D1162868

Play Therapy with MENTALLY SUBNORMAL CHILDREN

HENRY LELAND, PH.D.
Coordinator of Professional Training, Education, and Demonstration, Parsons State Hospital and Training Center, Parsons, Kansas

and

DANIEL E. SMITH, M.S.
Acting Chief Clinical Psychologist, Parsons State Hospital and Training Center, Parsons, Kansas

GRUNE & STRATTON

NEW YORK • LONDON

First printing August 1965
Second printing January 1971

Grune & Stratton, Inc.
757 Third Avenue, New York, New York 10017

Library of Congress Catalog Card Number 65-12655
International Standard Book Number 0-8089-0262-8

Printed in the United States of America (E-A)

To:

Our wives who obviously know a great deal about the needs of immature personalities or this book could not have been written.

REGARDING "NOTES" IN THIS BOOK

The reader will find two types of "notes" in this book, handled in two different ways.

Most of the notes are bibliographic in nature, occasionally including brief comment. These are grouped at the end of each chapter under the heading "Additional Notes," to avoid drawing the reader's eye constantly to the foot of the page, yet placing them at logical points for further study by those interested in references.

Other notes are primarily of a commentary nature, only occasionally including brief bibliographic citation, and these are important for the reader to have immediately at hand at pertinent points in the text. Hence, these are placed as true footnotes at the bottom of the appropriate pages.

Despite this division, both types of notes are consecutively numbered throughout.

Contents

Foreword

John F. Kennedy, while President of the United States, said about the problem of mental retardation that "This situation has been tolerated for too long. It has troubled our national conscience—but only as a problem unpleasant to mention, easy to postpone, and despairing of solution."[1]

In times past, part of the despair clearly came from our ineffectiveness in helping the mentally subnormal to avoid the emotional complications of his disability. Yet, to achieve confidence and self-esteem, *any* individual needs to make the optimal use of his own potential.

This book is devoted to the task of making explicit, a way to treat the handicapping emotional complications in a mentally retarded child through play therapy. There are an estimated 5,600,000 mentally retarded individuals in our country, and between 100,000 to 200,000 infants who will be mentally retarded are born each year.[2] Due to the impact of modern drugs on general health and the consequently lowered infant mortality rate, the number of mentally retarded persons has increased and their life-span has been lengthened.[2] Mental retardation has become one of the most serious handicapping conditions in the United States.[2]

Yet, of the 5,600,000 mentally retarded individuals, only 285,000 are so severely or profoundly retarded that they will need lifetime care and supervision; 350,000 are moderately retarded and capable of self-maintenance in unskilled or semi-skilled occupations; 5,000,000 are mildly retarded and capable of social and vocational adequacy with proper education and training.[2] Retarded individuals need *early* attention to their specialized needs and require a variety of helping services.

"The concept of mental retardation as a stationary irreversible condition is no longer scientifically sound."[3]

Play therapy in childhood is an important resource among the variety of helping services required to help the mentally subnormal person *learn* to live to the fullest of his potential, to adapt to life with others, and to gain the maturity needed to live in the real world. "Traditionally the characteristic behavior of retarded children was thought to reflect primarily inability or deficit; it is possible to conceive of symptoms in the retarded child which usually connote dysfunction as also having dynamic and economic meanings in terms of ego functioning; the behavior of the mentally retarded child can have adaptive significance."[4]

The authors focus our attention on their method of play therapy, believing that it can significantly add to the retarded child's coping mechanisms and aid those ego functions—adaptibility, learning rate and capacity, tolerance of change—which develop impulse control, allow gratification delay and frustration tolerance, and increase the use of cognitive and motor skills.

Having had the opportunity to work with the authors of this book as they successfully helped mentally subnormal children to cope more effectively with emotional conflict and adapt more economically to their perceptions and their feelings, I knew that the authors should communicate to others their theoretical orientation and describe their therapeutic methods. Perhaps the prospective reader of this book would like to know why I, as a child psychiatrist and psychoanalyst, so valued the work of the authors when as a psychoanalyst I follow a different frame of reference from the one used in this book.

It is because the authors are *not* tied to any specific philosophy, but have drawn on the contributions of many schools of thought whenever these various philosophies could be applied helpfully to the problems of aiding the mentally retarded child toward adaptive behavior. This book is neither against any school of thought, nor is it an attempt to unify all schools. Rather, the book recognizes that there is a serious mental health problem to be resolved and that a variety of philosophical orientations are each able to make a contribution to the task at hand. The book does not prefer one orientation over another; it pools many contributions to arrive at a statement about practical and effective play therapy with mentally subnormal children.

As Fuller states, "Some of the basic principles of psychotherapy with retarded children are the same as psychotherapy with any (troubled) child since in either case the purposes of psychotherapy are to strengthen the child's ego, to create a more healthy equilibrium of forces within his psychic structure, to release within him the potentials for further growth, and to facilitate his adjusting more adequately and more happily to reality."[5]

This book attempts to understand the relation between ego and reality in a mentally subnormal child and strives to use various adaptive activities within the reality of the mentally retarded child as the basis for its therapeutic work. In the presentation of their concepts of play therapy, the authors present ways to help the emotionally disturbed, retarded child whenever this is possible, by a further mastery of motor skills, by a further development of cognitive functions, by an increase in language mastery, and by further experiences which increase the troubled retarded child's sense of his own competence through learning activities that result in social gains for the child and achieve new patterns in his relationships with others. In these methods of play therapy, the mentally subnormal child can enhance his self-esteem and assert himself in ways more acceptable to his social world and to him. Out of such therapeutic progress come gains in ego strength.

The retarded child—by discovering how to deal with things and with people, by finding out what effects can be produced by what kind of actions, by learning ways to delay, by increasing his ability to tolerate the frustration of his reality—can be helped by the kind of play therapy described by the authors and can achieve a growth in competence in his dealing with impulse and with reality. The authors present ways that help the retarded child to expand his interests through play therapy, to increase his interactions with reality and the persons in it, and to add to his satisfactions from reality. Through such play therapy, the mentally subnormal child *learns* how to deal with emotional disturbances; environment becomes something for exploration and interaction, not a cause for withdrawal and defeat.

—*J. Cotter Hirschberg, M.D.*
Menninger Foundation,
Topeka, Kansas

ADDITIONAL NOTES

1. Quoted by Hargrove, E. A. in "Congress Speaks for the Retarded." *Mental Health Forum*, Southern Regional Education Board, Vol. 5, No. 1, p. 1, April 1964.
2. Fact Sheet on Mental Retardation, The National Association for Retarded Children, Inc., New York, April, 1964.
3. Pollack, M: Brain damage, mental retardation, and childhood schizophrenia. *Am. J. Psychiat.* 115:422-428, Nov. 1958.
4. Hirsch, E. A.: The adaptive significance of commonly described behavior of the mentally retarded. *Am. J. Ment. Def.* 63:639-646, Jan. 1959.
5. Fuller, D. S.: Psychotherapy with the Brain Damaged Child. Paper presented at a Workshop of the American Orthopsychiatric Association, February, 1960.

Introduction

"The manner in which our nation cares for its citizens and conserves its manpower resources is more than an index to its concern for the less fortunate."[1] Today there is an increasing number of children who function in a manner which we would describe as mentally retarded, or at least mentally subnormal. They are not able to do the things their community expects them to do. This is not a new problem; it has been with us a long time and this is certainly not the first book that has been written on the subject.[2] The problem, however, is becoming increasingly more prominent as we find that this area includes greater numbers than were ever predicted previously. In the past, these children were given such labels as *brain damaged, mentally deficient, emotionally disturbed and possibly psychotic.* However, regardless of label, the actual behaviors of these children are similar and, therefore, raise questions involving combinations of emotional disturbance, brain damage, and retardation, in the sense that each of these children has some of the characteristics of all of these groups.

This is not to say that all of the previous work in differential diagnosis has been in vain. Certainly there are brain damaged children and their characteristics and functionings must be understood. There are undoubtedly emotionally disturbed children who are not mentally retarded, and there are certainly mentally retarded children who have none of the specific symptoms of emotional disturbance or brain damage.

However, as far as the community is concerned, these children as a group are unable to function at a level consistent with the needs of the community. This is proven first by the fact that they are singled out and, for example, become known to the school systems as *exceptional children.* It is also illustrated by the fact that many of these children must be institutionalized. Further, one finds a vast development of special services for these children, to the extent that some communities now have special classes for the *retarded,* special classes for the *emotionally disturbed,* special classes for the *orthopedically handicapped,* etc. What is shared in common by all these children, however, is general behavior which we could call subnormal behavior. Within our theoretical position which holds that mental processes are properties of the brain, this subnormal behavior would be classified under a general heading of mental subnormality. Thus, we may say that all subnormal children may be described as functioning at a retarded level.[3]

The community problem has many facets. We will deal only with those aspects of the problem which are related to the possibility of treating subnormal children through the use of play therapy.

This book is not aimed at the general question of play therapy as such. That question has been discussed quite extensively in the past. The use of play therapy with emotionally disturbed children is an accepted method of treatment and has been covered well in the literature by such people as Virginia Axline, Moustakas, Slavson, and Lois Murphy, among others.[4] The use of play therapy with the emotionally disturbed, retarded child has not been as thoroughly investigated.[5] The last really comprehensive review was done in 1955 by Cowen,[6] though more recently there have been individual studies reported in some of the literature on the retarded, indicating that treatment for these children through the function of play therapy is both feasible and possible. Therefore, the major aim of this book is to explore as thoroughly as possible, the whole question of the use of play therapy with the group of children who represent a level of subnormal mental development. They may, as we have previously stated, be brain damaged or emotionally disturbed, etc. We prefer to think of them as containing elements or characteristics of various subnormal groups. The general therapeutic goals should be based on each child's behavior.

It is our feeling that before a discussion of play therapy with retarded children can be developed, a much sounder theoretical basis must be laid. In the past, the methods and theories of play therapy as used with emotionally disturbed children of normal intelligence have been applied to retarded children, but this application has not always been too effective. Beyond the obvious facts that subnormal children are not as communicative, are not as able to express their problems, and are not as able to gain insight into them through usual methods, there is also the factor that their daily life experiences do not usually contain sufficient elements to permit them to utilize the play material traditionally available for the expression of their emotional problems. Therefore, we have a number of concepts with which to deal. *First*, we want to set up a generalized theory of play therapy, particularly as it refers to psychological theories of learning the cognition, for we feel that play therapy with the mentally subnormal is primarily a learning function. *Second*, we will examine the techniques and procedures of play therapy with the emotionally disturbed, brain damaged child in terms of different methods of play that might be used to meet the goals for different types of problems, and consider the different procedures that each method involves. *Third*, we will discuss the indications for the use of these different types of play procedures in terms of the child's Adaptive Behavior, his Measured Intelligence, his needs for supplemental and special therapy, such as psychopharmacology, electroconvulsive therapy, etc., and finally his specific type of medical and psychological diagnosis.

In addition, we will discuss adjunctive uses of play therapy, as we have found that there are other uses for these playroom methods beyond the child's specific therapy needs. These include an extension of the processes of diagnosis and evaluation; the use of play therapy as adjunctive to disciplines dedicated to training; the use of play therapy for research in psychotherapy and in learning theory as it relates to children; and the improvement of the relationship between the child and his milieu.

These are the general aims of this book. It is the hope of the authors that through the realization of these aims, there will be available not only a therapeutic instrument for use with the mentally subnormal, but also a cohesive theory which may be applied to children of normal intellectual development who are, nonetheless, functioning at a subnormal level because of the nature of their emotional disturbance or brain damage.

DESCRIPTION OF SUBNORMAL CHILDREN

For the general purposes of this book, most references to the subnormal child will be in terms of definitions established in the *Manual on Terminology and Classification in Mental Retardation*, which are the official definitions used by the American Association on Mental Deficiency (AAMD).[7] Subnormality is a term which we are using primarily because we wish to underline the importance of including children who, because of emotional disturbance or certain types of brain damage, function at a subnormal level even though their actual intellectual measurement or Measured Intelligence would not necessarily indicate such subnormality. The definition of mental retardation used is also that of the AAMD which states: "Mental retardation refers to a subaverage general intellectual functioning which originates during the developmental period and is associated with impairment in "adaptive behavior."[8] This definition is acceptable to the present authors, and we would only insist that the concept of Adaptive Behavior which has been defined as: "(1) the degree to which the individual is able to function and maintain himself independently, and (2) the degree to which he meets satisfactorily the culturally imposed demands of personal and social responsibility,"[9] include all concepts related to emotional disturbance, childhood psychosis, etc., and that it not be considered merely an extension of the concept of Measured Intelligence. Thus, we would say that the psychological characteristics of the mentally subnormal child would include functional retardation, possibly retarded Measured Intelligence, and certainly subnormal Adaptive Behavior.[10]

Emotional disturbance is not as easy to define since it encompasses a much wider range of behavior. For our purposes we are going to be general rather than specific and merely say that emotional disturbance includes any behavior on the part of the child which is considered by his community to be out of keeping with the behavior they would expect of him in the circumstances in which it occurs. This is, we realize, a very broad statement and actually defines emotional disturbance by not defining it at all, but from an empirical point of view, a review of social case histories of children on waiting lists for institutions, child guidance clinics, etc., does, in fact, point in the direction of this kind of construct. Such case histories do not consistently specify qualities which the child demonstrates, but rather indicate the consistency with which the child is unable to function in a way compatible with the minimal demands of his school, his parents, or his community. The people involved with these children want to know what is wrong and what they should do about it. Such children are usually classified by the clinical personnel as emotionally disturbed, and it is in this sense that we are using the term. In other words, the indication that the child is in need of psychological help is sufficient evidence of emotional disturbance to so label him.

That portion of the book which deals with treatment needs is, however, dependent on a more concrete type of definition. It is very well to say that a child is emotionally disturbed and therefore needs help, but in the past there has been no particular effort to identify a certain type of help with a certain type of need or goal. We would not think very highly of a physician who prescribed the same medication for all diseases, yet we think nothing of putting children with unlimited variations of emotional disturbance into the same kind of play therapy programs without any particular thought as to their specific needs, the specific indications for treatment or the particular goals. There is a tendency on the part of many treatment areas to seek some sort of Utopian level of mental health which, in effect, has the aim of making the child more healthy than his surrounding community, and thus some sort of mental freak. This, of course, cannot be accomplished and the whole process becomes an extremely frustrating one for the therapist and the patient, to say nothing of the new problems developed because of differences between the child's behavior and that of the rest of his family. Thus, for example, a child with extremely compulsive parents must retain many compulsions if he is going to survive with them.

Many clinics and hospitals, while not falling into this "Utopian" pitfall, nonetheless tend to treat the child in terms of specific behavioral manifestations as though he were able to understand and deal with his problems at the same level as a normal child. They expect verbal communication, insights, and all of the other trappings of play therapy to occur with emotionally disturbed children who have normal intelligence. When it is found that these results do not materialize, the child is dropped from therapy with the statement that he was not a proper candidate. This seems to overlook a basic tenet of play therapy, namely that play itself is a form of communication and that thus, many of the things the therapist feels are lacking are, in fact, present and the error may be in the technique rather than in the candidate. This problem has particularly permeated the thinking of many of the institutions for the mentally retarded, and it is one of the reasons that psychiatric and clinical psychological services are so restricted there. To what extent this feeling still survives, the present authors cannot judge, but we do know that any census of child psychiatrists in the institutions for the mentally retarded would have very slim pickings. Thus, the whole problem of relating the treatment needs of the child to the particular type of therapy to be used has never been properly dealt with, and there is relatively little prescription material available for children as far as psychotherapy is concerned.

Psychotherapy must, for our purpose, have both long and short range goals. We cannot expect a child to be reconditioned or to change his personality so that his behavior is completely acceptable in any specific series of psychotherapy sessions. The functionally retarded child is performing at a level consistent with his life space regardless of the community's attitude, and the psychotherapist must start at the point where the child is most likely to achieve success. In other words, the psychotherapist must recognize the child's level of aspiration and must try to set his therapy goals in such a way that the psychotherapy will not represent new and additional frustrating experiences for the child. Thus, a basic prerequisite needed by the therapist in his goals with the functionally retarded child is that he must, in keeping with the techniques already used in special education, know where his child stands at the present moment, what the present functional level is, and not set therapy procedures and goals beyond the child. Above all, the therapist must avoid producing an additional traumatic experience for the child which would merely add to his original negative impression of society.

When specific procedures are demanded, quite often the therapist himself feels resentful, saying that he wants to be free to deal with the problem in the way he sees fit, or to deal with the whole situation as the child presents his problems. This type of freedom is, of course, essential in a therapy program just as a physician must be free to prescribe the proper medicine that the disease demands. However, this type of freedom without orientation or understanding of the goals or needs of the child, or without use of different types of therapeutic procedures, changes from freedom to chaos, and the net result is usually a conglomeration of attempts which often fail. Under such circumstances, it is not uncommon for the therapist to state that the child is too retarded to benefit from the service. The techniques and procedures which we will be describing have been first tried in pilot studies with functionally retarded children, and it is the result of this research that has led to the preparation of this book.[11]

11. The authors feel that this is a proper use of the concept of research and further that field research duplicating as many "life" variables as possible is productive, and that these variables cannot be studied in the isolation of laboratory conditions, viz. Chap. XIII for a more detailed discussion of these points.

DEVELOPMENT OF A REHABILITATION CONCEPT OF PSYCHOLOGY

We will open with the general premise that if the child has ever been amenable to training in any area, be it walking, talking, getting out of bed, or even rolling over in bed, he can use the same abilities to be trained to do other things. This is a very broad statement, but it is based on the principle that it requires a tremendous amount of effort as well as a certain amount of native intelligence for a child to learn, for example, how to walk. There is an old joke that if a centipede had to think about it, he would never walk, because he would be unable to decide which foot to put down when. There is probably some validity to this notion as it applies to walking behavior and therefore, we are not assuming that the child learns to walk through tremendous intellectual exercise or through the extension of cognitive ability. However, we are saying that it requires a great psychological investment for him to learn to walk, and that this same psychological investment can be channeled into other areas that would logically follow from the ability already present. Such a concept may be misleading. It would imply that anyone, no matter how retarded, could be trained to do something more than he is doing. We are certainly not suggesting that anyone, no matter how retarded, is a proper candidate for psychotherapy. We do feel, however, that the child's unsuitability as a candidate is not a function of his retardation. Rather, the difficulties seem to lie in our own level of knowledge of his retardation, the availability of therapists, the availability of materials, and other factors which are generally related to the mechanics of psychotherapy, rather than to theory. The child is thus not a proper candidate only because psychotherapy is not yet ready for him. As far as the theory of psychotherapy or, specifically, play therapy is concerned, there may be something which, even at this extremely low level, can be of benefit to the child.

This brings to mind an extremely retarded patient who functions at a Measured Intelligence Level V, using the AAMD classification, and the lowest possible level of Adaptive Behavior.[12] He was nonetheless brought into the playroom for diagnostic purposes and could, after a number of sessions, respond to the examiner when he was called, although previously he had not been able to do so, and was thought to be functionally deaf. This is certainly not a great therapeutic success, and undoubtedly if this were all that we had to talk about, it would not merit writing a book. But it does indicate that even at these very low levels, there is something which the child can be offered.

This is consistent with the thinking previously reflected by Leland and Goldberg when they stated that these general ideas are:

> . . . based on the hypothesis that human learning is a continuous process from birth to death only interrupted by physical, mental, and/or social barriers which can be manipulated or removed. In other words, human learning has no ceiling, and it is only the barriers which block further learning (p. 530).[13]

We realize that this statement puts the emphasis on learning, but as we stated above, we are, for the purposes of this book, correlating the concepts of play therapy with the concepts of learning. Therefore, what is true of learning would seem to be true of psychotherapy, at least insofar as the goals of psychotherapy are related to the removal of the above-mentioned social and mental "barriers".

It should be remembered that we must constantly be devising new ways of enhancing programs of child rehabilitation at all levels. The concept of rehabilitation is used here with the idea that children, when they come to the institution, to the child guidance clinic, or to the other services being made available to them, have patterns of behavior which are already structured. They already do things in certain ways, relate to people in certain ways, relate to things in certain ways, and these "ways" are generally controlled by their likes and dislikes. Since these behaviors were sufficiently out of line with the expectations of their home community to require special treatment or even separation from that community, we have to proceed on the assumption that the primary treatment and training requirements of these children consist of restructuring or reordering these behaviors.

This process is usually described as rehabilitation. However, it could be described just as accurately as a process of reconditioning. We feel that the psychotherapy techniques with which we will be dealing in this book are based on a theoretical formulation of an ongoing conditioning process, and that these processes should become the heart of any theory of psychotherapy with the mentally subnormal child.

The next chapter will discuss in detail, a generalized theory of behavior as it refers to play therapy, and the elements which we have discussed in the "Introduction" will be further emphasized. The point we must make here is that the concept of rehabilitation and the concept of reconditioning are for us synonymous, and that the concept of psychotherapy with the mentally subnormal and the concept of rehabilitation are also, if not synonymous, at least closely interrelated.

Finally, should there be a feeling that we are overlooking the differences between treatment and training: In this book we do not attempt to substitute play therapy for either special education or other training programs for the mentally retarded. We are merely proposing a theory and method of dealing with the child who, in addition to the training methods used in the community or in the institution, needs this special help. We will discuss various aspects of this question in later chapters.

Much of the work involved in the preparation of this book is based on the experience of the authors at the Parsons State Hospital and Training Center, (PSH&TC) Parsons, Kansas, which is an institution for emotionally disturbed and mentally retarded children. We were fortunately situated in an institution that approaches psychotherapy from a research point of view, and thus all of the facilities of the institution were made available in order to permit us to carry out experiments utilizing psychotherapeutic procedures on children who functioned at all subnormal levels, including some individuals who fell into the normal range insofar as Measured Intelligence was concerned. We would like to thank, at this time, the members of the staff of the Parsons State Hospital and Training Center for making this opportunity available to us and particular mention should be made of Dr. Jacqueline Baumeister, Clinical Director, and Dr. H. V. Bair, Superintendent, for the personal help and support that they gave. Our gratitude also, to Dr. S. Cotter Hirschberg, Menninger Foundation, Topeka, Kansas, whose remark that "somebody ought to write a book" served as the kindling for this project, and who later made many valuable suggestions and contributions to the text.

ADDITIONAL NOTES

1. Kennedy, J. F., "A Statement by the President regarding the need for a National Plan in Mental Retardation," 1962.

2. Southard, E. E., "General Aspects of the Brain Anatomy in the Feebleminded," *Memoirs of Amer. Acad. Arts & Sciences*, XIV: 2, 1918, p. 23, gives bibliography references back through 1860.

3. The present writers do not wish to become involved in the discussion of differences between *mental retardation*, *mental deficiency*, and the general term of *mental subnormality*. We do not feel that there is a useful difference between these terms, and we have used all three at will throughout the rest of the book. For a further discussion of this question viz. Masland, R. L., Sarason, S. B. and Gladwin, T., *Mental Subnormality*, N. Y., Basic Books, 1958.

4. There are a large number of books and discussion articles currently available on most aspects of play therapy. The books we are citing here seem to be the most representative of the more important schools or approaches to this subject and are thus offered to the reader who desires a general overview: Axline, Virginia M., *Play Therapy*, Boston, Houghton Mifflin Co., 1947; Moustakas, C. E., *Children in Play Therapy*, N. Y., McGraw-Hill, 1953; Moustakas, C. W., *Psychotherapy with Children*, N. Y., Harper Bros., 1959; Slavson, S. R., *Child Psychotherapy*, N. Y., Columbia Univ. Press, 1952, and the two volumes by Lois Murphy, *Personality in Young Children*, 2 vols., N. Y., Basic Books, 1956, while not dealing specifically with play therapy, nonetheless set the stage for it and give many valuable suggestions as to techniques, materials, settings, etc., which may be used.

5. Stacey, C. L. and DeMartino, M. D. (Ed.) *Counseling and Psychotherapy with the Mentally Retarded*, Glencoe, Ill., The Free Press, 1957, have discussed the problem in their Chap. 5 passim.

6. Cowen, E. L., "Psychotherapy and Play Techniques with the Exceptional Child and Youth," in *Psychology of Exceptional Children and Youth*, Cruickshank, W. M. (Ed.) Englewood Cliffs, N. J., Prentice-Hall, 1955, pp. 520-575. This review, together with that done by Neham, Sara, "Psychotherapy in Relation to Mental Deficiency," *AJMD*, LV, 1951, pp. 557-572, constitute a very thorough coverage of the field to 1955, and though they drew different conclusions from their investigations, they do provide a very solid foundation for the development of a more comprehensive theory of play therapy with mentally subnormal children.

7. Heber, R., "A Manual on Terminology and Classification in Mental Retardation," 2nd. Ed., Mono. Supple., *AJMD*, LXVI, 1961, passim.

8. *Idem*, p. 3.

9. *Idem*, p. 61.

10. Viz. Chap. IX.

11. This note has been cited on page 5.

12. Heber, *op. cit.* p. 58 and 62.

13. Leland, H. and Goldberg, I. I., "Rehabilitation of the Institutional Mentally Retarded," *Amer. Psychologist*, XII, 1957, pp. 528-530.

PART ONE: GENERAL AND THEORETICAL CONSIDERATIONS

I. Some Ideas on the Development of the Essential Qualities of Man

Today, in the world of psychology, the increased emphasis on the value of proper experimental design, the use of the proper statistic, the questions of collecting data, the whole matter of the evolution of theories and laws, etc., make it somewhat daring to write a book on the question of psychotherapy and call it scientific. Some psychologists, in thinking that they know what the concept "scientific" means, have relegated to the "arts" the individual who would deign to evaluate elements from a biased or presumptive point of view, based on concepts which are not fully known or understood, constructs which have not been fully developed, or value judgments which have not been experimentally substantiated. It is possible that this is an appropriate criticism of any book which endeavors to complete this task. Another point of view, however, more representative of our thinking is expressed by Dr. Baker in the following statement: "The scientist has to tell the whole truth as he knows it in that moment in time, and nothing less or different can be expected."[14] The truth about psychotherapy, as we know it at this moment in time, is the basis of our effort in this book. From this point of view, we feel that we have the responsibility to make such a presentation and we hope that it will be regarded as a meaningful scientific contribution.

What then, are some of the assumptions which one must make in order to conceive of a scientific theory of behavior as it relates to any kind of psychotherapy? One must start with an essential value judgment that the human being is a worthwhile organism, that he is worth salvaging, that every living person has some potential contribution for the long-range future of mankind, and that the concept of a long-range future has some validity. Furthermore, one must assume that as culture grows, this growth is in the best interest of all mankind; that any failure on the part of individual men to aid in this growth becomes reactionary and as such tends to slow down the total possibility of mankind's increasing its control over the forces of nature, thus slowing down the eventual creation of a better, happier, less painful world. These assumptions do not bear explicit definition, and certainly in a book of this kind they do not even call for an attempt at such a definition. They require unto themselves a complete book much longer than this one will be.

But some such underlying philosophy is necessary to any individual who sets out to dedicate himself to improving the lot of the more severely handicapped members of the human species. It is not that such an individual must have a defense for this dedication, but rather that he has to have within himself a feeling that what he is doing is worthwhile, that he is making a contribution both to his own peace of mind and to the future of his fellowmen. In addition to hoping that this contribution has the possibility of success, he would like to be able to look at the creative and productive achievements of such an effort and say to himself, "This I have done; it has been worthwhile; it has been useful; and my training and efforts have not been in vain—they have made a contribution."

SPECULATIONS ON MAN'S EVOLUTION AND PSYCHOLOGICAL DEVELOPMENT

With the underlying premise that man is worthy of help and, being worthy can be helped, it is necessary to take a short look at what seem to be the essential characteristics of man as we find him. Again this is not a matter of careful scientific analysis, though much of what we propose as conjecture is capable of scientific verification through research areas related to the science of man, such as anthropology, ethnology, biochemistry, physiology, and many others. The first of these premises is based on the available knowledge of man's evolution. Here, we find that the earliest traces of man, as represented by the discoveries in the vicinity of Kenya, Uganda, and Tanganyika, by Dr. and Mrs. L. S. B. Leakey, produced fossils about 1,750,000 years old that are strictly *hominid* in nature,[15] indicated as being most certainly bipedal, with the strong probability that hands were used for the manipulation of implements. Further, evidence of these implements in the form of crude and simple pebble tools have been found with the remains.[16]

It is felt that the initial adaptation leading to the emergence of the *hominidae* involved a pelvis and lower extremity permitting the assumption of an upright posture. "Apes with a long slanting pelvis can take only a few steps upright and must use the hands to supplement their locomotion. With his shorter pelvis man can stand and walk erect."[17] Then, the upper extremites and hands, freed from locomotion duties, were able to take over many of the activities, such as food seeking and preparing, combat and defense, and other developmental manipulative skills which had previously been the responsibility of the jaws and teeth. This led to the consequent reduction of the lower face, "which imprisoned the cranium" and permitted the development of the brain bearing portion "and an hypertrophy of its neural contents."[18] Thus, the "Leakey" find demonstrated a cranial capacity average of 550 cc. (450 to 600 cc.) while the average anthropoid is 450 cc.[19] This would seem to indicate, according to some anthropologists, that the pattern of development from an early period involves growth from hand to brain. That is to say, as man became a handed animal instead of, as present day monkeys seem to be, handed and footed, there was a certain loss of previous prowess which had to be compensated for in some other manner. This process of compensation developed from the effort to make up for the loss of foot prowess by the use of hands for manipulating implements.[20] It is likely that this compensatory effort had to be thought through in some manner, thus indicating the beginnings of symbol function and the origin of some form of cognition. There seems to have been a constant progression, from these beginnings, along this pattern. First, man's environment produced the need for certain knowledge; then, through utilizing his hands as a handed animal in an effort to manipulate the environment, he developed increased cognition and increased brain power which, in turn, has made it more possible for him to increase his manipulation of his environment and thus progress over and beyond other forms of animal life.

Departing from our history for a moment, it would appear likely, in terms of ontogenetic recapitulation, that the child follows the same phylogenetic patterns of hand to brain development as did his ancestors, and thus the use of the hands, in a symbolic sense, here represents the whole sensorium.[21] Therefore, more organized developments "in the maturing brain lead to the formation of elaborate cortical receiving areas for each of the sensory modalities. . ."[22] This, in the eyes of some physiologists, has actually brought about a transfer of responsibilities in terms of brain function and they have tried to define this through somatotopic representation of the cortex of the brain.[23]

Since the child's manipulative activity, or in terms of the above, the major activity leading to the brain's development, is carried out while he is at play, it appears logical that when there is a need to modify present patterns of development, the use of therapy techniques based on play (hand or sensory activity) would seem to be the most effective.

DEVELOPMENT OF COMMUNICATION

Somewhere along this line—exactly where is difficult to pinpoint—man also developed the power to communicate his method of fighting the everlasting war with the forces of nature; therefore he was very early able to become a social, communicating being, rather than just a social being as an animal. He was able to pass on through the process of communication, the information which he had learned and which thus began to be the beginning of a lore which we can call knowledge, even though far in advance of the time when this knowledge could be recorded and considered permanent. Also at this time, we can postulate that things seemed to be happening to the speech mechanism as such. Man shares with many other animals the ability to make sounds or emotional vocalizations which seem to be controlled in the mid-brain or stem.[24] Evidently he shares with lesser numbers of animals but still a great number, the ability to differentiate these sounds so that certain of them can be identified with specific purposes.[25] This seems to be a cerebral function, but man alone has the additional power of taking these differentiated sounds and giving them sufficient symbolic content through the "association cortex" of his brain that noise is translated into actual speech and communication. Thus, man is the only animal that can be described as a language-bearing animal. This specifically human characteristic is a facet of higher nervous activity which differentiates man from the other animals and makes it possible for him to increase his knowledge cumulatively over the course of generations, as he continues his struggle with the forces of nature around him.[26] In this way he is not only able to win certain battles with his environment, but he can put these victories on a more permanent basis which can be shared by all members of the human race. Thus mankind can be said to determine its own history in the general sense of being able to decide for itself how it is going to live in its environment. This again becomes a strictly human characteristic related as it is to the fact that man has language and symbolic communication.

The development of communication seems to depend on socialization. Here again, we have an assumption which eventually may be tested scientifically under controlled conditions, but which, in terms of our present breadth of knowledge, has to be assumed in terms of logical constructs based on external observations. Thus, we see that a young ape and an infant child both require about thirty-eight weeks' gestation before they are ready for birth.[27] The young ape at birth is capable of doing many things that the human child is not.[28] The apparent reason for this is that the ape brain is not going to develop much more than it did during the gestation period, and that although the ape required training, association, etc., at its level, this training was of a nearly fully developed brain. The human child, on the other hand, is a relatively incomplete organism in terms of a comparison of the brain at birth with the brain at a later period. His brain weight doubles (380 Gm. to 630 Gm.) in the first six months after birth and more than doubles again (630 Gm. to 1,330 Gm.) by the age of four.[29] It evidently requires a period of around ten to twelve months for this organ to be able to function in terms of language as one would expect a human brain to function. Thus, at the point where the child acquires the use of language, one presumes that the brain has reached a high level of development, and that though there is further growth and improvement, a major milestone has been reached. During the original one to two year period, the baby gradually begins to learn how to live in his environment, gradually acquires many of the abilities that the ape had before him, then surpasses these abilities and begins to set out on new roads with new activities that are much more "human" in nature. Here we seem to have a repetition again of the phylogenetic pattern in that this improvement in behavior is a "hand to brain" improvement. That is, during this period the young baby gradually learns to move himself around, to control his motion, to exercise, to eventually crawl and to talk, always through the guidance of searching or seeking movement most of which is predominated by sensory behavior. In this way information is conveyed to the brain where it is used for the cerebral development and growth leading to the climactic point at which the child begins to speak, and, thus, fully identifies himself as a member of the human species. It would seem totally illogical to conceive of the child as going through the same pattern of growth and development away from the contact with other humans.[30] He certainly would not begin to speak if he had not previously heard words nor would he have the same social consciousness, etc., if he had not previously had the opportunity for social contact. Thus, even though this is a period of physiological, even anatomical development, it nonetheless seems that it must occur within the framework of a social reference if the result is to be one consistent with what we call human behavior. Hence, we find that man's language-bearing characteristics are also based on other aspects of man as a species. These aspects are primarily the social nature of his development and the tremendous importance of the personal interaction between man and his peers.

After considering the relationship of society to the development of speech in man, we have also to consider the fact that ontogenetically all men do not develop at the same pace as "the average man." That is to say, defective patterns of brain development produce aberrations of thought, communication, and behavior. The present treatise is not intended to deal with the origins of speech and communication in man. There are others who have covered that aspect of the question, the most noteworthy of whom are Penfield and Roberts,[31] and also reference should be made to the work of Schiefelbusch, Bair, and Spradlin.[32] The responsibility of this present material is instead to deal with the relationship between the development of cognition and language and/or communication. As Wallon stated: "The age of (the origin) speech is marked by a change in the practical aptitudes of the child. . ."[33] However, we wish first to discuss the problems of the individual with subnormal development in terms of the ontogenetic growth of that individual.

First, it is necessary to return to the questions which we discussed in the beginning of the chapter, where we put forth a number of premises concerning the nature of man. One further premise is that, though we consider man a natural organism in the sense that he is responsive to natural laws, with the added implication that there is organization in nature and that these natural laws therefore have some relationship to forces which are both predictable and measurable, this is not an implication that man is of necessity a "naturalistic" organism. That is, he does not come forth ready-made with all of the established processes which he is going to utilize during his span on earth, and with a role to potentiate these forces to the highest degree.[34] Rather, he comes forth with a tremendous potential for doing many things some of which may be realized and some of which may not, depending on the molding process to which he is subjected because of his relationship with the rest of society. Therefore, the young child cannot develop, regardless of his background, without this molding, and even the normal child cannot be left totally to his own devices without this molding process and still be expected to achieve. Thus, we have the responsibility of guiding the child so that he can benefit from the highest level of society's growth, whereas "a merely natural education would force us to overcome in each pupil evils already overcome by the race."[35] A child born with perfectly normal physical potentials, when placed in a culturally deprived environment, will assume many of the characteristics of subnormal mental development just as readily as the child born in a brain damaged or brain injured state. Consequently, the process of molding or civilizing which must occur through the interaction of the individual with society, is a very necessary process if the child is going to advance at a pace which will allow him to take his place in the modern world. Therefore, when behavioral aberrations develop, quite often they may be considered to be related to the attempts of the brain of the child to adjust itself to the image of the surrounding community.[36] If the development cannot keep pace with the demands of society, we find that the child responds to the situation as best he is able and his response is quite often out of keeping with the manner in which society hopes that he will respond. It would follow that there would be a chance that these behavioral aberrations could be corrected if the child could come to feel that he was progressing in terms of performing as society expected him to perform. Anything that would help him move along this ladder, as in certain of the educational methods associated with the Montessori system[37] and some of the more recent work done by Haring and Phillips,[38] would help him correct the problem and possibly would eliminate the unacceptable behavior. Thus, we might say that special education may do the major job, and certainly if the elements disturbing the child are related to factual knowledge or to the lack of concrete understanding of the relationship between factual knowledge and social living, then special education can do the job very well. However, there is within this group a large number of children in whose path lies the problem of the integration of some meaningful abstract relationship between the social content of their lives and the factual knowledge which they have to learn. These children find that they are unable to integrate their behavior consistently along the lines that the surrounding social community has established, and that the learning of educational tasks does not help to erase these differences. Under these circumstances, a specialized type of learning situation has to be created which we call psychotherapy. does not help erase these differences. Under these circumstances a specialized type of learning situation has to be created which we call psychotherapy. Psychotherapy with children merely becomes a specialized form of teaching and it is not a matter of "psychotherapy or teaching," but rather a matter of which approach will be most beneficial in terms of the patterns of learning involved, i.e., a specialist in this specific area (and this is the role of the therapist) or the more generalized approach of the classroom teacher. When the specific problem relates to the social sphere, it is the responsibility of the psychotherapist. This type of problem may occur anywhere on the ladder of development because frequently the child will enter into the special education program with a very willing desire to learn; he may advance rapidly within this learning situation, only to find that he cannot gain the recognition or social acceptance for which he was hoping, and we find a breakdown of his enthusiasm. Or the special education situation itself may not be able to keep up the pattern which was started, in that it fails to continue to add new experiences, etc., because it has not yet perfected the old techniques. Furthermore, it fails to recognize, as was reported by Smith (1959),[39] that quite often new experiences have to be introduced even though old techniques have not yet been perfected. Other factors that may play a role in this area may be related to the fact that as the child's aspiration increases, his knowledge of social differences in terms of his actual intellectual potential increases, and behavioral difficulties replace what previously was merely educational retardation. These and various other factors are responsible for the feeling that psychotherapy does not necessarily have to precede special education. On the contrary, psychotherapy may even be necessary after the completion of successful special education or anywhere else along the line, depending upon whether special problems develop.

We can say that psychotherapy is required when the child is not able to perform in the minimal manner expected by the outside world, and it follows that psychotherapy can be said to have been effective when the child's behavior and understanding leads him to perform in a manner expected by the outside world. The child must understand what the outside world requires and must be able and willing to perform. The question of being able to perform is usually related to the processes of education, and the question of being willing to perform can be conceived to be related to the processes of psychotherapy. This whole problem orbits around the question of speech and cognition and is one of the most important variables in terms of social acceptance. That is to say, problems relating to the development of proper communication, or speech and cognition, or awareness, are most closely related to the child's being able to perform properly within a social environment. It is conceivable that the actual education processes can go on without any real speech exchange; that is, the child can be put on a self-programming unit which sets up a learning situation and provides rewards at certain intervals, while the function of the teacher becomes one of reinforcement and of making sure that the machine is dong its job properly. The only speech that might be involved would be that accompanying an occasional pat on the head, a statement by the teacher to the effect that "Johnny is doing just fine," or possibly an occasional admonition to "wake up," or "stop kicking your feet." This type of speech is not conducive to social learning since it does not set up speech experiences which the child might expect in the social world. If he child is able to integrate this factual learning with experiences which he has already met in the social world, then further help would not be considered necessary. If, however, it is difficult for him to make this integration as we discussed above, then actual preparation in the area of these social experiences through becoming aware of them and being able to attach communication symbols to them is extremely important, and this preparation becomes a function of psychotherapy. The teaching task, from this frame of reference, involves training perceptions. The child then learns how these preceptive experiences can be carried over to a broader setting. When he demonstrates that he cannot carry over these perceptive experiences because they have failed to become the basis for apperceptive experiences, this becomes the real function of psychotherapy in the sense of providing an apperceptive field in which the child can learn to integrate the factual or perceptive information he has gained with the rest of the experiential field in which he finds himself.[40]

IMPORTANCE OF LANGUAGE AND COMMUNICATION

We find, however, that all men do not possess the qualities or abilities to make it possible for them to function fully in terms of apperceptive experiences. This raises a question which may sound strange in a book on psychotherapy and play therapy but which is, in terms of the basic assumption of the authors, a very necessary part of therapy. That is, a recognition that that aspect of the individual's behavior which is observable has a physiological basis, and that there is, therefore, something within the makeup of the individual's brain that is causing the behavioral results which are observable to the outside world. Exactly what has gone wrong, we cannot say. It would be nice if we were able to remove skull plates and take a look inside, make certain manipulations as one does on a calculating machine that is not functioning properly, and close the skull plates again finding that our machine is once more in perfect working order. Man has not reached this level with the human brain and we do not anticipate that he will reach it very soon, although, of course, anything is possible in the future. However, in terms of our present needs, we are in a sense forced to consider ways and means of correcting the malfunction of our "machine" without actually manipulating the working parts. This would appear to be a hopeless task if man's brain or man himself were really a machine. That is, this is clearly one of the aspects of difference between man as a model of physics in the mechanical sense, and an actual mechanical machine which has attempted also to model physical laws. This difference is the fact that man's mechanism is, in a manner of speaking, self-changing. That is to say, if this mechanism needs adjustment, it can, of its own accord, make these adjustments—presuming, of course, that some external help or model is available so that man can know in what direction or in what manner to make adjustments. Thus, we do not have to remove the skull plates and deal directly with the mechanism if we want to make changes in the function of the brain. We have merely to get a message through in order to add sufficient bits of information to the present functioning mental processes which will then be able to change themselves in accordance with the implied direction created by the additive material. This way of looking at the human brain demands certain specific assumptions, as was previously required with our manner of looking at man himself. The assumptions that we are offering at this point are essentially threefold: first, that man's behavior is based on the functions of his brain; second, that the brain is so constructed that external influences are a necessary part of the way in which functioning is learned; and third, that it continues to modify its functioning.

As to the first, there is nothing particularly new or original about this assumption. In actual practice we find exceedingly early references to this type of thinking in the philosophies of the ancient Greeks.[41] More recently, in the 18th century, we find presentation of an organized system of philosophy of behavior based on the fact that the brain was the center of this control. The key names that come to mind in this system are Hobbes, Hartley, and Priestly, whose thinking gave rise to a school known in psychology as associationism.[42] The basic precepts of the associationist school were that mental processes were based on the association of ideas which were derived from without and that the brain went through certain functions, and set up certain associations which permitted the transmission of these ideas from one center to another. There was not too much done with this line of thought for about a century and a half, but we find in the beginning of the 20th century that Pavlov, working in Russia, presented similar ideas and developed from them the modern school of psychology based on conditioning,[43] which gave rise to American behaviorism. These facts are available in any elementary book on psychology and only bear repeating at this time as an effort to establish some of the historical antecedents to the idea that man's behavior is based on functions of a physiological nature occurring within the human organism. Now, if we make this assumption, we are going to have to presume that every aberration of behavior, any irregularity, is essentially associated with irregularities within the physiological organism, the brain.

Any presumption that man's behavior originates from within due to innate causes or that man's behavior originates from without, in terms of an extra force separate from his physiology, leads into extremely blind alleys related to various vitalistic schools of psychology, and produces such pseudoscientific statements, as for example, that psychotherapy does not work with a specific group because "it is the nature of that group," or that the individual behaves in a certain manner because "he was born that way," or no amount of effort on the part of a therapist can change certain behaviors because "they were genetically predetermined." If we assume that man's brain is the center of his activities, but that the brain is dependent on stimuli from without, and that it then organizes this stimuli into responses through a process of association of cells,[44] leading to a cognition which produces the external expression of these associations, whether this expression be verbal or verbal substitutes in the form of gestures or other communicative devices that do not actually use language,[45] we then have a much tighter, more experimentally testable frame of reference from which to start than if we pretend that these thoughts, ideas, or behaviors were already present as a result of some innate process or added willy nilly in terms of some external vitalistic force.

The second and third assumptions, that external stimuli are responsible for cognition in terms of the concept that the brain is able to both establish behavior and modify itself through an adaptive process are, of course, a direct outgrowth of the first assumption. As we stated earlier, the difference between the human machine and the mechanical machine is the ability for modification through external influences. This seems to be a process of the brain and the rest of the nervous system, as purely reflex behaviors also tend to modify cognitive behaviors. For example, if the child approaches a hot stove, feels the heat, and draws his hand away quickly, this achieves not only a conditioned response to a hot stove, but also cognitive or learned behavior in the sense that he becomes aware that he has to avoid this hot stove as well as other objects which radiate heat regardless of their shape, size, or phenotypic appearance. This is a process of developing cognitive function from what was merely a reflex response to a threatening stimulus. Therefore, we do not have to presume that only the cerebral areas of the nervous system are capable of self-modifying behavior, but rather that the whole nervous system is able to receive a stimulus, organize it through various cell assemblies and associations, and integrate it as a conditioned response into the association bank of the organism, thus permitting further learning and cognition. The term "association bank", as used in this sense, refers to the memory aspects of the mental machine. This memory function allows for retention of information that enables the organism to know that certain stimuli have occurred previously, that it responded to these stimuli in a certain manner, and seemed to achieve certain results from this response. The ability to remember behavior, even though it may not be at a completely conscious level in the sense of total recollection, is nonetheless present and helps to maintain the behavior patterns at a comparatively stable level. Thus, the major function of this association bank is to serve the organism by making it unnecessary for it to relive each experience every time it occurs, but having lived it once, to remember what its reactions were and thus be able to make these reactions without necessarily involving further cognitive effort.[46] A problem with retarded individuals is that in their search for a proper response to a specific stimulus, they lack the power to build proper associations and are usually unsuccessful in their attempts. Therefore, their association bank is overloaded with failure memories and each time the stimulus occurs, they have to start once again searching for a proper or useful response—a response which can, in a sense, work. This produces the confusion or chaos of their mental processes, which not only results in failure to find a proper group of associations permitting an acceptable response, but also makes it highly unlikely that they will recognize an acceptable response even if they do find it. Thus, even if by chance they are to come upon an accepted response, the experience is lost to them, except in that it enters their association bank along with the other unsuccessful responses and becomes merely one more association memory to plague them in their attempts to organize some sort of meaning around the life processes.

For many people, it is difficult to accept that aspect of this theorizing which denies man's inherent individuality. It is certainly the authors' intention to consider man, as a species, to be essentially an open energy system completely dependent on external fuel for the maintenance of his function, since the constructs of higher nervous activity as related to the physiological processes are presumed to be expressions of energy.[47] Since man is an open energy system dependent on external fuel for maintenance of life as it is described biologically, it follows that thought as a form of the expression of energy is also totally dependent on this external fuel. Thus, the fact of thought and the cognitive processes which are related to the expression of thought are all dependent on material from outside the actual operating body of

46. We realize that this is an oversimplification of the process, and that in any given field situation there are many alternative paths which will be opened by the "memory" of the previous experience; therefore, each new situation has to be weighed in its own terms. However, all else being equal, the "association bank" seems to be able to remember the necessary behavior to meet the problem.

man. This is not to say that this body does not, as a functioning organism, have certain controls over the manner in which this energy is expressed, and, certainly, the specific physiology of the individual has a great deal to do with the behavior resulting from the various cognitive efforts. Thus, a tall man takes into consideration the fact that he is tall before he attempts to get through an opening that is four feet high. A physically weak individual does not attempt exercises which require an adequate or excessively developed muscle. An individual who has a "weak" stomach avoids certain foods, and likewise we might presume that an individual with a certain type of brain structure avoids certain types of mental exercise or behavior. The latter is a logical conclusion, and much of the evidence we have, particularly in the area of functional retardation, supports it. It does seem certain that weakened brain structures, due either to metabolic or anatomical weakening, do not perform in the area of cognition at the same level as nonweakened brain structures. Part of the goal of psychotherapy is, in a sense, to reverse part of society's dictum in this area and to provide whatever success experiences can be provided in order that the organism will begin to know and understand in just what areas it can function. Thus, the negatively oriented mind that has associations consisting only of failure experiences can, through success experiences, be reorganized—in a sense, remade—so that it will function at a higher and more socially acceptable level. This is an external process and is not in any sense based on the innate learning of this organism.

Thus, if a patient in psychotherapy or any functionally retarded individual can be brought to realize his extreme dependence on society, the job of the therapist becomes much easier, the whole process becomes much more rapid, and the potential for success becomes much greater. In a sense, one might almost say that the prognosis for success in psychotherapy is dependent on a realization on the part of the patient that his thoughts do not specifically originate within his own physiology, but are dependent on the social stimuli surrounding him, and that his acceptance and understanding of these stimuli will help make the necessary modifications. To comprehend this is, of course, more than one would ask of the retarded individual, but one may certainly ask for acceptance; therefore through the therapeutic process of what will later be referred to as "cognitive stimulation," we hope that a certain amount of understanding can be achieved.

SUMMARY

To summarize then: (1), we feel that man's development is "from hand to brain," again conceiving of the hand as representative of the whole sensorium: (2), that the essential characteristic of the "human" aspects of man's behavior is his language bearing quality, and further that this quality is of an essentially social origin; and (3), that behavior creates cognition in the sense that the receipt of external stimuli is the source of both behavior and cognition, but that the latter also includes the conversion of these stimuli into symbols or language—thus socially acceptable or controlled behavior depends upon cognition. Therefore, the brain function may be modified through the process of communication from without.

With the above developmental sequence in mind, it is our presumption that the most successful way to treat mentally subnormal children would be a play therapy process which takes into consideration all of the above assumptions. We will discuss such a process in Chapter IV. Before that, however, we wish first to review some of the constructs for a generalized theory of behavior as it refers to play therapy.

ADDITIONAL NOTES

14. Baker, W. V., Comments to "The Moral Unneutrality of Science," *Science*, CXXXIII, 1961, pp. 261-262.

15. Weltfish, Gene, "Some Main Trends in American Anthropology in 1961," *Annals Amer. Acad. Pol. & Soc. Sci.*, 33, 1962, pp. 171-176.

16. Magoun, H. W., Darling, Louise, and Prost, J., "The Evolution of Man's Brain," in *The Central Nervous System and Behavior*, (Brazier, Mary, Ed.) Josiah Macy, Jr. Foundation, N. Y., 1960, p. 35 and p. 72.

17. *Idem*, p. 59.

18. *Idem*, p. 34.

19. *Idem*, p. 35.

20. *Idem*, p. 72-73.

21. Kasatkin, N. I., "Early Conditioned Reflexes in the Child," in *Central Nervous System and Behavior* (Selected Translations from Russian Med. Lit.) U.S. Dept. HEW, PHS, Washington, D. C., 1959, pp. 330-342.

22. Magoun, *op. cit.* p. 42.

23. *Idem*, p. 41 and Woolsey, C. N., "Organization of Somatic Sensory and Motor Areas of the Cerebral Cortex" in *Biological and Biochemical Bases of Behavior* (Harlow and Woolsey, Ed.) Univ. of Wisc. Press, Madison, 1958, pp. 63-82.

24. Magoun, *op. cit.*, pp. 43-44.

25. Polyak, S., *The Vertebrate Visual System*, Univ. Chicago Press, Chicago, 1957, p. 994.

26. *Idem*, pp. 1030-1031, discussed essential relationship between bipedalism and speech development in man.

27. Magoun, *op. cit.*, p. 41.

28. Harlow, H. F., "Affectional Behavior in the Infant Monkey," in *The Central Nervous System and Behavior*, *op. cit.*, pp. 307-357.

29. Magoun, *op. cit.*, p. 41.

30. Itard, J. M. G., *The Wild Boy of Aveyron*, (trans. Humphry, G. and Muriel), The Century Co., N. Y., 1932, (1894), pp. 49-50.

31. Penfield, W. and Roberts, L., *Speech and Brain Mechanisms*, Princeton Univ. Press, Princeton, N. J., 1959, pp. 235-242.

32. Schiefelbusch, R. L., Bair, H. V., and Spradlin, J. E., *Parsons Research Project: Progress Report*, Bureau of Child Research, Univ. of Kans. and PSH&TC, Parsons, Kans., 1962.

33. Wallon, H., *De l'acte a la pensee*, Flammarion, France, 1942, p. 249.

34. Rousseau, J. J., *Emile*, London, Dent & Sons, 1911, presents the naturalistic frame of reference which while aiding in the pioneer development of work with the mentally retarded, nonetheless overlooks the major fact that people can change.

35. Herbart, J. F., *Science of Education* (Trans. Felken, H. M. and E.) W. C. Heath & Co., Boston, 1902, in reference to the role of educational psychology.

36. Wallon, H., *L'enfant turbulent*, Alcan, Paris, 1925, points out that the "normal child discovers himself in the pathological child" in the sense that pathology represents stages of arrested development, p. 309.

37. Montessori, Marie, *The Montessori Method*, (trans. George, Ann E.), F. A. Stokes Co., N. Y., 1912.

38. Haring, N. G. and Phillips, E. L., *Educating Emotionally Disturbed Children*, McGraw-Hill Book Co., Inc., N. Y., 1962, "interference theory" as it develops from "extinction theory," pp. 129-132.

39. Smith, D. E., "An Experimental Program For Moderately and Severely Mentally Retarded Children," Unpublished Master's thesis, Kansas State College, Pittsburg, Kansas, 1959.

40. Ulrich, R., *Three Thousand Years of Educational Wisdom*, Harvard Univ. Press, Cambridge, Mass., 2nd. Ed., 1954, cites Herbart's (1850) idea of "apperceptive masses" which follows a similar frame of reference in terms of the total field, pp. 510-511.

41. Beare, J. I., *Greek Theories of Elementary Cognition*, Clarendon Press, Oxford, England, 1906, p. 5, 212-252, ". . . Alcmaeon of Crotna (5th Century B.C.) thought of the brain as the central organ of sentiency and, in short, of mind." Also Zilboorg, G. (with Henry, G. W.) *A History of Medical Psychology*, W. W. Norton & Co., Inc., N. Y., 1941, p. 38.

42. Solley, C. M. and Murphy, G., *Development of the Perceptual World*, Basic Books, N. Y., 1960, p. 5, and Simon, B., *Psychology in Soviet Union*, Stanford Univ. Press, Palo Alto, Calif., 1957, pp. 1-2, et passim.

43. Simon, *op. cit.*, p. 2.

44. Sokolov, E. N., Paramonova, N. P. and Lomonosov, M. V., "Extinction of the Orienting Reaction," *Pavlov*, Elsevier Publishing Co., Amsterdam, 11:1, 1961, pp. 1-7, discusses the formations of a "neuronal model of the stimulus" in a manner similar to this idea of cell associations; see also Hebb, D. O., *Organization of Behavior*, Wiley, N. Y., 1949, pp. 69-73, refers to something along the same line in his concepts of "cell assemblies."

45. Solley and Murphy, *op. cit.*, pp. 132-133, present "some major points made about developmental stages in cognition" from various authors. Our usage here clearly intends to include the concept that the most "human" forms of behavior are dependent on cognition in the sense of "awareness" or "knowing."

46. This note has been cited on page 20.

47. We are using this vocabulary for lack of a better one, and we recognize that the concepts represent a highly controversial area, though there seems to be some agreement as to the general idea. Viz. Roberts, E., "Biochemical Maturation of the Central Nervous System," in *The Central Nervous System and Behavior*, *op. cit.*, p. 179.

II. A Generalized Theory of Behavior in Play Therapy

Play therapy, or any psychotherapy, is a process related to and a part of the process of conditioning and reconditioning.[48] This being our premise, it follows that much of what learning theorists have taught us about the ways and means through which man learns, thinks, cognizes, and feels, represents a contribution which, if it could in some way be consolidated into a theory, might eventually produce laws of behavior which will make the job of a therapist that much easier.

ASSUMPTIONS ABOUT BEHAVIOR

There are a number of premises which should be examined in this regard. The first is the statement usually associated with field theorists, but also with other schools of psychological thought, that "all behavior is lawful."[49] That is to say, all behavior of the human organism is based on order and organization within nature. The process that we call abnormal behavior, abnormal in the sense that a psychotherapist has been called upon to correct it, is not a matter of unnaturalness, but rather a lawful process which for one reason or another is inconsistent with the accepted patterns of behavior occurring within a particular sphere or community. Every individual, regardless of how he is behaving at the moment observed, is responding to some set of natural relationships in terms of the pressures of exogenous forces upon him. It appears, then, that behavior is a consequence of the interaction of the individual and the pressures of these exogenous or environmental forces. Behavior thus produced, while it is the result of organization within nature, as we find it, may at times be inconsistent with the popular demands of the society in which the individual finds himself. It is not our intention at this time to go into an involved discussion of the philosophy of science, as these points have been thoroughly discussed elsewhere.[50]

But, if we can accept the premise that "all behavior is lawful," it becomes incumbent upon us to consider those aspects of behavior which tend to be described as abnormal. We have to recognize the concept of normalcy here as a statistical concept. We consider normal behavior in much the same way that we consider, for example, normal intelligence or normal temperature, or any of the other things where the word normal refers to a measurement element. It is true that behavior is not measured in the same sense, but society in a manner of speaking, does measure. It has certain limits beyond which behaviors are not permitted to go; if they do, they are considered abnormal. Thus, society may look with a certain amount of derision at a man who would walk down the street in a suit coat when everyone else felt the weather required an overcoat; it would regard with still greater wonderment, the same individual were he to appear on the street in his shirt sleeves in that weather; it would describe the same individual as abjectly abnormal were he to appear on the street on that day without a shirt and, in this latter instance, might even call the police and have the man investigated or examined. Now these are merely three different states of behavior which society originally considered abnormal, but which had to reach an obvious extreme before they would be labeled as such. This behavioristic concept thus becomes a matter of a measurement continuum and therefore when we speak of the individual who has been brought in or referred for psychotherapy, we should assume that his behavior has cumulatively, in this measurement set, been adjudged by his surrounding society to be abnormal—not that there are specific things of an innate nature within that behavior which are abnormal.

With the above in mind, it obviously becomes both absurd and fruitless to begin asking questions of a metaphysical nature, such as, "Why does the individual behave this way?" These questions deserve no answer, since they presume that there is some abstract reason or force, such as the ancients used to ascribe to a devil, which produced this "peculiar" behavior. The question of "why" is no question for a scientist to ask, and we have to presume that the therapist is making as much of an effort to function in a scientific manner as any other of his scientific colleagues. We use the term "scientific" in the sense of seeking the truth "as it can be known at this moment in time." The truth about a patient is not based on why he behaves as he does, the only proper answer to which is, "Because he is a human being." Rather, we should seek to learn what form this behavior takes, what has occurred to make it take this particular form, and what can be done about it? These questions have to be directly related to some of the knowledge about behavior which we have acquired from the experimental field.

The second premise would be that, in a broad sense, specific behaviors tend to provide a means for the human organism to relieve tensions which have built up in the areas of those behaviors. Taking man as an energy system, the intrusions from the surrounding field will change the force of the energy producing tensions which seem to be expressed by behavior.[51] The human will behave in a certain manner in order to relieve tension which has become intolerable to him. It is recognized that the fact of behavior does not relieve all tensions; it is even further recognized that the very fact of behavior may increase alternative tensions—i.e., tensions alternative to the ones being relieved—but nonetheless, specific behavior seems to be the result of increased tension in that area. To illustrate this concept, let us consider the act of eating, which is the specific behavior in response to the tension of hunger. Ceasing to eat is a response to the tension of fullness, or it could be said that the eating relieved the tension of hunger and the cessation of eating relieved the tension of fullness. We certainly recognize that the tension of hunger is not a specific innate quality, that it is related, in part, to the individual's place in a society which has established a certain suggestibility through the observation of other people eating, or through certain types of conditioning in terms of such things as odors, sights and atmosphere. Regardless, however, of how the tension has been produced, the end-product is a set of tensions which manifest themselves as hunger. Relief is derived through eating, and after the consumption of a certain quantity, the hunger disappears. However, the person tends to continue eating despite the dissipation of the hunger until the new tension of fullness has developed, at which point he normally ceases to eat. This limited example represents the types of behaviors to which we are referring and whether an individual's behavior is normal or abnormal, it still represents a release of tension. This is to say, that when the child behaves in a manner which elicits the disapproval of his social unit, he is doing so because of the presence of tensions. He may sit in the middle of the floor and scream, thus bringing his mother to certain specific actions which are negative to him. We have to presume at this point, that there are certain tensions within the child's immediate environment which have produced the screaming behavior and that these tensions, or the need to relieve them, are greater than the fear of reprisal from the mother. It is also possible, for example, that under certain circumstances the tensions have been produced by a fear of the loss of the mother's interest, and that the contact itself may have been the thing that the child was seeking. Thus, the behavior becomes a step toward a long-range tension-relieving activity, even though it may appear to the outside observer that the child is producing difficulties for himself instead of relief. In this regard, we can make an axiomatic statement that there is probably a direct ratio between increases in tension and increases in specific behaviors. Hence, as the pressures operating on the child increase in a certain direction, the behavior which these pressures produce will also increase in that same direction, and will continue until some sort of relief has been obtained. Stated in the terms used previously, these behaviors will persist until the alternative pressures from the opposite direction become greater, thus changing the pattern of behavior. This, in a sense, is a psychological restatement of the law of inertia, and though this is not our full intention, there is recognition that psychological behavior is not divorced from physical behavior. The difference, of course, lies again in the fact that the human as a communicating animal enters into the situation somewhat differently than a noncommunicating machine, and thus the particular factors relative to increased tension in one direction, versus increased tension in another direction, are as much related to the associations and language which the individual establishes around the situation, as they are to the operation of other exogenous forces.

The function of the relationships among behavior, the relief of tension, and communication is discussed below, but it should be pointed out here that the individual is always actively choosing among behaviors. Again, it becomes very difficult to judge this process in terms of a specific behavior, but we can, for example, take the retarded child whose primary behavior is one of sitting and rocking. Here, it is obviously impossible to know what specific tensions are being relieved. However, even in a situation such as this, we can presume that tensions are being relieved because the child shows immediate expository signs of discomfort if the behavior is blocked. Therefore, although it is impossible to determine the particular tensions being relieved by the rocking, it becomes immediately obvious to the investigator that an arbitrary blocking of the rocking behavior produces tensions which are unbearable to the child until he is permitted to once again resume rocking. However, if another element is introduced in the form of some sort of distraction, such as a TV show, the child who shows such obvious discomfort at being prevented from rocking will often stop himself and possibly concentrate on the show without any signs of discomfort. Thus, one has to draw the conclusion that at some level, a choice has been made in terms of various behaviors, and that under certain circumstances, rocking is the behavior of choice, while under other circumstances, the TV show, for example, becomes the behavior of choice and is evidently effective in relieving the tension.[52]

The child described above was dealing with a series of very primitive tensions as opposed to a child whose antisocial behavior consists of saying the word "damn" at any given occasion. Although a difference in communicative ability is clearly indicated, the fact of primitivization does not seem to change the basic element with which we are concerned. This is that the child, having been permitted to behave in the manner which he has elected, seems to be relieving tension. When this behavior is interfered with, the tension increases and the lack of behavior becomes unbearable.

The behavior serving as a means of releasing tension, even though other tensions may be built as a result, aids the individual toward higher functioning by utilizing his ability to produce associations when he makes a selection as to which is the most advantageous or most pain-relieving solution: either the release from the tension that the behavior reduces or the release of the new tension by ceasing the behavior. The psychotherapeutic function, as we will indicate, is essentially one of reconditioning whereby there is an attempt to manipulate this process of choice and to direct it, through conditioning, along democentric lines.

A third premise in this discussion of behavior is the observation that successful tension-relieving behavior, regardless of whether it is accepted or not, appears to function as a self-reinforcing process. That is to say, the individual, having found a behavior which relieves specific tensions, will continue to seek relief in this manner at an increasing pace as the tensions increase, even though social pressures against this behavior may, as a result, also increase. Thus, the child who finds that making certain noises relieves certain tensions, will often continue to make these noises in an increasingly faster and louder pattern regardless of whether his mother intervenes or not. The rejection of the mother's intervention in this case is not pure negativism as it is often described, but rather the child's attempt to determine whether or not he will be permitted to choose an activity which he has found useful in relieving his tensions. Rejection of intervention then, is a request for liberty or a request for freedom of action, rather than specific opposition to the mother's wishes. This process of self-reinforcing behavior becomes one of society's greatest difficulties with disturbed children, and often leads to the kind of situation where people say: "Well, the particular act, although not very important, was the result of a long accumulation of many other acts and proved to be the straw that broke the camel's back." What they are saying, in effect, is that this child seems to be, at an increasing pace, less and less in control of his behavior in this specific sphere, and society or his specific social unit, has become more and more worried. Their increased concern has intensified the tension surrounding the child, thus producing newer needs for relief which bring about the behavior at an increased level. This produces greater agitation in the social sphere which leads to an exacerbation of tensions around the child, generating new needs for relief, and again increasing the behavior until finally the social unit, being more powerful, moves imperiously, thereby creating a specific block either through institutionalization of the child or exposure to therapy of the child.

SOME CONSIDERATIONS OF THE RELATIONSHIP BETWEEN THE RETARDATE AND SOCIETY

Leaving this point for a moment and returning to our original assumption in Chapter I, that all men have some importance and that those more fortunate or more able have an obligation to help those less fortunate or less able, we find that the problem of the handicapped individual in society represents one of the major points of discussion surrounding this particular philosophy. There have been in the past and probably remain today, many well-meaning individuals who, without particular malice in their heart, argue loudly and strongly for both eugenic processes[53] and euthanasia. Some of these individuals state that through proper genetic selection, handicapped individuals need not be produced, and further, when they are produced, if they are destroyed immediately, they need not suffer the pain and agony of having to continue to live in a handicapped state. Again, though it is not the function of this book to deal with these particular types of arguments, the authors, as is probably obvious, are totally opposed to this line of thinking. The eugenic frame of reference seems to us to be totally without scientific basis. There is certainly no experimental evidence which will in any way support the idea that through proper genetic selection, handicapped individuals will no longer be born. On the contrary, there seems to be an increasing body of evidence that many of the conditions which previously were presumed to be of strictly genetic origin, now appear to be related to some form of intra-uterine lesion or "prenatal insult,"[54] and that although the difficulty is congenital in nature, the origins are within the environment of the womb, and are not specifically related to genetic imprinting or other forms of chromosomal predetermination. Thus, while it may be that genetic selection would produce different types of individuals from those presently being born by our present processes of random selection, it nonetheless remains unclear as to how we are going to presuppose that the selected individual is actually carrying the total characteristics that we would consider to be best or highest within our culture, or within any culture of the future. It is similarly questionable as to how this process of preselection will be able to deal with the question of the post-conceptive environment which is clearly beyond the control of eugenics.[55] In terms of the question of euthanasia, we feel that man does not have within his province the right to play God to the extent of deciding who is going to live and who is going to die merely on the basis of his physical make-up. There are varying types of related arguments that can be thought of in this regard ranging from the question of the moral right of one individual to take the life of another, to the practical scientific question that a dead organism is biologically and chemically different from a living organism, and that if science is going to learn anything at all about the prevention and cure of these conditions, it has to be able to deal with living organisms. Euthanasia would, therefore, destroy valuable medical, psychological, and sociological information, the presence of which aids in the eventual improvement of all mankind. Thus, even the most severely handicapped and most grossly deformed individuals may make a contribution, if only in the form of increasing man's knowledge of the unfortuitous ramifications resulting from the gestation and birth process, thereby, hopefully, increasing his ability to prevent these noxious occurrences.

With the above discussion in mind, we want to look at the general situation regarding the retarded individual as he finds himself in society. There are various facets of this situation that have to be examined and it is the purpose of this book to examine as many of them as possible. Therefore, these opening remarks will not attempt to crystallize any particular aspect. We will discuss in later chapters the question of the retarded child in relationship to society, to the institution, and to his family. Also, we will discuss the relationship of the child to society in regard to his adaptive behavior, his measured intelligence, and his physical disabilities. We will suggest various procedures that might be followed from a psychotherapeutic frame of reference, so that these relationships will be less painful and more adequate to both the child and his society. At the moment, however, we want to discuss the broader, philosophical aspects of this relationship.

One of the underlying, though unfortunate truths of community living within our culture, is a strong tendency to cast out its weak, deformed, and other helpless members. This tendency has strong historical antecedents. We find these individuals have not only been cast out, but physically destroyed, as, for example, in ancient Sparta. As we move through the ages, some cultures have followed one practice or another; all have tended to reject certain of their exceptional individuals either through casting them out physically or isolating them in some manner which kept them out of the general run of life. It is true that this isolation sometimes took the form of bestowing honor, as when handicapped individuals became medicine men or shamans in their tribes (it is speculated that probably the oracle at Delphi was a mentally retarded, possibly even epileptic individual).[56] Other people in various periods have clearly had handicaps and difficulties which have led their tribes or cultures to honor them, and at the same time continue to isolate them, to put them into a temple or some other separate area so that they would not be part of the regular workaday world. This seems to have been the practice over the ages. As civilization grew, we found that there was an increase in psychological destruction and individuals were accused of being witches and/or being beset by the devil, and were beaten or burned or treated in some manner which was ostensibly designed to drive out the devil who was responsible for the retardation or handicapped behavior.[57] In all of these instances we find that the underlying characteristic is the impossibility for society as a whole to absorb into itself that which is different, and institutions of the mentally deficient owe part of their origins to this fact.[58] Victor Hugo, in *Notre-Dame*, expressed this type of feeling as vividly as we find it expressed anywhere in literature, as did Hogarth in his etching from the *Rake's Progress*.[59]

In our present civilization, the rejection of the unusual can be observed among children where we find that one group can be extremely cruel and totally destructive to an individual child who, for any reason at all, tends to be different or seems to be out of place. Thus, the fat child, the skinny child, the redhead, the child with an odd shaped ear or nose, is an immediate source of extreme derision, name calling, and general teasing which is carried to as great an extent as is reinforced by the behavior of the child being teased. This kind of cruelty is certainly a learned process on the part of our children; it is something that they pick up from the behavior of their parents in their attitudes towards people of different races, colors, religions and names. The children, hearing their parents speaking derisively of people who are foreign to their culture, carry these hostile attitudes to their play activities and find for themselves individuals who may be abused for similar reasons. The psychological nature of prejudice has been thoroughly discussed by various authors where it is usually generally agreed that this type of feeling is based on an admixture of fear, wonderment, insecurity, and confusion, all of which lead the individual to be unsure of himself in his relationship to the "odd" person. Rather than admit his lack of confidence, he decides, much as his ancestors did, that there is something dangerously different about this person, and thus again the devils must be driven out or the witches burned.[60] When this happens to a child who is otherwise normal, there may be a fight or some event which will permit the outsider to eventually "win his spurs" and take his place in the "in" group. Should a mentally handicapped child be teased in this manner, however, the chances of his realizing what is actually happening to him are extremely slim. He is not able to consider ways of getting even and becoming part of the group. Although he may realize that he is being rejected, teased, and "punished," he cannot comprehend the reasons for this abusive treatment. His reaction does not lead to eventual success and acceptance by the group, but rather to constant terror and fear of being around these individuals. Thus he further makes himself a source of derision by his attempts at isolation. Since this seems to be a "human" pattern, we cannot discuss the situation in terms of its pros and cons, stating that "it shouldn't happen," and then drop it; we have to start first with the realization that it does happen. It happens at a more or less frequent rate, depending on various facets which may include the economic stability of the community and the amount of racial and religious tension present which thereby implies that some communities may be relatively free from this type of behavior while others are overwhelmed by it. Regardless, however, of these variations, there seems to be a constant pattern, particularly among children, of derision and attack upon the mentally handicapped individual.

Thus, one of the conclusions that we might draw from this whole situation is that the major effort of anyone working to help these children should be to discover ways and means of making them appear "invisible." The child who is not teased, who is not bullied, but who simply goes through his day as part of the crowd would, in our terminology, be considered invisible. He is not behaving in such a way as to become immediately visible to his peers and therefore, is not a source of threat or fear to them. Since the mentally handicapped child can at no time effectively fight back or carry the burdens of visibility, it becomes incumbent upon anyone working with him to try to help him achieve invisibility as rapidly and as completely as possible. This seems to run contrary to the usual mode of thought regarding mental hygiene and mental health efforts. We often say that the individual should learn to express himself, to be creative, to develop his own personality, etc. These are important ideas in thinking about the "whole man," and the efforts of every individual to find his place in society and make a contribution. However, with regard to a mentally handicapped individual, these ideas sometimes run contrary to his actual capability, and in this regard it becomes difficult to prescribe that he follow these traditional mental health dicta in the manner in which they are usually suggested. Rather, this individual has to learn to conform, to be part of his group, and to be as good a part of the group as he is mentally capable of being. This may actually mean that he is going to have to indulge in behaviors which may not be totally acceptable in terms of a stricter mental health point of view. Thus, the mentally retarded child growing up in a community where certain moral practices are not as tightly guarded as they might be in other communities, cannot be expected to be a more moral person than his peers. For mental hygienists, psychologists, or policemen to expect this, is to demand visibility of this individual when his real need is invisibility. We are, in a sense, asking the mentally retarded or mentally handicapped individual to carry on his shoulders the cross of society which we ourselves are unable to bear. Such a demand becomes totally absurd in the face of the self-preservatory needs of this individual who is certainly in no position to bear the ills and foibles of society along with him. Thus, we have to find ways of helping this individual conform to his peer group so that instead of being the subject of its taunts or bullying, he can participate in its general way of life, become absorbed into its society, into its culture, and hopefully, through this process, into the whole of society.[61] Thus, in discussing the generalized or philosophical relationship of the mentally handicapped individual to society, the key word is again invisibility, or if you will, conformity; the need seems to revolve around the fact that on his own, the child cannot set out on the path of individuality, but rather he must first be a part of the crowd. We, as psychotherapists, can help him achieve this goal which will enable him to move with the crowd wherever it is going, rather than having the crowd moving on and against him. As a further note, if we as mental hygienists do not like where the crowd seems to be going, our responsibility to the whole of society is to try to make some efforts at changing the direction of the

61. As we will discuss in the chapter on Adaptive Behavior (Chap. X) there are times when creativity should be encouraged, but only to the extent of allowing flexibility in conflicting social situations where conforming to one set of patterns means not conforming to another.

movement of the crowd, but not to expect the mentally handicapped individual to accomplish this by his powers.

In fully considering the question of the retarded individual in society, we must never lose sight of the fact that while invisibility is an essential goal, there is no mythical separation between the "in" group and the "out" group which has only psychological or sociological implications. The observed differences are real and the retarded individual is a living, breathing organism. As an organism he sometimes presents physiological and anatomical characteristics which are specifically different from those of anyone else in his surroundings, and he is unable to deal with this difference. Thus, the red-headed boy in school may be able to point from time to time to other red-headed individuals who have made tremendous successes. Certainly the undersized boy can always indicate the "Napoleon" throughout the ages, and thus thinking of himself in these terms, become, in a sense, psychologically equipped to make the fight that he must make for his personal recognition. The retarded individual has the additional problem, that not only is he singled out because of certain characteristics, but also that he cannot point to successful retardates. Therefore, the retarded individual has to be helped not only to conform to the behavior patterns of his peers, but also to learn how to create behaviors which will permit him to be accepted, though different. This process can be described as a process of finding substitute behaviors to replace those which do not permit invisibility or are unacceptable to the community. To do this, it is necessary for the retardate to cognize, and clinical experiences seem to indicate that this is the most difficult for the emotionally disturbed, retarded child.

GENERAL APPROACH TO MODIFYING BEHAVIOR

The process of finding substitute behaviors could be described as a process of unblocking cognitive functions. The cognitive elements of the child's behavior may be considered as blocked because of the presence of disturbance. Without, at this time, going into the question of etiology, we can presume that these blocks are the result of organic, sociological, or psychological interference with higher nervous activity. The function of these three spheres must be discussed in another place. The main reason for mentioning them at this time is to indicate that we are fully aware that the etiology is important in considering cognitive function, but from the point of view of our present discussion, it must be considered something apart from our current problem which is describing the higher mental activity of the child.

One should bear in mind that we are presuming that the child has a limited number of associations in his "bank" due to the process of blocking of cognitive functions, and the major role of the therapist in this area is to bring about what we have called the unblocking of these functions. We feel that this may be accomplished through a number of procedures which are not unusual in experimental work. Thus, we may think in terms of reward and punishment, and to some extent of cognitive stimulation. The first of these elements, reward, is based on the idea that behavior is the process of releasing tension, and that if the child is permitted to react, he will relieve these tensions. It seems logical to presume that one of the major elements present in the play therapy situation is the *giving of permission to the child to play.* This is a form of permitting him to behave, and in this way the right to play becomes a reward in the situation. If the behavior exhibited is not consistent with the desires of the therapist, the therapist may stop the play or, in our terms, intrude upon the child's play, thus blocking the behavior and in this manner producing a stoppage of the release of tension, thus producing a punishment. The child, in order to avoid the punishment and to be permitted to continue the behavior which was tension-relieving, presumably will attempt to conform more to the demands of the therapist, and in this manner relieve the punishing situation in favor of a rewarding situation where he will be permitted to continue with his activity.

The process of cognitive stimulation occurs when the therapist, functioning as a model, indicates through his intrusions, what he wants the child to do in this situation, or how he wants him to behave, thus not forcing the child to flounder around in various kinds of test situations, but rather helping him go directly to the kind of behavior or play activity which is considered most appropriate. Through his function as a model, he guides the child toward what must be done in order to gain a reward, and the child's understanding of this becomes a process of cognition. Therefore, the process of the therapist serving as a model becomes a process of cognitive stimulation.

To relate all this more directly to play therapy, we bring a child into the therapy setting and he begins to do something. It isn't important whether he "plays" in the traditional sense, but he begins to do something, if only to wander around the room or open cabinets. The child presumably is behaving in a way which releases certain tensions and, for example, it might be further presumed that the particular tension being released at this particular moment is the uneasiness which he feels because he is in a strange room, expected to do strange things with a strange person. He has this feeling of uneasiness since he does not know what is expected of him, and he seems to relieve it by wandering around the room and, in a sense, by doing what is often called "testing the limits," i.e., trying to find out what he can get away with, what he cannot get away with, and thus defining the situation for himself. Now in the situation of permissiveness, which often occurs in play therapy, the child is usually permitted to continue this activity without interruption until he touches an area that either produced the "a ha!" effect in the therapist, or until he does something which directly violates some preconceived idea of limits, at which point he is blocked. Our construct would be a little different. As soon as the child commenced to do anything, he would immediately be intruded upon by the therapist's asking him what he was doing. (In our constructs, intrusion and punishment are usually verbal intrusions.) This intrusion provides a model for the child which lets him know that he is expected to discuss various things in the course of his activity. If he replies to the therapist in a positive manner, the therapist permits him to continue. Thus, if the child is wandering around the room and the therapist asks him what he is doing, and the child replies that he is wandering around the room, the child would be permitted to wander around the room, and in this manner he learns that giving a positive reply produces permission to choose his own behavior. The usual situation, at this point, is that the child has not yet figured this out and he either gives no answer or gives the "I don't know" type of answer. When this occurs, the therapist continues to intrude more deeply, and the child finds that his exploratory activity is interrupted beyond his ability to continue. The whole situation thus becomes annoying, or expressed in the frame of reference we have been using, punishing. The therapist continues providing the kinds of clues that are needed for the child to work his way out of this situation, if he will become aware of what the therapist is doing. Thus, developing the child's awareness that there are two people present who must interact becomes one of the first processes in therapy. Through this process, cognitive functions are literally unblocked in the sense that the child is slowly being forced to use them in his attempts to discover how he is going to be permitted to do something to relieve the tensions which he feels. The child may merely sit down in the middle of the floor and bawl, which becomes another way of relieving the tension. At this point the therapist again becomes intrusive and asks him what he is doing, demanding some sort of cognitive reply. Thus even this activity does not become an escape from the ever-probing force of the therapist, who is literally trying to condition him into cognitive lines of behavior. Over a period of time it is presumed that the child, in order to get rid of the therapist's intrusion will: (1) begin trying certain activities; (2) explain to the therapist what these activities are, and (3) find that he is permitted to continue the activities without intrusion and thereby be able to move ahead on his own. In other words, he chooses his own line of activity and discovers that the therapist is perfectly happy to go along with this choice and, in fact, welcomes it.

The kind of relationships which we have been discussing, to be considered capable of modifying or redirecting the on-going processes, have to be consistent with the child's present level of maturation. That is to say, we cannot make cognitive demands that are greater than the child's present level of development or that are inconsistent with the way in which he views his need to relieve tension. We have to make certain judgments as to where we feel this particular child should be, in terms of his chronological age and his needs to remain a part of his social unit. These judgments, however, must be consistent with the child's ability to perform,[62] otherwise the therapist will find that he has made certain errors in programming, and has set up conditioning processes which are somewhat beyond the child.[63]

We cannot presume that a certain action in the child's home, parental rejection for example, or an authoritarian father, or sibling rivalry, or some other event of this kind, will necessarily produce specific effects in the playroom which have to be worked through. It is not inconceivable that a child may want to stick pins in a doll because he wants to stick pins in a doll, and not because he is angry with his brother. He may have been angry with his brother and not wanted to stick pins in a doll, and for the therapist to become preoccupied with supposed cause and effect relationships, produces a diversion from the main process which is the building of cognitive associations. For therapy to go forward, particularly with the functionally retarded, the child must be able to know what it is he is doing; and it is much more important in the play therapy situation that he knows he is sticking pins into a doll, than that he be aware, at some esoteric level, that the doll is representative of his brother with whom he had a fight that morning. Thus, the therapist cannot be too preoccupied with cause and effect problems, but rather wants the child to be able to rationalize what he is doing. If this behavior is socially acceptable in a broad sense, the therapist then supports it by permitting the child to continue, thus producing the reward. If the behavior is only acceptable in the therapy room, but would be considered socially inacceptable in the broad sense, the therapist continues to intrude to some extent, though also permitting the child to be active, thus achieving the "working-through" process that is consistent with most therapeutic procedures. If the behavior is unacceptable even in the therapy room, then the therapist's intrusions become more definite and the child finds that, in effect, the behavior has been blocked or at least all the tension-relieving aspects of it have been removed, and through this process the child hopefully will choose a new mode of behavior, or find a more acceptable rationalization for this behavior. A part of the play therapy process can be viewed as a teaching process. Though the therapist is not actively saying that the child should behave in a specific manner, he is, by intruding on most of the paths to the goal of tension-relief, creating the impression that the child should behave in a certain manner because a certain pathway becomes the only one that is really open to him. Thus, the child finds that he is permitted to do many things as he wants to do them, for his reasons, as long as he can share these reasons with the therapist. Similarly, he finds that many anxiety-filled reasons in no way block the behavior. Thus, if the child says that he hates his brother and he is sticking pins in the doll for that reason, the therapist is going to support the behavior because the child has been able to express it verbally. Consequently, the child will find that being angry at his brother is not only permissable but in a sense, legitimate behavior on his part, and that it does not have to be the source of guilt and fears. But again, more important, the therapist is not constantly seeking cause and certainly supports or reinforces many behaviors of a cognitive nature that in no way involve the child's expressing the cause of his behavior. The therapist is trying to build associations which is best accomplished through making the child aware of what he is doing, even if he isn't precisely sure as to what led up to it, or what the more symbolic meaning might have been.

To tie these points together we might say, giving the most primitive example in terms of functional retardation, that if we reach the point of intrusion where the child is sitting in the middle of the floor bawling (we are not interested in the cause but merely the effect, which, in this case, is bawling), we are not going to retreat from the intrusion and say, "We're sorry we annoyed you to such an extent." Rather, we want to continue intruding, although it may be necessary at this point, again through the therapist's functioning as a model, to offer clues such as asking the child if he is crying. In other words, if we are at such a primitive level, the actual behavior which the child is performing may have to be pointed out to him in order to gain his affirmation as to what is actually occurring. If the child says he is crying, this behavior would be supported and he would find himself in the predicament of crying because he didn't know what was wanted; yet, as a result of his having been able to verbalize this behavior, he would receive the therapist's support. The therapist would then indicate that crying wasn't necessary for achieving approbation. It may be that this concept increases the child's confusion, but we have to remember that psychotherapy is not accomplished in one session, that we have years of previous conditioning with which to deal, and obviously the reconditioning process is going to be a gradual thing. The therapist should not be too alarmed if his young patient is in tears when the mother comes to get him. What has to be remembered is that the child has to be picked up at whatever point the therapist meets him, and he must build from there and not from some abstract norm which the therapist or the parents have established without consulting the child.

The processes that are being attempted are those of developing within the child, an ability to organize and generalize these learning experiences through play therapy. The child, by receiving experience in the use of language, in the use of his ability to create choices, in the use of his ability to develop associations to convert his tensions into language, in the use of his ability through play to link related pieces together, and through utilizing the therapist as a model who will help him complete this function, will organize his mental processes in a manner which will permit him to carry over generalizations to the sphere outside of the playroom. It is not merely a matter of reproducing the life situations with which the child is confronted and thus training him how to meet them in play. The situations that are set up may be extremely primitive in terms of the child's spending his play hour splashing in water or some other similar activity. It is a matter of setting up situations which emphasize the cognitive functions within the child so that he will learn that life situations outside the playroom also produce associations and permit him to try to think through certain kinds of answers to certain kinds of problems. It is hoped that he will learn that this process is also one whereby he may make generalizations and having made them, begin seeking tension-relieving behaviors which are consistent with his knowledge of the needs of those around him as well as an understanding of his own needs. Thus, the main carry-over that we are conceiving in this kind of play situation is one of increased social understanding in the sense that the child comes out of himself to a great extent and recognizes in the play situation that there are other people all of whom must be taken into consideration when he chooses a particular behavior that is going to relieve certain tensions for him. This understanding is, of course, an extremely high level of understanding, and when it is fully achieved, represents success in psychotherapy and the patient is then ready for discharge; but even at a less complete level, it is presumed that the practice the child obtains in using his higher cerebral function for cognition will eventually synthesize itself and the child will find himself trying to think through situations outside of the playroom just as he was forced to think through them inside the playroom. Now it is at this point that we can really tie psychotherapy to learning, in that the new behaviors that are produced in the play therapy sessions are a product of learning through the establishment of associations, and the patient is thus able to live in a more demanding social environment because he has learned cognitive activity within the play therapy area.

In conclusion, we have set up a generalized theory of behavior in play therapy. It is based on the premise that all behavior is lawful, that behavior tends to be tension-relieving, and that aberrations of behavior tend to be self-reinforcing; that the way to deal with these aberrations is through a process of building and/or unblocking cognitive functions, that this may be done through a reward and punishment situation where reward becomes the permission to carry out behavior of the patient's choice, and punishment becomes intrusion in this sphere. This is further fortified by cognitive stimulation which takes the form of the therapist's serving as a model so that the patient will know what is expected of him, and assuming that the therapist has been able to program the conditioning or play therapy in a manner consistent with actual maturation, the child will carry through by developing the processes of organization and generalization, thus permitting him to perform in the community at an acceptable level.

ADDITIONAL NOTES

48. Bandura, A., "Psychotherapy as a Learning Process," *Psy. Bull.* 58, 1961, pp. 143-154, has enlarged upon this concept with the introduction of the principal of "counter-conditioning." He also refers to a number of others who have approached this question and provides a useful list of references; see also Wolpe, J., *Psychotherapy by Reciprocal Inhibition*, Stanford Univ. Press, Stanford, California, 1958.

49. Brown, J. F., *Psychology and the Social Order*, McGraw-Hill Book Co., N. Y., 1936, pp. 35-36. While many science writers have used this concept, Brown gives one of the best discussions in terms of the applied or social field.

50. Cohen, M. R., and Nagel, E., *An Introduction to Logic and Scientific Method*, Harcourt, N. Y., 1934, has been a standard reference in this area; see also Feigl, H. and Brodbeck, May (Eds.), *Readings in Philosophy of Science*, Appleton-Century-Crofts, N. Y., 1953.

51. Many writers have dealt with this question from their own frame of reference using different words to convey what seems to be a similar idea. Our intent here seems most closely allied to that expressed by Selye, H., *The Stress of Life*, McGraw-Hill Book Co., N. Y., 1956, pp. 171-176, where he discusses the relationship of "maladaptation" to nervous and mental diseases; and on p. 11 where he cites Claude Bernard as saying that ". . . the most characteristic feature(s) of all living beings is their ability to *maintain the constancy of their internal milieu . . .*"

Also, Brown, *op. cit.*, p. 27-28 again sets these concepts into an applied or social field.

52. Hollis, J. H., "A Method for Observing and Recording Responses to Social and Nonsocial Stimuli in Retarded Children," presented to the annual meeting AAAS, Philadelphia, Pa., Dec. 26-31, 1962, points up some of the ways in which this level child transfers his attention to objects.

53. Jennings, H. S., *The Biological Basis of Human Nature*, W. W. Norton & Co., N. Y., 1930, p. 251 and Gamble, C. J., "What Proportion of Mental Deficiency is Preventable by Sterilization?" *AJMD*, 1952, 57, pp. 123-126, try to make a case that mental retardation would be reduced if eugenic procedures were followed.

54. Ingalls, T. H., "Epidemiology of Congenital Malformations" in *Mechanisms of Congenital Malformations*, (Dancis, J., Reynolds, S. R. M., & Smith, C. A., Eds.) Association for the Aid of Crippled Children, N. Y., 1954, pp. 10-20, *et passim*.

55. Dunn, L. C., and Dobztansky, Th., *Heredity, Race and Society*, Penguin Books, Inc., N. Y., 1946, pp. 69-76, discuss some of these problems and reach some of these conclusions.

56. Zilboorg, *op. cit.*, p. 38.

57. *Idem*, Chap. VI, pp. 144-174.

58. Fernald, W. E., "Growth of the Provision for the Feeble-Minded in the U.S.," *Mental Hygiene*, 1917, 1, pp. 34-59, discusses the origins of the institutions in the U.S. and describes the previously existing conditions.

59. Hugo, V., *Notre-Dame* (The Novels of Victor Hugo Vol. I), P. F. Collier, N. Y.; Hogarth, W., *Marriage A La Mode and Other Engravings*, Lear Publishers, N. Y., 1947, (*Rake's Progress* Plate VIII).

60. Allport, G. W., *The Nature of Prejudice*, Addison-Wesley Publishing Co., Inc., Cambridge, Mass., 1954, reviews most of the major aspects of this question from the psychological frame of reference and McWilliams, C., *A Mask For Privilege*, Brown & Co., Boston, 1948, reviews some of the sociological and economic aspects.

61. This note has been cited on page 32.

62. Seguin, E., *Idiocy: And Its Treatment by the Physiological Method*, William Wood & Co., N. Y., 1866, p. 95.

63. Haring, N. G., "The Education of the Emotionally Disturbed Child," (mimeographed) presented at annual meeting Kansas Soc. for Except. Child., Emporia, Kans., Oct. 14, 1960, discusses this point as well as the need to ". . . interrupt or interfere . . ." continuously and directly. See also Haring and Phillips, *op. cit.*, pp. 129-132.

III. Play Therapy and the Learning Process

One of the major problems facing the clinical, developmental, or even the experimental psychologist in working with subnormal children is a question of how far these children can be developed. The usual conceptualization of goals in a rehabilitation process is based on the aim of returning the individual to the community as a self-sufficient, adequate person. This goal in rehabilitation and in psychotherapy is a very effective goal when applied to what are, essentially, whole minds, because the concept that there was previously a function which has been damaged, but which might be replaced, is a very sound and useful one. This is particularly true in physical rehabilitation where various prosthetic devices are used to aid in walking and in hand and arm movement. In dealing with children of subnormal mental development, however, we are faced with an additional rehabilitation burden. For the most part, these youngsters will probably never be able to function in the community at what would be considered a normal, totally self-sufficient level. A large number of them may be able to be absorbed into the community; the process of absorption is going on all of the time with individuals who, in terms of measured intelligence, are subnormal. This process of absorption changes as civilization grows and we find that the areas where these individuals were previously absorbed in terms of manual labor of one sort or another are gradually being eliminated by technological development, although it is true that, in general, a certain percentage will be and is being absorbed into the community regularly. However, this is not the group that usually comes to the attention of the therapist, because the child whose behavior is sufficiently out of line with his community to bring about the necessity for considering psychotherapy, is already, by this fact, cutting back on the potential for automatic absorption.

LEARNING PROCESSES WITH SUBNORMAL CHILDREN

In view of the above, it is necessary to consider the practical or realistic areas of development in terms of what can be improved on a short-term basis, recognizing that psychotherapy with a child should not be a process lasting many, many years. Here, we must deal with specific behaviors or specific symptoms, and we find that we run into a number of difficulties.[64] It has long been the tendency of both the community and of care personnel in institutions to reward those behaviors which are most obnoxious. Children in a typical institutional experience find that if they yell and scream, the care personnel become preoccupied with them, do things for them, and try to deal with their behavior; if they very rationally ask a question or simply say something to the aide, they find themselves sloughed off. This same situation often occurs with the child at home. His normal behavior is taken for granted and the family makes no "to-do" over it, but they become quite excited and quite involved with his abnormal behavior and, from the frame of reference of conditioning processes, actually reinforce the abnormal behavior by this procedure. These interactions are not as disastrous with a child who is making an average adjustment because he seems to be able to comprehend the realities of the situation, and thus distinguish between punishment and mere failure to reward. He may be eventually annoyed by the latter, but is able to gain a feeling of reward through the peaceful, jovial atmosphere of a routine, predictable family interaction. The maladjusted or retarded child, on the other hand, is suffering from what might be described as a perceptive error in figure-ground relationships in that he does not seem readily able to distinguish between punishment and failure to reward, and thus may behave in what seems like a punishment-seeking manner, because his "good" behavior was not actively rewarded.[65] Therefore, in thinking of developmental and learning processes, the first things we have to consider are the child's specific behaviors, and having decided which specific behavior we are going to support, we must set up a process of reinforcing positive actions, rewarding the things that we want to see happen, and extinguishing (i.e., withholding reward) or even punishing the things we do not want to see happen. In short, rather than perpetuate the type of conditioning which typically occurs in the child's environment, we attempt to do the exact reverse.[66,67]

Traditional thinking in the area of conditioning concerning the question of reward, speaks generally in terms of setting up a situation whereby the child will receive some recompense for the behavior which one has attempted to elicit. It is suggested for a child who is learning to walk, for instance, that an item of candy or a penny be placed at periodic points along the route, so that the child will have specific goals toward which to strive, and having accomplished these goals, will reinforce his own levels of aspiration and move on toward higher goals or, in this case, greater walking achievement. There is no question that this type of procedure is successful. However, the child is going to walk in a community, and in a situation where it is usually more convenient for the parents to pick him up and carry him because they have to get to certain places at certain times and they do not have time to let the child go at his own pace, where a great deal of travel is by vehicle anyway, the general tendency is for the child to find himself a source of criticism for his walking attempts. Thus, regardless of what happens in the therapy situation in terms of paying the child to walk, the environment actually pays him not to walk, and the traditional conditioning process must go a step further and try in some manner to control the total environmental contacts of the child so that the community will not counterbalance the processes that occur in the therapy situation. There are two questions which seem to evolve at this time: first, the question of "paying the child to improve or to perform," and second, the question of dealing with the child's environment as a source of the reward or punishment which produces the behavior. To these we want to add a third question concerning considerations of parsimony between the more traditional approach, or, what we have already described as a combination of learning and cognition concepts.[68a]-

The question of rewarding or reinforcing behavior is a comparatively primitive one related to the fact that a person has to have a reason for doing something. The reasons may be varied, but underlying the whole process, he has to want to perform the particular behavior that the therapist is desirous of seeing performed. Now one of the usual and certainly successful ways of getting an individual to want to do something is to make it worth his while. In essence, most of us perform at that level. As psychotherapists we receive a salary; if we engage in private practice we are paid by our patients. This salary or income is the reward we receive for our behavior and it is highly questionable that we would carry out this behavior if we did not receive this particular reward. In fact, we most assuredly would not carry out the behavior to the extent that we do if we did not receive that reward, because life's necessities would require that we perform some other behavior that did earn a more satisfactory monetary reward. Therefore, it is totally unrealistic to think in terms of altruistic psychotherapy; from this frame of reference, it might be equally absurd for us to consider that the patient should perform for us, in the sense of working for us (particularly with children, play is a form of work)[68] for nothing, when we would at no time consider working for them without remuneration.

This problem is emphasized with children and particularly with subnormal children, because they have not come voluntarily into the play or therapy situation. We might say that if the child had come to us and said, "I need help," the fact that they received help would have been sufficient "pay" to recompense the work they had done. When, however, the child does not of his own volition come with this request but is brought, or in many instances dragged by an anxious parent, where the child is in constant protest against the invasion of his time, or as in the case of institutionalized children, feels that this is just one more task demanded by the institution representing no special values to him—then the question of recompense becomes a much more significant one, because we cannot say that the services we are rendering to the child "pay" him. In point of fact, from his frame of reference, our services represent impositions and, as a result, we find ourselves in very much the same situation as parents who are constantly harping about their child's ingratitude for all the things that they do for him—statements and ideas which are familiar to all who have ever followed soap operas or other such "adult" entertainment. The point is that the child did not ask for the services and, while there may be a moral debt or obligation due the parent, this is not a debt or obligation which the child feels was incurred through his own volition. Most typically, the manner in which the parent wants the obligation discharged is contrary to the way in which the child would be willing to discharge it, even assuming that he actually felt obligated. The psychotherapist working with retarded children finds himself in a similar position. That is, he cannot expect the child to carry out certain behaviors just because the therapist thinks they are a good idea. The behaviors have to contain within themselves elements which the child himself wants to do or can in some way be induced to do through the presence of a proper reward.

Now it has been protested that this question of reward becomes a process of bribery, that this idea of "paying the child to be in therapy" is literally bribing him to do something and that bribery is immoral. Also, it has been protested that this disrupts the doctor-patient relationship, because the doctor is being paid to serve the patient, and if the patient is also paid to serve the doctor, this somehow equalizes the relationship and disrupts the underlying basis for it. Certainly, we accept the idea that if the patient has to be bribed to perform, the possibility of a carry-over of this behavior to a situation where the bribery does not exist is much less than if the patient would perform without the bribery. Further, if the patient is going to follow the doctor as a model or guide, it is necessary that the patient not be "in control of the situation" as would be implied by a "he is paying us, therefore, we do what he wants us to do" type of argument. It is true that very rarely does the retarded child show up with the statement, "I am a taxpayer and you are working for me," but basically much of his behavior implies something of this sort in the sense that he is aware that he has to be taken care of, quite often he is aware that in institutions physical punishment cannot be used against him, and he becomes quite aggressive in his daring the therapist to do something. In terms of management procedures this can be handled, but it is quite disruptive to a proper therapeutic atmosphere.

One of the major answers to this kind of question is the fact that reward does not always have to be in specie. Since the therapist is paid for his services in the kind of payment that is requisite for his maintenance in the community, we should recognize that the child should be paid for his services with the kind of payment that will permit him to maintain himself in his community. The child's needs in the community are not those of buying groceries and supporting a family and, normally, the child's needs in the community do not really involve nutrition, so that neither monetary nor food rewards are specifically necessary, although they might be highly enjoyable. The child does need, however, to feel a certain status, to feel that he is recognized as a person who may make decisions, that he has a place, that he will be permitted to play or to carry out his work, and that he belongs. The child's needs in the community consist of a number of intangible elements which can be given quite freely through the reinforcement process.[69]

Therefore, anything that would be considered rewarding to the child by the child, is a sufficient and proper reward. What is important, is that the therapist recognize that this reward must be presented at the time that the behavior to be rewarded is performed. Thus, the two elements essential to faster learning are that the reward be at the proper time and that it consist of something the child himself considers a requirement. For example, if the child finds that he constantly gets his mother's attention by wetting the bed, the tendency to wet the bed will be continued. If the mother makes no particular mention of the times the child goes to the toilet properly, or seems oblivious to the fact that he is dry, the tendency to be dry will not be continued. What seems to be the reward to the child is the mother's noticing or reacting to his behavior. The actual rewards provided by the environment do not ordinarily consist of candy or pennies, but rather, on a day-to-day basis, they consist of the mother's reinforcing wet behavior and not reinforcing dry behavior—thus, the child remains wet. For the normal child, the mother's behavior in this regard is not noxious because he has developed for himself a set of values which include being dry. As a result, he finds that life is much more convenient to him in that he is not punished physically, etc. Thus, a set of rewards is built around social values. For the retarded child, however, who has not established these values, the reward becomes the parent's attention, and this constitutes sufficient reinforcement for him to persist in wetting behavior.

Conversely, the child should be punished in some manner when non-desirable behavior is performed. Again, the punishment does not have to be specifically physical; it is sufficient to withhold privileges and rewards. In attempting to inhibit behaviors which are not desired, the withholding process becomes primarily one of punishment if it is without recourse at that point in time.[70] Thus, for example, if it is desired that a child learn to wash his hands, it would seem to be the proper reward that he be complimented on his cleanliness, that he receive certain extra privileges for being clean, that the handwashing procedure itself be imbued with reward in the sense that he gets attention during this period and is again complimented. At the same time, when he fails to wash his hands, he is punished by not being complimented, not receiving these privileges, and in fact, by losing other privileges related to cleanliness. Furthermore, the period of time permitted in the bathroom to wash his hands is sufficiently restricted and controlled so that the relationship between washing his hands and behavior in the bathroom is also established to a point where it is no longer a matter of his wandering randomly into the bathroom to wash his hands and thereby gaining all the privileges and rewards. Rather he learns to wash his hands at the specific and proper time and if he fails to do this, the issue is closed for that day. As a result of this failure, he is punished by not receiving the rewards or compliments, and by being further punished in the sense that certain things which he expected are not permitted him. Thus, the role of punishment in a therapy situation becomes just as important as the role of reward. Or, using the original example, if we oversleep and do not show up on the job, or if we do not keep our appointments with our patients, they are not going to pay us and will probably go to another therapist who keeps his appointments. Not only will they fail to pay us for that particular session, but their actions will result in the cessation of our income, leading to the cutting of electric, telephone and other services. Hence, if we do not do the work, we are not only unrewarded, but we are actually punished and it is this concept of punishment that must accompany the concept of reward. In other words, lack of reward is not representative of the whole idea of punishment. Punishment must have an identity of its own so that it is not a question of the child's being rewarded or not rewarded. Unfortunately, the situation in usual therapy practices, leads to cutting back on the success of reinforcement of the behavior wanted because it implies that the situation being "neutral" is of little importance and therefore it will be of no importance to the child either. We have to emphasize with the child that not only is it essential that he perform in the way we wish him to perform and that we are willing to provide a reward for this behavior within his frame of reference, but also that when his performance meets with our disapproval, we will take steps to punish him. This is a matter of introducing punishment independent of reward in the sense that he will be forbidden to do certain things, that he will lose certain privileges as in the example given above from Pestalozzi, and that he may even lose the good will of the therapist at that point.[71] In this way, punishment becomes as positive a teaching device as does reward and at no point should it be considered neutral. We feel that one of the greatest errors in play therapy, or in general work with children, is this process of neutrality where the therapist is saying in effect: "This behavior is not terribly important to me, I'll accept it if you do it, I want you to do it, we'll be good friends if you do it, but I'm not willing to either reward you for doing it or punish you for not doing it and, therefore, it doesn't have the importance that I pretend it has." The child responds accordingly. Literally, the therapist has, in a sense, to set off sky rockets when the proper behavior occurs and to be equally reactive when improper behavior occurs.[72, 73]

CONDITIONING AND ENVIRONMENT

With the above in mind, we come to the second area, the function of environment in relation to conditioning procedures. The idea is becoming more generally accepted that if specific behaviors are to be changed and, as we pointed out in the opening portions of this chapter, it is in this manner that the functionally retarded child must be approached, then one of the more expedient ways of achieving change is to set up procedures designed to deal with those specific behaviors. For instance, if it is desired that the child stop swearing, it serves very little purpose to deal with the way in which the child relates to the dining room situation, and if we want a child to eat, it serves very little purpose to deal with the question of swearing, even where swearing and eating may be somehow interrelated. In other words, a decision as to which is most important, the eating or the not swearing must be made. Since retarded children usually present a variety of symptoms or behaviors which their parents or care personnel dislike, some sort of hierarchy of change has to be established by the therapist. It must be decided which items have to be changed first, which items may be changed automatically by the improvement of other items, and which items can be left alone. The point we want to make at this time is that some sort of priority has to be established because it is impossible to change five or six different behaviors at once, and even if it were possible, it would not be recommended because one would not know which procedure effected which result and, therefore, we would have no idea of what had happened in the therapy situation, or whether the therapy situation really had anything to do with the change.

We are going to leave the highly controversial question of whether or not dealing with the symptom produces a substitution of other symptoms. At present, we have no experimental evidence which either supports or denies this contention, and it has been our experience with retarded children that even if new symptoms do appear after other symptoms disappear, these new symptoms seem to be every bit as much, if not more, a product of the child's environment as they are a product of the therapeutic change. Further, the removal of certain symptoms puts the child at a higher level of performance, so that even if there are later symptoms to be corrected, this correction comes more easily and the child is better able to adjust to his environment. Thus, the whole problem as to whether or not new symptoms arise through the suppression of old symptoms is becoming, at least in working with retarded children, a highly academic and nonproductive question which cannot be handled profitably at this time.

But to continue with our main point, it is necessary to establish a priority. There must be some sort of priority established if the child in play therapy is to be programmed so that he may deal with a specific kind of behavior. The traditional manner is one of programming the child by getting him to perform in a certain way for a reward. The concept is presented that if he does certain things he will achieve certain ends, that these ends will lead toward greater values which he can carry out of the play therapy situation into the normal situation, that the environment will reinforce this positive behavior on his part, and that he will then be prepared to go on to another level.

With the retarded child this is a matter of trying to get him to carry out a certain behavior, and the feeling is that if he can be brought to realize that the source of his reward comes from performing in a certain manner at a certain time with a certain speed and with a certain level of efficiency, he will continue to so behave even though the therapist is not there to provide rewards. It is assumed that he will continue because he will find by himself that society is supporting him in this behavior by permitting him to do things which he could not do and go places where he could not go if he had not met the requirements. Thus, in an institution, the child who does not wash his hands at the right time finds himself faced with a management device which keeps him from contact with other members of his group or from other activities within the institution. Similarly, at home, clean hands will produce good things and dirty hands will produce bad things.

This process of establishing a hierarchy of programming is usually left entirely to the experimenter. However, in psychotherapy a different type of problem arises. We have parents bringing children into therapy who say, "Johnny would be perfectly all right if he could only talk," or if he would "stop wetting the bed," or if he would "feed himself with silverware instead of using his hands," or if he would "stop climbing all over people when they come to visit the home." The objections on the part of parents are perfectly legitimate and certainly from their frame of reference indicate the most essential symptoms of the child's behavior in terms of what is keeping him from being absorbed into normal society. However, for the therapist to therefore say, "All right, I will condition Jerry to talk or to be toilet trained or to feed himself," does not always take into consideration all of the factors related to Jerry's own view of the situation. We are going to have to say that it is impossible to condition a child to do anything in the rehabilitation area that he does not want to do. Regardless of the views of some of the people in the field, children are not pigeons or white mice. We do not know whether you can condition a pigeon or a white mouse to do something it does not want to do, because we have no way of judging what a pigeon or a white mouse wants to do, but we can find out what a child wants to do, and you cannot condition him to do something that he has not for himself decided is to his own best advantage. Therefore, the whole question of conditioning in therapy as related to subliminal forces, etc., becomes just as idealistic and just as unrealistic as would be the alternate argument that the child's therapeutic processes must be based completely on dealing with his unconscious and that there is no place in therapy to treat symptoms. Both arguments would appear to be totally fallacious, particularly in dealing with the mentally subnormal, since both of them overlook the fact that the child, as a human being, has certain faculties, albeit damaged, which can be utilized for his growth and development. Therefore, for the therapist to specifically elect those symptoms with which he is going to work, is as much of an error as for him to completely ignore a symptom and decide that he is going to deal only with "dynamic processes." Instead, it is necessary that the child be understood in terms of his physiological and sociological make-up and that there be agreement, in a sense, between the parent, the therapist, and the child as to what is going to be treated. This is based partly on the physiological and neurological faculties of the child which we will discuss later. It is also based on the psychological atmosphere that can be built around certain activities. It may be, for example, that the parent has made such an issue of the child's talking that bringing him into therapy to teach him to speak only intensifies the obnoxious home situation and drives the child even further from the speech potential than if the therapist ignored the question of speech and worked with the child in terms of other aspects of communication, or even other types of therapy goals and activities, as we will discuss in the second section of this book. Therefore, in setting up the conditioning process around the child, it is necessary to establish a set of priorities consistent with the child's attitudes. These priorities must be in accordance with the way in which the child sees the situation, and any conditioning process undertaken for psychotherapeutic purposes should help the child do what he has already committed himself to do. It becomes one of the major problems of therapy to get this original commitment. That it occasionally may be bought is certainly true as we discussed in the first part of this chapter, and this is not necessarily immoral, but it must be understood by both the parent and the therapist that some means of getting a commitment from the child has to be utilized if the procedures are to be effective.

LEARNING AND COGNITION

Once the behavior has been set up, the milieu may tend to reinforce this behavior of its own accord without therapeutic intervention. Thus, if a child is proficient in using the spoon and does not get food all over the place, eats at a normal speed, etc., he does not receive criticism and may very properly receive approbation for his behavior. The mother may even of her own volition offer the child a second dessert, for instance, because he was so good and ate his meal at a steady pace. What has to be accomplished is that the mother must learn to support less than perfect behavior so that the child will have some idea of success as his behavior improves. This is a process of building motivation. The child must be brought to agree that the behavior recommended is the behavior to be sought, that there is some point in his using a spoon in spite of the difficulties that it represents, and in spite of some of the other problems that may be created by this act. Exactly what motivates a child is very difficult to discover and is really outside of the realm of this book. Suffice it to say here, that motivation, like all other factors, in a sense, can be itself conditioned. That is to say, the child can be taught to want to do something. It must not be overlooked, however, that the process which motivates the mother may be entirely different from the process which motivates the child. Thus, the mother may want the child to feed himself properly so that she can entertain guests or take him out to dinner with her; in other words, live a more normal social life with her child. It is unlikely that such considerations impress the child at all. On the other hand, he may be quite highly motivated to feed himself properly because of the possible reward of an extra dessert or, in terms of social processes, because of the mere fact that he does get approbation for carrying out certain activities or because of related activities such as the privilege of watching a certain television show while he is eating. Once he has learned the activity, regardless of his motivation, this will be reinforced by the mother's having guests over, and the child may then himself gain additional rewards by the presence of certain people whom he enjoys or who enjoy him. However, there is the possibility that the guests may react to him negatively as many individuals do not respond to retarded children warmly and with acceptance. Hopefully, this will not necessarily cancel out the behavior since the basic situation which was set up, was set up in the child's terms and, therefore, it is of less importance to the child whether the guests accept him, even though this was the mother's original motivation. What is important to the child is whether he can perform in such a way that he can receive the rewards the mother has established with him, such as watching television or the extra dessert. So, we do not always have to think of motivation in our terms; in fact, it is very important that we do not, but rather that we try to understand what is present in the child's world and what would be something that would motivate him to carry out the behavior.

Though interest has often been mentioned as one of the major bugaboos with regard to the mentally retarded, it has been our experience that it is not one of the problems. After the initial process of getting to know a strange person, the child is usually quite happy to come to therapy. The child in the institution is particularly highly motivated in that direction. Therapy is a change of pace in his normal day, the therapist tends to be more accepting than ward personnel or some parents; there is even the opportunity to do or say certain things which may not be permitted on the ward or in the home and, generally speaking, coming to therapy is an exhilirating experience to the child. He frequently responds to it with enthusiasm and is, in effect, the type of "vivacious individual" which Seguin said was necessary if we are to make certain gains. It is interesting to note that as long ago as 1866, Seguin pointed out that no matter "however incapable we consider idiots, they can be made to act efficiently . . . if we know how to appose the vivacious to the immobile, the loquacious to the mute, the imitative to the careless, the affectionate to the indifferent. . ."[74] This, in a sense, could be considered one of the objectives of therapy which is most easy to obtain with retarded children since, generally speaking, they are quite willing to come into the therapy situation. The problem of motivation is not one of motivation to therapy or to play with the therapist, it is rather motivation to perform as the therapist has decided he should perform. This is a different kind of question, and raises the problem of parsimonious operation.

The various kinds of operations we have described in this chapter are successful, have been proven successful in the past, and certainly will be successful in the future.[75] As we mentioned at the beginning of the chapter, the general tendency on the part of the environment is to support the behavior which is not desired. The environment does not demand the behavior but rather, the child is supported by finding that he gets attention and help even though he has to put up with criticism and abuse to achieve it by certain behaviors which are contrary to those which the therapist is seeking. Thus, even though the child's mother may yell at him for eating with his hands, he nonetheless does get fed and there is a possibility that, if he has difficulty in handling a fork or a spoon, he will not get fed as efficiently and as thoroughly as would have been the case had he used his hands. Therefore, he is more willing to put up with his mother's ranting in her efforts to get the food in his mouth than he is to go through the frustrations of having the food drop on the floor or the various struggles that he has to go through in attempting to use utensils. Now there are a number of processes related to this and if we, for instance, want a child to use a spoon, obviously he has to be encouraged to use a spoon. He has to be fed foods that are more serviceable with a spoon than with some other utensil or with the hands, e.g., soups, sauces, etc. There is absolutely no point in serving finger foods if we expect the child to feed himself with a spoon. Further, we have to be assured that the child will be complimented and given recognition when he utilizes the spoon, that he will be criticized when he does not utilize it, and that the peripheral areas, in terms of clean hands and clean clothes are equally pointed out and complimented when the spoon is used. In order to accomplish this properly, it is necessary that everyone who comes into contact with the child during the feeding situation is brought into the situation. It is not sufficient for the child, for instance, to come into therapy to obtain practice in using a spoon and to have the therapist compliment him on how much skill he shows, only to then return home, pick up his spoon and have his mother say, "Johnny, will you hurry up and eat, we haven't got all day!" It is similarly unrewarding for him to eat with his spoon and be completely ignored except insofar as he is bawled out for dropping some food on his lap or getting something on the tablecloth, so that while the fact that he is using a spoon is not mentioned, the fact that the food isn't being directed in exactly the right place is mentioned. Johnny thus adopts a "What's the use" attitude with regard to the spoon. If the process of change is to be accomplished, it takes more than just the therapist and the child. All of the individuals in the child's environment have to be incorporated into the process. In effect, the therapist must change the attitudes of the mother, father, any of the siblings that are involved, and any other individual who may have occasion to eat with the child under these circumstances. In an institution, this may involve as many as thirty children, three aides, a number of cooks and nurses, all of whom must change their attitudes if the conditioning of the child is to become what might be called total conditioning, i.e., in the sense that the child is to be reinforced only for positive behavior instead of being reinforced for negative behavior while having the positive behavior ignored.

However, if it is possible to set up such a situation, there is very little question in terms of experimental evidence that the process will work and the child's behavior will change. The major point in question does not so much concern processes as it does expediency in being able to deal with the attitudes and behaviors of so large a number of peripheral individuals in order that the conditioning be complete. Furthermore, in attempting to work with the child in the community, its members—neighbors, shopkeepers, policemen and passing children—present the tharapist with an almost virtually impossible task in establishing a fully controlled environmental setting as is required by the learning theorist. Even in an institution the situation is far from practicable. It is undoubtedly easier to control the behavior of ward personnel, nurses, and the other individuals who are in direct contact with the patient. But when one considers the individuals who are in charge of maintenance of buildings, grounds personnel, various other peripheral therapies, as well as social workers and individuals from other disciplines who may not be completely involved in the situation, visiting parents, general visitors, etc., even the institutional setting does not offer an atmosphere conducive to controlled experimentation. Therefore, we find that we have in the procedure of conditioning, as it stands by itself, a rather complete and total violation of Occam's Razor; that is to say, in order to produce the results required, a very involved and intricate procedure has to be utilized which, in the long run, becomes too involved and intricate for the therapist to handle skillfully. We feel that much of this situation can be alleviated by continuing on one hand to utilize these principles of conditioning and other factors which we have derived from learning theory, but also by including the material which has come to us through the work of the cognition theorists. That is to say, if the child can be brought to an understanding of what is going on, can be made to realize his role in making the behavior changes that are required, and can be made to desire these changes every bit as much as the therapist, then he will become responsible for his own behavior and it will not matter as much what the people around him do in this relationship.

Now this is not to rule out the influence of the environment. There is certainly no question in our mind that the environment has produced the original behavior and as long as the child remains in it, will continue to produce behaviors both positive and negative. However, we must remember that the same general environment produces normal behaviors in normal children and abnormal behaviors in abnormal children, so that in many respects the environment can almost be considered constant, and that which is different is the relationship of the child to his environment. Therefore, when the therapist deals primarily with changing the relationship between the child and the environment rather than only changing the environment, he is much more parsimonious in his behavior.[76] The easiest and most parsimonious way of changing the child's relationship to his environment is to get him to realize the nature of this relationship and to get him to want to make the relationship different because of the rewards that the difference can make. This is a matter of utilizing the child's ability to think at whatever level, and thus producing cognitive understanding of the needs to do things regardless of level thereby creating a situation where only the therapist and the child need make the major specific attitude changes. Now, of course, if this can be facilitated by making it possible for the parents or ward personnel to work along with the therapist on these attitudes and on these changes, it will certainly speed the cognitive processes required. However, the heart of the matter still relies on the fact that the child must become responsible for his own behavior, must want to make the changes himself and, to the extent of his ability, must understand why these changes are necessary and thus regulate his behavior accordingly. We could use as an example, the automobile. While we do not have to understand how the motor functions in order to drive the car, when something goes wrong and we call in a mechanic, our objective is to find someone qualified to deal with the motor, even though our own personal understanding in this area is extremely limited. Thus, it would be misleading for us to imply that our only concern is our relationship to the driving aspects of the car and to pretend that the car does not have a motor; it would be equally foolish for us to attempt to repair the motor ourselves. The more logical or appropriate manner of dealing with the situation is to recognize that the car has a motor, that the motor is partly the source of what is wrong, and that this relationship is what has to be understood if we are to make changes in the functioning behavior of the car. We bring in an expert who then deals with the motor directly, but who also deals with us in terms of making us understand how our behavior as a driver has affected the functioning of the motor. Now the parallel here is apparent if we consider the brain of the individual to be equivalent to the car's motor. What has to be seen is that the individual must understand that his behavior is affecting the functioning of his brain, and if we are to change this, it is not sufficient to merely talk about changing the behavior. We must also consider changing the functioning of the brain as was discussed in the previous chapter—the patient thus, in our analogy, being both the driver and the motor. The whole process of mental development in the child is dependent on the extent to which cognition can be achieved.

Now, in regard to changing the child's functioning, both the child and the therapist must come to understand what social values the desired behavior represents. This is related again to the ability of the child to fit into a social complex. He is not going to be absorbed into this social complex if his concept of social values is different from that of the surrounding society. Therefore, every bit as important as the actual changing of the behavior or dealing with the symptoms which we have discussed, is the context in which the child sees this behavior. This is a matter of dealing with social values at his level of understanding. The child must know what is expected of him, and often that is sufficient. Consequently we find that a child who is experiencing hallucinations can get along very well in society if he tells no one about them. Frequently, the therapist is successful with psychotherapy if he is able to convince the child that society will not condone these hallucinations, that if he will keep them to himself, he will avoid getting into constant difficulties with people around him and thus be able to function. The therapist, under these circumstances, hopes that, through the child's holding the hallucinations unto himself while living in reality, the environment will eventually reinforce the proper behavior and the hallucinations themselves will disappear, but the therapist does not need to explain this to the child. All that the child need understand is that people do not accept hallucinations, and that he will not be a cause for alarm if he can keep them to himself; therefore, the child must know what is expected of him in a given situation even though he may not fully understand the reasons for it. He will eventually learn to perform the required behavior because the rewards make it worth his while or the punishment for its absence has been sufficient to act as a deterrent. We feel that from time to time there is a tendency for us to lose sight of important thinking from the past because we have new methods and more scientific procedures with which to approach our problem. Such people as Pestalozzi, Froebel, and Seguin, who are generally associated with the history of education, should also have a place in the theories of learning and play therapy because they understood the one thing which we have tended to forget: that the child is capable of having a value system.[77] Even the retarded child is capable of having a value system, and this value system becomes a much stronger motivating force for him than any other element we could introduce into the therapy process. Once this motivating force has been activated, the whole matter of conditioning and learning becomes a fairly simple process for the therapist, and the child can go forward at a comparatively rapid pace. Thus, the combination of the functions of conditioning and the functions of cognition, in terms of the full utilization of the learning system of man, become the two major instruments in a successful play therapy procedure. In the next chapter we will discuss the more specific relationship between these elements and play therapy with the retarded.

ADDITIONAL NOTES

64. There are various ways of defining or describing symptoms depending on one's philosophical frame of reference. We choose to consider behaviors as indicators of symptoms without a one-to-one relationship between specific behavior and specific symptoms. Here, our position comes closest to Yates, A. J., "Symptoms and Symptom Substitutes," *Psychol. Rev.*, 1958, 55, pp. 371-374.

65. Mandelbaum, A., "The Use and Meaning of Controls in an Inpatient Treatment Center for Adolescents," (Mimeographed) Southard School, Topeka, Kans., p. 2.

66. Ayllon, T. and Haughton, E., "Control of the Behavior of Schizophrenic Patients by Food," *J. Exper. Anal. of Behavior*, 5, 1962, pp. 343-352.

67. Festinger, L., "The Psychological Effects of Insufficient Rewards," *Amer. Psych.*, 1961, XVI, pp. 1-11, in his discussion of "dissonance" points out that the most common way for the organism to reduce dissonance is to change this behavior. We have set up a situation where withdrawal will not reduce the dissonance or "punishment" and therefore, in keeping with Festinger's findings, but contrary to the traditional behaviorist stand, the punishment will lead the child into new, more acceptable channels.

68a. Battig, W. F., "Parsimony in Psychology," *Psych. Reprints*, 1962, 11:2, pp. 555-572 though seemingly "anti"-parsimony nonetheless presents arguments which force us to continue the consideration of this factor in our choice of paths.

68. Dewey, J., *Democracy and Education*, N. Y., Macmillan Co., 1916, differentiates between "work" and "play" in terms of the importance of the end product. Thus, when the child uses "play" for exploration or learning or emotional expression, he is "working," pp. 34-35.

69. Pestalozzi, J. H., *Leonard and Gertrude*, D. C. Heath & Co., Boston, 1901, and Seguin, *op. cit.*, pp. 215-217, give examples and ideas related to the fact that children will respond positively to an adult with a rewarding attitude, if they seem to understand what is happening.

70. Ayllon and Haughton, *loc. cit.*

71. Pestalozzi, *loc. cit.* Pestalozzi would even go so far as to refuse to speak to the student he was punishing.

72. Boardman, W. K., "Rusty: A Brief Behavior Disorder," *Journal of Consulting Psychology*, 26, 1962, pp. 293-297, discusses punishment from this frame of reference; see also the comments by Bandura, A., "Punishment Revisited," *Journal of Consulting Psychology*, 26, 1962, pp. 298-301, and Miller, D. R., "On The Definition of Problems and the Interpretation of Symptoms," *Journal of Consulting Psychology*, 26, 1962, pp. 302-305, who discuss this question from the behaviorist and analytic frames of reference respectively.

73. Munn, N. L., *Psychology*, Houghton Mifflin Co., Boston, 1946, pp. 129-130, correlates punishment with annoyances.

74. Seguin, *op. cit.*, p. 218.

75. White, J. G., "The Use of Learning Theory and The Psychological Treatment of Children," *J. Clin. Psychol.*, 1959, XV, pp. 227-229, among others, cites the use of these techniques to deal with the types of children's problems often brought in for psychotherapy.

76. We recognize that this is a process of interaction and that the environment will in fact change as the relationship changes; see also Zazzo, R., *Le Devenir de l'Intelligence*, Presses Universitaries de France, Paris, 1946, pp. 24-32.

77. Boyd, W., *From Locke to Montessori*, George G. Harrap & Co., London, 1914, discusses the work of these and other individuals as it applies to the development of education techniques.

IV. Theoretical Considerations in the Formulation of Play Therapy with Subnormal Children

GOALS OF PLAY THERAPY

The goals of play therapy with functionally retarded children are varied, but they generally center around attempts to raise the child's level of functioning[78] and to help him learn to control his behavior in such a manner that he is "more livable." That is to say, it is hoped that the child will learn to do more things and to improve his present ability, and further, through increased ability to deal with situations, that he will become happier and more useful as a person. Though therapists and clinicians are often loathe to admit it, goals of play therapy also involve the hope that the child will become less obnoxious. This is not to say that the functionally retarded child is necessarily an "obnoxious" person, but the behavior associated with his retardation often sets up extreme irritation in the clinician or parent and stands as a constant reminder of their inability to deal with him. He consequently becomes someone with whom they would rather not be at that particular moment. One of the unwritten goals of therapy is to change that particular status.

There are differences in opinion, but in general we can say that any planned or "goal-directed" attempt to create behavioral change in the patient, regardless of the materials or procedures used—as long as an effort has been made to establish a close interpersonal relationship between the patient and the therapist,[79] as long as an effort has been made to create an organized treatment setting,[80] and as long as the processes of communication are emphasized—should, for the purpose of this book, be considered psychotherapy. However, differences in materials and differences in procedures will produce a different type of therapeutic result. In other words, if the materials are structured and definite, with a specific function, they help produce one type of psychotherapy, while if the materials are unstructured and indefinite, without a set function, they help produce a different type of psychotherapy. Also, if the therapist goes into the setting with preconceived ideas and attempts directly to achieve certain specific ends, he will produce a certain type of psychotherapy. On the other hand, if he goes in without attempting specific results and has more generalized aims, he will produce still another pattern. In reference to the above concept, this chapter will deal with the purpose of establishing specific goals for different types of play therapy, and it will also present the concept of structure as it is related to the various types of materials and approaches that may be used in setting up psychotherapeutic procedures for play therapy.

We hope that all can agree that the personality changes which are sought in the functionally retarded individual are those which will make him more able to conform to the demands of the community as far as behavior is concerned; that he will become less individualistic or autistic in his thinking, and more able to take from his environment, as does the normal child, the cues and guides to learning, both in the behavioral and intellectual spheres. We know, for example, that the introductory questions on the WISC[81] request information which, in terms of the standardization of that test, the child must have before he enters school. It is true that he could learn it in school, but for all practical intents and purposes he should have that information under his control long before he enters into any sort of formal learning situation. This knowledge has come to him from his milieu; it may have been presented by television, by overheard remarks or by plain logic. But whatever the source, somehow or other the milieu has produced cues sufficient for his knowing, for example, that a dog has four legs, though no one has actually sat down and explained it to him. However, the retarded child seems to be blocked in this area. He does not draw from the surrounding community information which the culture provides. In short, everything he knows he has had to learn either through a very arduous struggle, or through its having been taught to him in a very painstaking manner, usually through a process which involves conditioning, although the person doing the teaching has not necessarily thought of it in those terms. The reasons for this blockage are varied. They may, for example, be related to the organic cause of the retardation, or to an autistic-like self-preoccupation with inner thoughts of one sort or another, as found in the severely emotionally disturbed child. Regardless, however, of the cause, the net result is that the child's functional level has been lowered by his inability to use the minimal cues which his society has provided to guide him in the behavior expected of him in a given place at a given time.

We do not know what the factors are that enable one retarded person to carry on in the community while another cannot. Who will be brought in for therapy or be found to be in need of services or treatment over and above those normally provided in the community for the retarded or for youngsters of subnormal development, is difficult to determine. This question is, of course, an extremely important one; the discussion throughout the rest of this book implies certain social deficiencies in some children, and these are definable as therapy goals in the sense that it is necessary for psychotherapy to try to build cognitive awareness in the child lacking these qualities. We cannot really fully define what it is that distinguishes some children and marks them for psychotherapy, while others with very similar characteristics are able to utilize the facilities which the community provides and thus integrate themselves.

However, there are one or two hints which we might give at this time; one element seems to relate to an ability in the child to be accepted by the social forces surrounding him. That is to say, when the child seems to be a part of the surrounding community, seems to be accepted for himself at whatever level he functions, and is not constantly being made aware of his mental deficiency, he seems to be able to develop a suitable adjustment, at least during that period of time when play therapy would be the prescribed mode of treatment. It is true that some children break down later, in adult life, due to changes in the social relationships surrounding them, but this is still easier to handle if, as a child, there was a sense of belonging. This is part of the process of invisibility which we have already discussed. On the other hand, the child who is not able to feel that he is a part of the day to day world in the sense of being accepted, who seems to feel that he has nothing to say about his future but is completely in the hands of forces which are both frightening to him and completely out of his area of control, becomes disturbed and finds himself in need of special treatment over and above the expected processes utilized to deal with his subnormal level of mental development.[82] It is, in essence, to this child that we have been addressing ourselves, and, without any attempt to surround him with a special kind of mystique concerning rejecting parents or various other kinds of deprivation, we can say that he does not seem to have been given the same opportunity to integrate himself into society at whatever level that society is functioning, as the other child who does not find himself in need of therapy.

We are going to have to start our thinking at the point when the parent rings the doorbell requesting help or the social worker sends the institution an admission request, and, while it would make tremendously fruitful social investigation to find what was behind the ringing of the doorbell or the making of the application for admission, this problem is outside of the scope of this book and, therefore, is an area for other investigators.[83]

In essence, the behavior changes in which we are most interested are those related to the development within the child of a consciousness of social stimuli and an ability, once he is aware of these stimuli, to modify his own processes in some way to be in keeping with them, thus producing a pattern of behavior which is both socially acceptable and personally rewarding. Exactly how this is to be brought about is not always known. There is no easy formula for procedure, but it does seem clear that different children seem to have different demands and different requirements in this area based on their own self-concept, the image they have of themselves, the image they have of the people around them, their families, their friends, their peers, etc., as well as the rest of their life experiences. It is impossible to chart any child's life from the day of his birth to the time when he comes or is brought in for psychotherapy, either into an institutional setting or into a community service setting. An effort is made through case histories, etc., but these are very cursory at best, covering only peripheral areas, and even if they appear to be thorough, they obviously cannot at any time indicate how the disturbed or brain damaged child feels about a particular item of his history or a particular element of his environment which, in effect, is being seen through an "out of focus" frame of reference.

Because of these social factors, one of the first questions a therapist must ask himself is: does this child require individual attention, or would he be better served by functioning with a group of children with similar problems?

This question will be dealt with in later chapters as we discuss specific types of play therapy, but at this time let us consider some of the general implications of individual therapy as a mode alongside group therapy as a mode. We are purposely avoiding a comparison between the two because we feel that both forms may be useful with the same child under different circumstances and that each form has a specific application depending on the immediate goal. The most immediate goal is that which is most consistent with what the child is able to do at this particular point in time. The essential difference between individual therapy and group therapy is not the obvious difference involving numbers of children, but rather it involves the way in which the child responds in terms of the therapy goals and his maturational level. We must seek the particular form which would seem to create the easiest transition for the patient from his present mode of behavior to a more socially acceptable mode of behavior. In other words, is the child best able to make the adjustments required in company with and under the influence of other children and their behavior, or will he best be able to make these changes by himself with only the therapist acting as a model? This is a point that cannot be settled easily. We do not mean at this time to be talking completely around the question, but both group and individual therapy do play major roles in the particular theory we are presenting, and a judgment must not be made on the values of either form of psychotherapy, but on how the child will best be able to bring about changes within himself.[84] Thus, the issue is not whether individual therapy is necessarily "deeper" than group therapy or necessarily more likely to deal with "basic needs" or any of the phrases that are usually used in connection with it, but rather the question is: is individual therapy going to help this child gain a self-concept, or is he more apt to gain it in conjunction with other children; is individual therapy going to help him control his impulses or learn to behave in a socially acceptable manner; or is he better able to reach these and other goals in conjunction with other children.[85] We are, of course, ignoring many of the other aspects of the question, such as the amount of time that the clinician has to devote to therapy versus the number of children who need therapy, the logic being the ability to treat more children in a group in a given therapeutic hour, etc. These questions have been discussed in the literature to some extent, and it is not the purpose of the present volume to duplicate that discussion.[86] Rather, the point we wish to highlight, which is not necessarily new in dealing with questions of functional retardation, is that the child has specific problems, and is expressing these problems to the therapist who must discover the best way of dealing with them in order to reach certain goals. The best way may be individual therapy or it may be group therapy, but the therapist has to learn to understand his patient sufficiently to know which form is the best in terms of the problems of the patient.

A further area for discussion in regard to the general goals of psychotherapy with the functionally retarded has to do with the need to recognize and to cope with the developmental and maturational processes in the child. This is a special problem for clinicians dealing with all children, not just the functionally retarded. That is to say, one child, because of his chronological age, is at a different stage developmentally or maturationally than another child of a different chronological age. This leads both to the necessity of understanding patterns of maturation and to the necessity of accepting maturational differences. These maturational differences will affect the personality patterns. One might even say that the young child has every right to behave in an immature manner because he has not yet reached a mature level of development. Thus, as we indicated in the introduction, therapy goals which are "Utopian" in nature and are not in keeping with the child's current level of development or maturation, are only going to create new disappointments and traumatic experiences instead of accomplishing a therapeutic aim. Beyond this point, we must consider that therapeutic results must not be confused with natural developmental or maturational factors within the child. Thus, if we are to avoid the false feeling of success which may occur if we have a child in psychotherapy for a period of, say six months, at the end of which we find that he is functioning on a higher level than he was six months previously, we must remember that he is six months older and that the higher level may be due to this increase in age as much as to the therapeutic procedures used.[87] Therefore when working with children, regardless of their functional levels, the maturational factors and developmental factors have to be very carefully considered.[88]

The psychotherapy goals for the mentally subnormal are primarily those which, taking into consideration his current maturational level, tend to accelerate his ability to mature and to learn, at least insofar as personality patterns are concerned. It is this desire for acceleration which becomes one of the most important problems of psychotherapy with the functionally retarded child, because there is a backlog of decelerated learning which has to be overcome in what is really a minimum time, since it is neither feasible nor fair to expect a ten year old boy, for example, to go through an additional ten years of psychotherapy to erase the poor conditioning of the first ten years. Rather, we have to figure ways of accelerating the growth pattern so that the faulty learning of the first ten years can, in a sense, be erased or replaced and new learning conditioned in a much shorter period, hopefully six months or maybe a year. This can be accomplished if the therapist is aware of the principles of how children learn. He can arrange his therapy procedures and his therapeutic approach along lines that will be in keeping with the growth and developmental patterns of his patient or group of patients, and thus be in a position to help to accelerate these growth patterns.[89] This also requires that the child constantly be aware of what he is doing in the play sessions, and that he be able to indicate his awareness by either responding to the therapist actively or behaving in a manner such that the therapist knows that this awareness has been achieved. The therapist then responds by both permitting and entering into the activity, thus making the awareness a source of approbation (reward). If the child is not willing or able to establish this awareness, the therapist continues to be a source of intrusion (punishment). Since this requires a control of cognitive processes in the therapeutic situation, in the sense that the child has to intellectualize his behavior in order to achieve recognition and approbation from his therapist, the process can be described as actually *forcing the child to think*. Therefore besides the freedom from intolerable disappointment which the psychotherapeutic process should represent to the functionally retarded child, it must also represent an introduction to social and individual responsibility[90] to the extent of knowing his role at that moment. If the child behaves in a certain manner, he is more likely to be gratified than if he behaves in another manner; e.g., if he behaves in a more socially acceptable way, he is less likely to run into disappointment than if he behaves in a less socially acceptable way. With this realization comes improved cognition, and with improved cognition comes higher functioning in all areas. Thus, this technique of '*forcing the child to think*' becomes a way of accelerating growth and developmental processes and higher nervous activity. There may be instances where the child is overly resistant to this approach; in those cases additional modes of intrusion must be sought.[91]

In later chapters we will discuss more fully how this improvement in maturational processes is related also to the acquisition of skills and a general improvement of readiness for more advanced development in the area of perception. These factors are related to the child's improved self-concept and very closely related to the psychotherapeutic process. Again, we must emphasize the constant interaction between personality change, behavioral change, and intellectual learning so that the psychotherapist becomes, at times, the teacher's assistant by producing readiness for the more specific teaching done in the classroom.

Another aspect of the problem of establishing proper goals for the mentally subnormal child has to do with his relationship to his milieu. The child's problem, regardless of etiology, has a very definite sociological factor in terms of the general interaction of the child and his family in his home community.[92] This interaction has been sufficiently negative to create the need for treatment in the community facility, or in some instances, institutionalization. Thus, the very fact that treatment is needed is *de facto* evidence that a community problem exists. The presence of this community problem is not totally lost on the child and he is, to some extent, aware that he "is a problem." As our experience in other areas of emotional disturbance indicates, with this awareness there develops a self-reinforcing process whereby the problem multiplies itself, e.g., the child may have a fear of parental and community rejection, and then with a snowballing effect, other fears related to himself and his inability to cope with the situation, the continued rejection, etc. All of this, in a sense, may be verified by institutionalization, in that leaving the home and being sent to an institution then becomes the clearest indication that his fears concerning rejection have been borne out. This may set up its own processes within the institution, leading to additional disturbed behavior. A similar thing may occur when the child is brought into a child guidance clinic or a community service where he becomes aware that he is receiving a special kind of treatment which may be something that he feels he cannot discuss with his playmates or friends, because the family attitude indicates that it is not completely socially acceptable, thus producing additional fears and additional trauma. It becomes incumbent upon the institution or community service first to attempt to deal with these fears before trying to understand either the etiology of the condition or the basic behavioral changes that are required. The therapist must become aware of the child's previous relationships within his milieu, the cultural conditions from which he has come, the social realities of the home situation in terms of the socioeconomic status of his parents, and his previous experiences in life concerning the way the milieu has dealt with him.[93]

When the child must be institutionalized, the hospital, in order to cope with the situation, attempts to redirect the child's feelings along more "realistic" lines, and, in this sense, becomes a therapeutic milieu. Thus, institutionalization becomes unto itself a form of immediate therapy, and every child in a hospital can be considered to "be in therapy" from this frame of reference. However, there are a group of children with identifiable characteristics who do not respond to this type of "milieu-therapy."[94] That is, they have specific problems of adjustment to the hospital and to themselves which combine to make it difficult for the therapeutic atmosphere of the hospital to break through the barriers they have set against the rest of the world. Thus, some children seem to feel the contradictions between the hospital as a therapeutic community and the hospital as a verification of their rejection by their family more strongly than other children. This may in some way be represented by their level of comprehension and thus related to intelligence, but that is still another area. The point remains here, that these children, for the most part, with their feeling toward the contradiction, make poor adjustment to the hospital community and are given the highest priority within the hospital for either individual or group psychotherapy.

This would also be true, to a lesser extent, of those children who are being treated by a child guidance clinic or other community services, in that they often become totally resistant to these therapeutic services and should receive some other type of therapy to help work through any feelings they might have that their being in treatment is a total confirmation of environmental rejection. Thus, many of the therapy goals are defined in terms of the sociological factors present.

Part of the problem involved here is the child's general lack of understanding that the rules and regulations relating to behavior which have been laid down in his home community are not aimed specifically at him, but rather reflect the needs of the social order. In other words, he must realize that when he is scolded for stepping off the curb before waiting at a stop sign or looking for the cars, this is not a personal rejection or a personal attack upon him, but instead is the way society functions so that both pedestrians and cars can exist in the same world. This is the most difficult phase in dealing with the functionally retarded child in terms of his cultural experiences, particularly because quite often the *ideas of reference* which are associated with forms of schizophrenia are found with these children. We do not want to say that these children are all schizophrenic but rather, that the nature of their thinking produces a reaction which is not too different from the traditional schizophrenic in regard to egocentric or autistic thinking. For this reason the therapist has a responsibility of establishing limits. The concepts of limits has been discussed in the literature from varying frames of reference.[95] At this point we do not wish to go into the specific question of what limits to establish, as the chapters describing the specific types of play therapy will cover the limits required for that type. It is important, however, to take the following into consideration in establishing these limits: first, the relationship of the patient to the therapist which may even reach the point of being a question of personal safety; second, their appropriateness to the relationship of the patient to materials in the play; and third, their relatedness to the time and place (setting) of play therapy. These limits are, however, in a broader sense most related to the child's gaining the understanding that in spite of the fact that the therapist has imposed limits, the child is still accepted, that he is still "loved" by the therapist, and that these limits are not imposed on him as a way of punishing him, but rather as a way of increasing his freedom within the therapy situation, because he no longer has to fear doing certain things. In this sense, limits provide a very close correlation between the requirements and demands of living in the home community; thus, if the child will stop at the curb and watch for the cars, he no longer has to fear crossing the street. This one-to-one relationship may sound oversimplified. In actual practice it probably is not. Once the child has learned that social regulations are not aimed specifically at him, but are rather part of the warp and woof of society—where there is grass that cannot be walked on, flowers that cannot be picked, things that cannot be taken, words that cannot be said—and that these rules are applicable to all people. From this understanding, he will gain an improved concept of himself and may even take pride in the fact that he has to do the same things that other people have to do and therefore is not so different. This feeling of extreme difference seems to be a problem with a large number of functionally retarded children. Consequently, the presence of limits in the therapeutic situation is not only conceived in terms of personal safety and preseveration of material but, more important, it helps to emphasize the healthy or positive sides of the child's personality by trying to point up to him ways in which he is similar to other people instead of constantly emphasizing the ways in which he is different.[96]

Furthermore, concerning the third type of limits (time and place), we have some additional factors. "Time" refers to the limits set on the length of the therapy session. Here, we have what could be described as an inescapable limit in the sense that time passes regardless of what else occurs. This can be used to help the child realize that there are many forces in nature or things in society which are, as far as he is concerned, immutable. However, he finds that though unchangeable, it nonetheless provides continuity and thus, while it stops one session, it also starts the next.

The "place" refers to the playroom or play therapy setting, which is also considered a limit in the sense that it is usually the only place where the child interacts with the therapist *as a therapist*.[97] Both the child and the therapist must be aware of the special roles and relationship the setting provides. Some things are possible in the playroom that are not permitted outside the room. The playroom becomes a source of freedom for the child and the therapist helps him use this freedom constructively. Also, the room and the therapist become united in the child's mind and it comes to symbolize both the freedom of activity and the source of models.

STRUCTURED-UNSTRUCTURED MATERIALS

As we have discussed in Chapter III, in trying to evolve the methods of modifying the behavior or procedures for developing new behavioral

97. The exceptions to this rule are mentioned in Chap. V (U-U Therapy) and Chap. VI (U-S Therapy).

functions, the atmosphere of the therapeutic setting and the attitudes of the therapist become extremely important in terms of the conditioning processes which are to be established. We consider this general idea to be best represented by the concept of structure. That is to say, the presence or absence of an organized system of play procedure becomes the keystone of the whole therapeutic process. Thus, where there is a very tightly organized, well-developed system of procedures and methods, we would say that this process was highly structured; where there is a less developed system, not as well organized, and where the methods and procedures are not as strictly followed, we would say this was lacking in structure or to use the terminology we will be employing throughout the book, unstructured. Thus, we would define structure, as we are using it, as the degree of preconception of form or order found in the therapeutic field.

The aspects of this definition relating to form are being considered in terms of the amount of structure found in the materials in a play therapy situation. The aspects of the definition relating to order, we are considering in terms of the amount of structure in the processes and techniques of psychotherapy. For our purposes we have attempted to group these two concepts and have evolved four different types of play therapy as follows: (1) Unstructured materials with an unstructured therapeutic approach (U-U); (2) unstructured materials with a structured therapeutic approach (U-S); (3) structured materials with an unstructured therapeutic approach (S-U); (4) structured materials in a structured therapeutic approach (S-S). We have established these four types as representative, in one way or another, of most of the schools of psychotherapy and related areas now present in the literature. Thus, for example, the S-S pattern is most descriptive of that used in conjunction with special education or other modified classroom settings. The S-U pattern is most typical of the usual play therapy and, therefore could be considered the traditional pattern. The U-S pattern is most typical of that found in occupational therapy, music therapy, and some of the ancillary therapies. Finally the U-U[98] pattern is a method which we are presently developing in relationship to work with some of the more severely mentally retarded, or children whose retardation may not be as severe, but whose adaptive behavior is extremely low.[99] Each type of play therapy will be discussed in separate chapters where full definitions and/or conceptions of their function and use will be explained.

Returning to the question of structure, this concept, in reference to materials, refers to the fact that materials may have a specific shape or form, and that they may be designated for specific purposes or uses. Thus, a doll, a truck, or a broom, which are often used to create thematic play, would be considered highly structured materials. Conversely, some unstructured materials could be developed into certain reality objects with the help of the child's imagination. Thus, leather in O.T. could become a belt, and blocks in a therapy situation could become a train or a house. We would define structure, when it refers to material, as the amount of preconceived shape and preconceived purpose to which the material has been set. If the shape is clearly defined and, in terms of social objectivity can be very little else but what it is intended to be, we may consider this a very highly structured shape. If the purpose for the object is clearly defined in terms of social objectivity, and it can be used for very little else other than that, we may consider this a very highly structured purpose. Thus, materials are to be considered highly structured if they follow this preconceived pattern. They will be considered unstructured if there seems to be no preconceived pattern or idea implicit in their function. Thus, since sand has no specific form or shape, nor is there any specific function attached to it, it would be considered unstructured. Probably the most completely unstructured material in a play situation is water, for while water may have definite functions outside the play situation, as a play item it would be considered totally lacking in structure for our purposes.

Now to tie in this idea of structure and materials with the theoretical considerations already presented, we will have to say that the function of the material is in many respects more important in defining its structure that its actual shape. Thus, some things may be unstructured under certain circumstances, and be considered structured in others. Let us, for example, take finger paint. Finger paint may be totally unstructured if it is offered to the child without definition and without concept, and the child is then permitted to find his own way. Thus, in the U-U situation where the paints are merely offered to him, and it is left up to the child to decide what to do, finger paint would be considered unstructured material. However, to jump ahead to the S-S situation, where the finger paint is specifically defined as finger paint, it must thus be used for painting with the fingers only, and the end product is extremely important in terms of the therapist's desire to get the child to express himself in certain ways. Thus, finger paint would here be considered highly structured material since its nature and function was completely defined.

However, there are in between elements. Thus, in the U-S situation, where the goal may be to increase the child's ability to use the finger paints, and it is neither the end product nor the manner of applying paint which is important, but rather, the learning to use paint for paint's sake, the paint would be considered unstructured material. Or in the S-U situation where the finger paint again is considered "finger paint" to be applied to paper with fingers, but where the therapist does not particularly care what the result is after this has been established, we would again have to consider it as structured material, though the total situation was less structured than in the S-S situation. Thus, the same item may be considered either structured or unstructured, depending on how the therapist intends the child to use it.

STRUCTURED-UNSTRUCTURED THERAPY APPROACH

In using the word structure as it refers to the therapist's processes and techniques in therapy, the same general constructs apply. Where the form of the therapy has been preconceived and well ordered, this would be considered highly structured. Thus, when the therapist enters the therapy situation knowing exactly what he is going to do, how he is going to approach the child, and what he plans to achieve with the child, this would be considered a highly structured therapy situation. Conversely, where there seems to be no specific preconceived order to the therapy situation, but rather the child is permitted to proceed as he wishes, this would be considered unstructured. The concept of structure with regard to the role of the therapist, refers generally to the amount of direction. In other words, the most completely structured type of procedure is that used by the special education teacher who, though using an accepting atmosphere of play activity, is nonetheless trying to teach certain specific skills. A less structured procedure is employed by the occupational therapist who, although teaching skills, is generally not too concerned about the end product and therefore does not emphasize the attainment of the skills. Conversely, the therapist who permits completely free expression of the feelings and desires of the child in play, would be considered to be functioning in an unstructured manner and this, as we have indicated, is what occurs in both traditional play therapy and in the even more unstructured type of therapy we have been implementing in our work with the grossly mentally retarded. The difference then between the S-U and U-U pattern in terms of the attitude and behavior of the therapist, is in the psychological field created by the original play materials offered to the child and the general make-up of the playroom. Both forms are "child-centered," but the first is more sophisticated because the child is socially more mature.

The importance of this range of structure in regard to both materials and approach is an effort to establish understanding as to where the child is functioning at the time of his therapeutic need. Thus, the previous discussion on the establishment of goals as relating to individual developmental and maturational processes, as well as the basic personality changes desired, and the total relationship of the child to his home community and the general milieu, presents the elements which must indicate just how much structure has to be introduced into the therapy situation. Unless all of the factors are taken into consideration, it will be impossible to establish a therapy situation which would be the proper prescription for a particular child. However, after all these factors have been taken into consideration, the continuum of structure that we have established should make it possible to see immediately the type of therapeutic procedures which are most needed in order to aid in the rehabilitation and the attainment of the more generalized goals of adjustment to community needs. Part of this process is, of course, related to the therapist's judgment of just how much structure the child already seems to present in terms of his own life space, how much need for additional structure appears to be indicated, and how much imagination and function the child would be able to contribute at that point in time to the therapeutic processes.

These particular questions will be discussed in careful detail in the following chapters, which describe the specific therapeutic processes and, at that time, each of these areas will be much more thoroughly defined.

ADDITIONAL NOTES

78. Eisenberg, L., "Treatment of the Emotionally Disturbed Preadolescent Child," *Proceedings Conf. Child Research Clinic*, Woods Schools, Langhorne, Pa., 1953, pp. 30-41 describes these goals in terms of "*strengthening* of the child's ability" to withstand negative factors in the milieu and ". . . the *enhancement* of his capacity to *react in a healthy fashion* to new situations as they arise." (p. 30)

79. Eisenberg, *op. cit.*, pp. 38-39.

80. Ginott, H. G., "Play Therapy: The Initial Session," *Amer. J. Psychotherapy*, 1961, 15, pp. 73-88, discusses some of the problems surrounding the establishment of a proper "setting," unfortunately, he overlooked the values of intrusion and democentric interaction.

81. Wechsler, D., *Wechsler Intelligence Scale For Children* (*WISC*), Manual, Psychological Corp., N. Y., 1949, *passim.*

82. Cromwell, R. L., "Selected Aspects of Personality Development in Mentally Retarded Children," *Exceptional Children*, 1961, pp. 44-51, discusses this in terms of "locus of control," p. 49. See also Bialer, I., "Conceptualization of Success and Failure in Mentally Retarded and Normal Children," (unpublished doctoral dissertation, George Peabody College for Teachers, 1960), who has evolved a scale for measuring "Locus of Control."

83. Farber, B., Jenne, W. C., and Toigo, R., *Family Crisis and the Decision to Institutionalize the Retarded Child*, CEC Research Monograph #1, 1960, discussed some of the previous research in this area as well as their present conclusions. Also, Farber, B., "Effects of a Severely Mentally Retarded Child on the Family," in Trapp, E. P., and Himelstein, P., *Readings on the Exceptional Child*, Appleton-Century-Crofts, Inc., N. Y., 1962, Chap. 17.

84. Sarason, S. B., "Individual Psychotherapy with Mentally Defective Individuals," *AJMD*, 1952, 56, pp. 803-805, discusses the role of individual therapy.

85. The composition of the group may be of some importance. It has been found by Leland, H., Walker, J., and Toboada, A. N., "Group Play Therapy With a Group of Post-Nursery Male Retardates," *AJMD*, 1959, 63, pp. 848-851, that if a group is diversified with both withdrawn and aggressive children, the possibility of therapeutic success seems higher than if the group is totally homogenous. Therefore, if there is only the latter population from which to choose, individual therapy might be the recommended mode; where if there is a heterogenous group of children, group therapy may be the preferable mode. See also, Ginott, H. G., *Group Psychotherapy With Children: The Theory and Practice of Play Therapy*, McGraw-Hill Book Co., New York, 1961.

86. Kotkov, B., "A Bibliography For the Student of Group Psychotherapy," *J. Clin. Psy.*, 1950, 6, pp. 77-91 cites extensive references through 1949 and there are certainly many more since. Specific references to group play therapy will be made passim. There are fewer references to either group therapy or group play therapy with the mentally retarded, but the following are representative of some of the work that has been done:

Cotzin, M., "Group Psychotherapy with Mentally Defective Problem Boys," *AJMD*, 1948, 53, pp. 268-283.

Fisher, L. A. and Wolfson, I. N., "Group Therapy of Mental Defectives," *AJMD*, 1953, 57, pp. 463-476.

Koldeck, R., "Group Psychotherapy With Mentally Defective Adolescents and Adults," *Inter. Jr. of Group Psychotherapy*, 1958, 8, pp. 185-192.

Mehlman, B., "Group Play Therapy With Mentally Retarded Children," *Jr. Abnormal & Soc. Psy.*, 1953, 48, pp. 53-60.

Ringleheim, D. and Polotsek, I., "Group Therapy With a Male Defective Group," *AJMD*, 1955, 60, pp. 157-162.

87. Ames, Louise B., Learned, Janet, Metroux, Ruth W., and Walker, R. N., *Child Rorschach Responses*, Paul B. Hoeber, Inc., Boston, 1959, among others, point to the importance of considering the temporal factors in development; see also Lebo, D. A., "A Theoretical Framework for Nondirective Play Therapy: Concepts From Psychoanalysis and Learning Theory," *J. Consult. Psych.*, 22, 1958, pp. 275-279.

88. Meyers, C. E., Orpet, R. E., Attwell, A. A., and Dingman, H. F., "Primary Abilities at Mental Age Six," Monographs, 182, *Soc. Res. Child Devel.*, 1962, 28, p. 18; see also, Meyers, Dingman, H. F., Attwell, A. A., and Orpet, R. E., "Comparative Abilities of Normals and Retardates of MA 6 Years on A Factor-Type Test Battery," *AJMD*, 1961, 66, pp. 250-258, and Meyers, C. E. and Dingman, H. F., "The Structure of Abilities at the Pre-School Ages: Hypothesized Domains," *Psy. Bull.*, 1960, 57, pp. 514-532.

89. Hunt, J. McV., *Intelligence and Experience*, Ronald Press Co., N. Y., 1961, thoroughly reviews and discusses the work of Piaget in relationship to child development and intelligence, pp. 109-307.

90. Social responsibility refers both to the ability to perform adequately in the social sphere in terms of the gestalt of interpersonal relationships and to the ability to assume a contributing role as part of the *social unit*, e.g., carrying out chores because they needed to be done, civic responsibility.

Individual responsibility refers to ability to perform with a minimum of supervision, a socially necessary task and to be able to utilize initiative or imagination therein, e.g., carrying out chores when *instructed*, both are part of the general definition of Adaptive Behavior, viz., Heber, *op. cit.*, p. 61.

91. Viz. Chap. V, p. 178.

92. Leland, H., and Smith, D., "Unstructured Material in Play Therapy for Emotionally Disturbed, Brain Damaged, Mentally Retarded Children," *AJMD*, 60, 1962, p. 621 *et passim*.

93. Here, the importance of case histories, parent counseling, and related informational sources must be underlined. This will be further discussed in Chap. XII. See also, Hamilton, G., *Psychotherapy in Child Guidance*, Columbia Univ. Press, N. Y., 1947, Chap. I.

94. Hadley, J. M., *Clinical and Counseling Psychology*, Alfred A. Knopf, N. Y., 1960, p. 668, defines "milieu therapy" as "The complex of social and physical factors that surround us, as manipulated and mobilized for the benefit of the client." Also, Mako, A. E., Crawfis, E. H. and Peer, I. N., "Defining and Applying Milieu Therapy," *Mental Hospitals*, 1962, 13, pp. 518-522, discuss practical applications of these concepts, as does Vail, D., "Mental Deficiency: Response to Milieu Therapy," *Amer. Jr. Psychiat.*, 1956, 113, pp. 170-173.

95. See among others, Schiffer, M., "Permissiveness versus Sanction in Activity Group Therapy," *Intern. J. Group Psychotherapy*, 1952, 2, pp. 255-261; Bixler, R. H., "Limits are Therapy," *J. Consult. Psy.*, 1949, 13, pp. 1-11; Slavson, S. R., "Authority, Restraint, and Discipline in Group Therapy with Children," *J. Nerv. Child.*, 1951, 9, pp. 187-195; Ginott,

H. G., "The Theory and Practice of Therapeutic Intervention in Child Treatment," *J. Consult. Psy.*, 1959, 23, pp. 160-166.

96. Ginott, (1959), *op. cit.*, describes many types of limits and their uses, some of these are from a frame of reference different than that of the present authors' but, in general, the discussion is quite complete and, in the over-all, useful.

97. This note has been cited on page 65.

98. Leland and Smith, *op. cit.*, p. 623.

99. Adaptive Behavior is based on ability to function independently and assume individual and social responsibility, Heber, *op. cit.*, p. 61; see also Chap. X, this work.

PART TWO: TECHNIQUES AND PROCEDURES OF PLAY THERAPY WITH SUBNORMAL CHILDREN

V. The Method of Unstructured Materials with an Unstructured Approach (U-U)[100]

We will open the discussion of specific forms of play therapy with the process we have described as the use of unstructured materials with unstructured techniques and procedures, or as we have labeled it, the U-U process. This seems to be the most primitive of the processes, inasmuch as it demands the least from the patient in terms of previous cognitive development, or present cognitive ability. We differentiate between the two, because in certain situations involving psychogenic retardation, the previous level of cognitive development may not necessarily be representative of present functioning ability. We do not imply, when calling this method the most primitive, that it is a form of psychotherapy to be used only with the most grossly retarded patients. The level of Measured Intelligence is not at issue here at all. Rather, we are interested in the level of functional behavior. That is to say, the child who seems to be functioning almost completely without the use of cognition, would seem to be the type of child for whom we are suggesting this type of procedure. The child whose behavior indicates a lack of consciousness of self, who seems impulsive, or who appears to be driven either through what is described as "organic drivenness"[101] or some other form of "drivenness" to act out feelings of hostility, destructiveness, or general aggressiveness, without seeming to have a basis for this behavior, or, conversely, who is withdrawn into himself and completely rejects the outside environment or major portions of it, again seemingly without cognitive basis, is the child who seems to be best served by a therapeutic process in which the structure has been, if not eliminated, at least modified to such a great extent that it appears to the child as if there were no structure. Traditional play therapy methods may also be effective with this type of child, but the structure provided by the materials in the traditional setting do not enable him to develop his own imagination to the same extent; they do not enable him to invent activities which will provide a good outlet for eventual social interaction, nor do they enable him to express whatever portion of hyperactivity is due to "organic drivenness" in a socially acceptable manner.

DEFINITION OF THE U-U METHOD

MATERIALS

The importance of unstructured materials in this type of therapy lies in the patient's greater ability to control, create, change, and develop play activity with them. Thus, he can learn that he is a person capable of creating and controlling materials and things. This paves the way for learning that he can control himself, and eventually allows him to interact with others. He can learn that he is not necessarily a dangerously destructive person and he can see that his impulses have been primarily destructive to himself. He can learn that his ideas and efforts can produce tangible differences in reality; e.g., the change in the size or shape of a piece of material is clearly due to his behavior and may be due to his idea.

The patient does not destroy unstructured materials. Some may get used up, but such materials are usually thought of as being expendable and the concept of destruction does not present itself. Thus, if he tears a piece of clay in two, he has not destroyed it, but simply has two pieces of clay which he can recombine if he wishes. Further, he may become aware of the fact that it was he who created the two pieces of clay and thus produced a new material, in a psychological sense, from what existed previously. If he makes some object with the clay, he can use it in that way as long as he wishes, but as soon as he no longer wants it, he can change it. On the other hand, structured materials demand a limited range of activities, e.g., it is socially acceptable to play with a toy truck in only certain ways. If it is used in other ways or is destroyed, the patient is then limited either by the bizarreness of his play or by the loss of the object.

The types of materials we have in mind are those which do not unto themselves have any particular preconceived function or value. Materials such as sand, water, wooden blocks, beads, string, finger paint, clay, paper, crayons, pipe cleaners, snow, scraps of wood, twigs, and various objects, either provided by the therapist or brought into the playroom by the patients themselves, serve as unstructured materials.

These materials and many others which we have not listed, all may serve as the basis for the development of behavior in relationship to *things*. These things may be representative of other things he has seen in his environment, they may be things developing from his fantasy, or they may be things which are suggested to him by his peers. However, this particular factor is not important because the end product is not the important element. What is important, is the child's ability to learn that he himself can be responsible for what happens to the material. This becomes the underlying aspect of all procedures regarding these materials. Thus, the unstructured materials become the primary medium by which the child learns to express the fact that he potentially has a personality.

However, we have to remember that these materials do not, unto themselves, represent "unstructured materials." Therefore, if finger paint is to be used to produce a specific kind of picture, it is no longer an unstructured material; instead it becomes structured. But if finger paint is used merely as a way of permitting the child to become dirty in a socially acceptable manner, then it is clearly an unstructured material since no particular end product is involved. Thus, the materials which we have suggested as "unstructured materials" are only given as suggestions of the types that the patient can use.

Another facet of this material is the fact that since the materials used have no specific structure, more carry-over into other areas can be expected. Unstructured materials are always available and the child learns that he gains acceptance from utilizing his imagination and creating play activities, where in the traditional setting he may learn to depend on specific toys and specific types of activities related to the highly structured toys. If these toys are not available, he becomes lost once more in a sea of frustration and can be seen to recommence rocking or destructive behavior, or other signs of hyperactivity which the therapy was attempting to correct. Thus, we have a means of carrying play to the home situation, or in the institution, to the cottage situation without having to transfer a great deal of equipment, etc., which may or may not always be available. A good example of this is the use of natural resources which the environment provides without the therapist's intervention. Thus, a snowstorm gives a vast supply of unstructured materials which can be utilized by the patient to become acquainted with the realities of cold, wet, hard, or soft, etc., as well as forming snowballs, throwing them in a socially acceptable manner, possibly even moving toward a bit more structure in making a snow man, being permitted to smash the snow man with the snowballs, etc. This serves a dual teaching purpose of acquainting the patient with the qualities of snow as we have mentioned, plus possibly leaving him with the impression that society may provide him with pleasure and an acceptable outlet for his feelings, since the snow was readily provided to him without any special effort on anybody's part. This is a rather abstract concept and we would not expect the patient to conceive of it in those terms, but again through the situation of utilizing materials which are readily available in the environment, the patient can eventually gain the idea that the environment can be rewarding as well as punishing.

Therapy Procedures

It is very difficult to present the therapist's actual behavior in a therapy session of this sort, because under different conditions the same activity might be considered desirable, acceptable, or undesirable. While the extreme behaviors are readily identifiable in general terms, the middle ground becomes quite relative within the changing field of conditions. For example, the child splashing in water could represent desirable behavior and thus be reinforced by the therapist if that were the highest level of activity occurring up to that time; and the therapist would attempt to support this behavior by reinforcing the concept that the patient was doing this, and for some acceptable reason was enjoying it. But in another situation, the same activity could be carried on apart from a higher level of activity going on in the room, as for example, during a group session. During individual therapy, it could represent a level of behavior which is lower than a previously attained high, in which case the therapist would not reinforce it, and thus the activity could be expected to be discontinued in favor of activities of the type that would be rewarded at that time. In still another situation, the same activity could be destructive to some higher level activity, and the therapist would actually intrude or more directly block it. Thus, the therapist's behavior has to be modified from point to point depending on where he finds himself in relationship to the patient at that time.

Generally speaking, the *first phase* of activity in which the therapist engages is the process of conditioning the patient to the idea, which in some cases may be a new idea, that his behavior, his ideas, his reactions to stimuli are his, that they originated in him and that he is responsible for them. The *second phase* is usually related to the process of getting the patient to organize his behavior around cognitive associations. This implies that impulse control is closely related to development of communication between the therapist and the child, and that once the child has, in the first phase, become aware that his behavior is his own, it then becomes necessary for him to learn that the behavior most acceptable to the therapist is that which has positive cognitive associations. The *third phase* is a process of conditioning the patient to organize his behavior around mutual cognitive associations. In other words, having established the fact that communication and related cognitive associations are the more acceptable forms of behavior, he must then learn that the interaction between his ideas or associations and the ideas and associations of other members of the group or the therapist, represents the highest form of socially acceptable behavior. In other words, the whole therapy process takes on the form of, as we said before, "forcing the child to think." Since one of the major problems with emotionally disturbed, brain damaged, retarded children is that they often have intellectual abilities somewhat greater than those normally reflected in psychological tests, and if they can be brought to use these abilities to a fuller extent, it is conceivable that the intellectual development itself will improve.

The therapist operates within a single scheme of priorities during these sessions; he responds to and attempts to elicit and reinforce the most desired forms of behavior that occur. These may be at one point egocentric, unimaginative, and impulsive, or at another point, democentric, controlled, and imaginative. Deciding what is desirable or undesirable behavior is guided by the general goals. The therapist is involved in a continuous process of evaluating the specific behaviors that are occurring, the current field conditions, and the individual or group progresses within this set of goals as they affect his relationship to the patient.

Therapy Setting

The actual therapeutic setting is as primitive as possible so that a relatively few number of limits have to be established in regard to the materials or the setting. In other words, a highly decorated room where decorations can be destroyed, affects the unstructured nature of the therapy and thus will not permit the types of results sought. The room is left plain, with very little destructible equipment, since the patient is much more inclined to operate freely in an atmosphere where it does not matter if anything is destroyed. It should actually be crude enough in its general construction and furnishing to allow for the lighting of a fire without causing any undue consternation or damage, and where the patient can be permitted to both kindle and extinguish the fire as part of the unstructured play of that particular moment. A minimum of tools and equipment should be provided including a sink,[102] a sand box, a cabinet to keep the materials, a table for working, a few containers, sponges, scissors, and a broom. The room has to contain very little because the patient and the therapist will provide whatever is needed.

This is not to say that limits are not imposed in this type of setting, but the limits that are imposed are relative to the relationship between persons, rather than things. Thus, it becomes clearly defined that the therapist cannot be injured, and if it is a group setting, that the other members of the group cannot hurt each other. If it is an individual setting, the relationship between the therapist and the patient is such that neither can do harm to the other. The things that are made or thrown or used, are thus not thrown at the therapist, but are thrown elsewhere. An interesting example of this is, with the imposition of these limits, a patient who had a very strong desire to express his aggression against the therapist used the one-way vision mirror as his target and thus threw clay at the image of the therapist in the mirror, staying within the limits of therapy, but still expressing his feelings and desires. This was of course, permitted, even welcomed, and after this particular behavior was expressed, it became possible to bring the behavior to a more cognitive level where the patient could actually admit that he wished that he could have thrown the clay at the therapist, and in subsequent therapeutic sessions the expression was brought to a higher level. Thus limits are established, but in terms of interpersonal relationships rather than relationships with things, the setting of the room being such that aside from the one-way vision screen, almost nothing in the room has to be protected and even the one-way vision screen becomes an issue only if some very hard object such as stones or wooden blocks are being thrown around.

It is even conceivable and possibly of advantage, weather and location permitting, to leave the therapy room as such and to use the natural, unstructured setting of the outside environment to carry out the play; thus mud puddles after a rain storm or piles of leaves in the autumn, etc., become excellent sources of therapeutic materials as long as the limits can be sufficiently maintained and the patient will stay within certain prescribed boundaries (thus not getting into neighboring yards or other areas where his behavior might not be understood or accepted). Here we find an exception to the "place" limits discussed in Chapter IV. The basis of this exception is first that the U-U form is as concerned with "freedom of expression" as it is with any expression, i.e., the major effort is to get the child to respond, no matter how or where. Second, we cannot expect an identification of the therapist as a model until the child has developed a concept of self. Therefore, this loss is only theoretical since the desired identification does not occur in the playroom either. We do feel, that once the child has progressed in this form, greater emphasis should be placed on playing in the playroom.[103]

INDICATIONS AND MAJOR CRITERIA FOR U-U THERAPY

Goals

The indications for this type of therapy become clearer if we think of the specific goals. We have already established the fact that the therapist's task, although complex, is based on fairly clear criteria for choosing between two major modes of responding to the patient. They are: One, a positive response which is reinforcing; and two, a negative response which is blocking or intruding. The decision of when to respond in either way is based on the basic goals or purposes of this form of play therapy. These goals are three-fold.

Recognition of Self. The *first* is recognition of self. This refers to the child's gaining a sense of control over his environment, realizing the freedom to follow his own ideas, and sensing that he is a real person. It is the primary goal, because the child must be encouraged to develop motivation for growth, and thus become able to deal with more challenging problems. The child who has no awareness of self is completely unable to utilize any of the growth producing elements of his environment. Behaviors seen in the playroom which demonstrate developing recognition of self include the example of the boy who, after six months of U-U therapy, was able to take a piece of clay, indicate that he wanted to make a hamburger, realize that it should be round and flat, shape the clay in that way, respond that people usually cook hamburgers and eat them, pretend that he ate one, and thus show mastery and control over the piece of clay in using it as he wished to do. He further showed ability to abstract in a manner which his psychological testing and earlier behavior would indicate that he could not do. This same patient, when he came into therapy, was totally unable to deal with the clay in any manner except to make little balls which he would then throw.

Another example was a patient who stated that the stack of blocks arranged was a church, that people usually go there on Sunday, and that he used to go there, etc., thus demonstrating some of the same cognition and abstraction as in the previous example. However, the second example also brings out emotional material for which the lack of a church in a traditional structured playroom might not have given the opportunity. The therapist's intrusions and demands for cognitive expression "forced" the patient to make a controlled response. This was reinforced and the child felt rewarded. The therapist could then begin to help him seek greater controls in the area of his impulses. This child, at the beginning of the therapy sessions, was completely unable to communicate anything except negative feelings and rejected all relationships with people or things.

A more primitive example is that of the child who wanted to go down a slippery slide, but who could not connect the idea of climbing the ladder and sliding down, and constantly wanted the therapist to put him at the top so he could slide down; he eventually learned that he could climb the ladder to get to the top, thus attaining a consciousness of his ability to control his behavior to the extent of producing a pleasurable experience for himself that was not dependent on someone else. These and many other examples underline the type of behavior changes that is being sought in terms of getting the child to recognize himself as a person who can be responsible for what happens to the things or people with whom he has contact.

Understanding that Impulses Can Be Controlled. The *second* major goal involves the understanding that impulses can be controlled. This becomes a form of conditioning whereby the patient becomes aware that he is able to control sudden intense drives, thus leaving him the opportunity to behave in a socially acceptable manner. This goal is included because these patients have been unable to direct their behavior in a socially acceptable manner in the past and this fact has given rise to frustration, guilt, and lack of self-concept which has been partially responsible for the presence of the emotional disorder. A play process which demonstrates improved impulse control is shown by the child who, in the beginning came in and began tearing apart large wooden boxes and even the sand box, but who was later able to engage in constructive play with these same materials. Another child, playing in water, slopped it on the floor, impulsively poured it into the sand and threw it all over. Later he was able to stack blocks together, call it a campfire, and then use the water to play that he had put out the fire after he had already played that he was roasting weiners at a picnic. Once the child has gained a greater measure of realization that impulses can be controlled, the way is paved for improved social behavior in terms of the demands of society.

Living within Social Boundaries. The *third* goal then becomes a matter of training the child to live within social boundaries. These boundaries in an unstructured situation are slight, but they are reflective of much greater limits which society itself imposes. This becomes a matter of gaining the ability to respond to the behavior of others in a controlled manner, and thus the ability to contribute either to a mutually conceived project in a group situation, or to a unified or cooperative project with the therapist in an individual situation. The reason for including this type of goal as one of the therapy goals is that these children usually have been unable to work through their own problems to a sufficient extent in terms of the resources which they have available, and so have not had sufficient psychic energy to participate in the affairs of their peers or of society. Thus, they tend to reject their peers, to fight with them when intruded upon, attempt to avoid them or hold them off, and generally behave in a way disruptive to any sort of activity, either group or individual.

Though the limits in this type of situation are described as slight, they nonetheless do aid the child in learning something about limits, particularly about the hierarchy of limits in terms of the fact that though they are slight, they are very important, and must be followed. An example of this type of cooperative participation is the forming of clay balls and then throwing them at a target. There is sufficient reward in the excitement and participation of each patient, or of the patient and the therapist, that the project develops more complete social interaction between them. However, the fact that a target and not another person must be on the other end of these balls, emphasizes the relationship between having fun and staying within the limits. Another example occurs, again in the theme of cooking, (which seems to recur quite often) where one individual might supply the concept of what to cook, another how to cook it, and another what people usually did with it, resulting in a suggestion that a party be had and food eaten, etc. Thus, both the limits which have forced the cognizance of the rights of others, and the improved impulse control which has made psychic energy available, seem to have contributed to the third goal, in the sense that the child learns to gain satisfaction by cooperating with others.

Individual Therapy

We have, from time to time, expressed the fact that this therapy method may serve in either a group or individual therapy situation. The differences depend on the type of behavior expressed by the patient. In individual therapy you would expect that the patient had very primitive impulses, almost no ability to cognize and, very little if any self-concept. This patient needs individual therapy in the sense that there is so little of him, that he cannot possibly share it. The function of the therapist here is quite clear cut. He has to expand on the quality of self that is present, and try to build sufficient understanding on the part of the patient that he can feel a certain self-mastery and thus meet the goals as we have described them. Here, individual therapy is called for because you cannot expect such a patient to find himself in the company of others if the self is so immature that the others add only additional feelings of frustration and increased lack of confidence. The function of individual therapy in this type of setting is essentially one of building a very close one-to-one relationship between the patient and the therapist, almost to the total exclusion of all other people in the outer world, at least during the therapy period, and then the gradual weaning of the patient away from this single worldliness into a more general milieu. This is an extremely slow process and requires that the patient receive the therapist's undivided attention if it is to be effective. During this whole period the therapist sets up the process of intrusion and acceptance in such a manner that a clear one-to-one conditioning situation exists at almost a primitive stimulus-response level. The only thing that really makes this situation different from the traditional S-R bond is the fact that the therapist does not have a preconceived idea of the type of stimulus he is going to introduce or a preconceived notion as to the type of response he wants to produce. Rather, using the stimulus which the situation itself produces, the therapist then tries to establish meaningful responses. Here again there is no particular interest in developing reality controls, this can come later. The therapist is interested in the patient realizing that whatever occurs is of his own doing, and thus the initial development of self has been accomplished.

A clear example of the above can be seen in a fairly high functioning patient, in the sense that she was able to communicate simple concrete things at a level almost normal for her age but who, nonetheless, spent a complete year in play therapy totally unable to discuss either her family, her friends, peers, etc., to the extent of withdrawing completely into herself and refusing to do or discuss anything if questions were raised in these areas, or if play was initiated that would normally introduce this subject. However, by using the unstructured form of play and letting the patient express herself as she saw fit, using whatever materials occurred to her in the setting, she was eventually able to gain sufficient consciousness of self and sufficient feeling for the potential which interaction might contain, that toward the beginning of the second year she became much freer about her feelings, and during the second year finally reached the point where she was able to discuss her family, friends and peers with a relative degree of freedom, though still without insight. However, as this progressed, even the factors relating to insight were improved though this was done in a different type of play not involving unstructured materials. This, by the way, is an example of how a, patient may actually emerge from this form of play therapy into a higher, less primitive form.

Group Therapy

On the other hand, with some patients the primary problem is not so much consciousness of self as it is consciousness of how this self exists in relationship to other people. This is still a problem of developing self-concept, and is still a problem of recognition of self, but it is a different kind of recognition problem in that the patient knows he exists, he just does not know "why." The problem thus centers around roles, what he seems to be able to do, what he is not able to do, whether or not he feels his behavior might be dangerous, (as in the case of a paranoid patient who felt that anything he did would be destructive to other people, that he was safest by doing absolutely nothing and demonstrated certain types of behavior similar to that usually found in the catatonic adult). These patients frequently best find themselves in group situations. This is not a problem of their not having enough self to share with others, but rather one of having so much self that they do not know what to do with it, and if they do not share it with others, it becomes destructive to them. We realize that we have carried the metaphor beyond its logical point but, in a sense, this is what happens, since a patient who has a problem relating to his total role, usually conceives of himself as potentially more than one person, and thus in reality has more self than he knows what to do with. By putting him in a group situation with peers, part of this problem resolves itself, due to the fact that children at all levels learn best from each other, and this is as true in play therapy as it is in school or in the community.[104] The child who primarily seems to need interaction and has to learn what his role in life is, is served best by a group therapy situation. Here, of course, the procedures are somewhat different; this is not a matter of a close one-to-one relationship between the therapist and the individual, but rather a more loose relationship between each individual and the therapist, with a fairly close relationship between the group as a whole. Here, the procedures usually differ. Early in the session, one or several of the patients may commence some activity involving the available materials. If this does not occur readily, the therapist invites activity with the materials, asking the group how they want to play, or by reminding them of materials that are available or activities that may have occurred previously. The therapist reinforces desirable activity in a number of ways but, in general, he gives the most attention to the child who has started the activity. He may restate to the group what the child has said he was doing, or he may comment that what the child is doing looks interesting, etc. The therapist thus attempts to support the activities that are imaginative and creative. He may offer simple suggestions or participations compatible with the activity as the child has developed it. The therapist selectively gives reward to activities which involve cooperation within the group, and thus the center of activity becomes not the individual patient but the group as a whole, and through this process the group develops; each individual member meeting the same goals as have been established for the U-U method, but through the means of interacting with each other rather than just the one-to-one interaction with the therapist.

Which of these two organizations is used becomes, as we stated, a matter of dealing with specific kinds of behavior, and the real guide has to be how the child sees himself and whether or not this recognition of self would be enhanced or slowed down by involving greater numbers of his peers.[105]

DISCUSSION

We have, in the above material, tried to outline a plan of psychotherapy using unstructured materials with an unstructured therapeutic approach. We have pointed out that this is most effective with the child who has a very primitive view of himself and his environment, and whose therapeutic requirements are that he learn that he has a self, that his impulses can be controlled, that there are boundaries to the environment, but that he can live with them without increasing his frustrations. The processes used are essentially those of conditioning of both functional and verbal behaviors.

Theoretical Constructs

Basically, the conditioning is expected to occur by selective reinforcement with rewards being given for behavior in keeping with the general goals, and with intrusion (punishment) being given for the behavior which violates or blocks other behaviors leading towards these goals. This interaction falls into three overlapping categories which we can label: (1) cognitive stimulation, (2) reward, and (3) intrusion (punishment). By cognitive stimulation we refer to the therapist's behavior which implies or suggests or serves as a model for partial imitation so that the patient more readily and frequently behaves within the goal formulations. That is, when the therapist asks the patient what he is doing, the patient is identified with his behavior, and the therapist is inviting and expecting the patient to verbalize his associations to his activities.

By rewards, we are referring to the therapist's behaviors or verbalizations which communicate his approbation, acceptance, and approval of the patient's behavior. We also see activity itself as a reward, in that any activity whether or not it is cognitively identified with the self or organized around individual or mutual cognitive associations, relieves some tension, seeks some goal, or avoids some stress. Therefore, the permission to be active in the playroom becomes unto itself a reward, particularly if this activity is permitted to go forward without intrusion.

By intrusion (punishment) we are referring to the therapist's disapproval, withholding of permission, nonacceptance, and active interference with the patient's continued activity. This includes those aspects of the therapist's interference with the patient's activities which actually, through the fact that the patient must stop what he is doing to answer the therapist's questions, serve as activity blocking intrusions; i.e., the therapist's continued inquiry or verbalization about the patient's behavior may become uncomfortably intrusive, and it is hoped that the patient will tend to avoid this discomfort by giving a cognitive association or by changing his behavior in favor of another behavior for which he can give cognitive associations, and thus receive a reward. Thus, the therapist, by permitting activity and, in general, supporting the patient, becomes an extremely rewarding person, producing the phenomena of cognitive stimulation and selective reinforcement. Where the patient is not able to develop cognitive associations, the same behavior on the part of the therapist becomes instrusive and thus punishing, and serves to block the unacceptable activity.

There may be occasions when this type of intrusion is not sufficient to block the activity or, we might say, the intrusion is not "punishing" enough. Such occasions would be those of pretended or compulsive deafness where the activity continues despite the intrusion and the patient pretends not to hear the therapist's questions, or, where the patient clearly hears the questions, but answers with an automatic "I don't know" to each of them. In these instances, additional intrusive measures must be used. One that is often successful is the introduction of personal contact by the therapist, e.g., placing his hand on the shoulder or arm of the patient and indicating by this action that he wants the patient's attention. This has the added advantage of giving a reinforcement to the process of interaction which is being attempted, and also makes use of additional portions of the sensorium, thus enhancing the learning experience that is involved.[106]

If there is a doubt about the appropriateness of the original question, other wordings may be attempted. Evaluative questions, such as "Didn't you want to answer?" or questions which are related to what the child is doing may gain some sort of response (a smile or a laugh or some other response) which may then be reinforced. Also, the therapist may try to give an indication himself of what he thinks the child is doing in questions such as, "Are you doing . . . ?" with the idea that if the therapist suggests what he feels the activity resembles, such as drawing or playing in clay, etc., the child may respond to the fact that the therapist has recognized his efforts. Here, it should be emphasized that any reply should be reinforced, even if the child makes a completely nonsensical verbal reply. In these cases the therapist will probably want to imitate the nonsense reply hoping that the child will see the humor of the situation; but at least having made this kind of reinforcement, he can help produce a change of pace and hopefully he can get the child to reply in a more sensible or meaningful manner. Further, the therapist can, at this point, guide the child to a better form by suggesting another word not in the nonsense class and asking the child if this is what he is doing, and if so to tell him. Thus, the child is reinforced or rewarded for making a verbal reply because the therapist commences to play with him and thus permits him to continue the activity, but at the same time the intrusion continues, seeking a more socially oriented reply, not necessarily in the realm of reality, but at least in the realm of socially acceptable speech rather than just nonsense.

If, on the other hand, "I don't know" is the child's reply, then the therapist must thoroughly analyze whether the question was appropriate on the possibility that the "I don't know" may be appropriate. That is, if the question itself was inappropriate, the "I don't know" may be the only truthful answer the child can give. In this case, the therapist again tries to guide the child through the proper answer even suggesting if it the nondirective guidance does not seem to help.

If the therapist can achieve his results without direct guidance, this is to be sought and various other expediencies such as rewording the question to a lower level of reply, etc., should always be utilized first. Also in this situation, since permissiveness is not what we are seeking, but rather cognition, the therapist should not be afraid to "argue" with the patient in the sense of asking "If you don't know, who does?" Or even asking "Do you want to know what you are doing?" These questions tend to put the patients on their mettle in the sense of introducing combat, and quite often the therapist will then get a reply with which he can deal. For example, a patient, when asked "If you don't know, who does?" replied, "Jesus," and the therapist was then able to raise the question "Well, what did He tell you?" This produced an answer which led to a discussion of the activity at hand, thus breaking down the "I don't know," and permitting cognitive activity on the part of the child. To continue with this point concerning the therapist arguing with the patient, the therapist may offer a statement, "I think you are "doing . . . "

in the sense that the child has offered "I don't know" as a solution to what he is doing, and the therapist is saying in effect, "I don't think you're doing 'I don't know,' I think you're playing with clay." This makes "I don't know" a substance, again introducing absurdity into the situation, and hopefully the child will recognize this; further, this puts the child's verbalizations at a level where they may be reinforced even though they are not accepted. Also, the child gains an added sense of confidence, that what he is saying is being listened to, and that his problem is to bring it to a socially acceptable level. There are probably numerous other ways by which this type of reply can be handled, the major point being that this kind of malingering cannot be accepted on its own level, and must be further intruded upon. The therapist then becomes responsible for seeking different and other modes of intrusion in an effort to accomplish his major goal, which is to block the activity until the child demonstrates ability to cognize in the situation.

Generally we feel that playroom behavior should correlate with what seems to occur in life with the normal child. That is to say, though we are not using the concept of punishment in the sense of active aggression, or as it might be used in experimental conditioning in psychology, with electric shock or something of that sort, we nevertheless have to recognize that life produces punishment regularly through blocking certain behaviors rather than through overt aggression. The best example of this is in the mother-child relationship where it is clearly a reward if the mother kisses the child. It is not as clearly punishment if the mother fails to kiss the child, but in the construct that we are presenting here, we could consider this punishment. In other words, a mother who is not affectionate, who does not kiss her child, is just as punishing as the mother who overtly slaps her child. There are reports in psychiatric literature, that the rejecting, frustrating mother is much more often the one who fails to kiss than the one who overtly slaps; in fact, we find in the literature representation of the fact that the mother who overtly slaps is considered a less "rejecting" mother than the one who merely fails to kiss in the sense that the slap is a recognition of the child's presence, and from this point of view he is receiving attention, etc., and doesn't feel as "frustrated" or as "rejected" as if he were totally ignored.[107] We do not wish to go into the discussion of the pros and cons of this frame of reference, but merely mention it to further illustrate the fact that refusal to reward is often considered punishment, and it is in this manner that we are using the term. Here again, the child is not only relearning old behavior in the sense of being reconditioned, but even when new behavior is being introduced it is still considered reconditioning or rehabilitation since one has to work with the assumption that the child has been exposed to this type of behavior previously, and that it is not entirely new to him. Rather, he has never before known what to do with it, or what it was for, or how it functioned. The learned insight of forced cognition thus becomes the primary objective of this type of psychotherapy. The child is considered to have progressed when the basic goals seem to have been met. In other words, when the child seems to realize that he is a person, that he is responsible for his own behavior, that his impulses can be controlled, and that there are limits in society which he must observe.

Indication of Therapy Gains and Criteria for Termination

This phase or form of psychotherapy should be considered totally successful if all of these goals are achieved, and at that point this particular type of psychotherapy should be terminated. In other words, even though the child may still have many problems and may still need the services of a therapist, new goals should be considered and an entirely different form of psychotherapy should be planned. The new type of play therapy should be entered into a different entity, (not necessarily with a different therapist, though potentially it could be) in a different setting, and as we will explain in later chapters, with a different relationship of materials and techniques and processes.

The length of such psychotherapy has to vary with the needs of the child. We would certainly recommend, because of the very limited intellectual and psychic resources of the children usually included in the U-U form, that short-term psychotherapy be planned. It should not be permitted to drag out over extensive periods of time if no observation of progress is made. In this case it must be remembered that the lack of progress is not the child's fault, but rather the therapist's and that evidently some error in approach or method has occurred so that the child is not responding to the therapist, rather than that the child is "too stupid" to benefit from therapy. However, there will be children who will tax the greatest therapist as far as progress is concerned, and these children should not be dragged out indefinitely in therapy, but should be terminated even though the goals have not been achieved. In general, however, termination should be considered at that point where the primary goal has been successfully achieved and the second and third goals are being approached, for quite often goals of improved impulse control and recognition of social boundaries can be reinforced through the use of some structure in the situtation, so that the major interest of the therapist at this stage is the achievement of the primary goal, which is recognition of self.

CONCLUSIONS AND EXAMPLES

While it is impossible to describe an exact therapy situation following these principles, in brief, the type of thing to which we are referring is described in the following specific situations, using first the case of a very primitive child who had no speech, was suspected of being deaf, and had a tendency to collapse in the middle of a road, hallway or wherever he was when going from one place to another, if he decided he didn't want to go. Here, the therapeutic method was essentially a matter of introducing him to the unstructured materials, trying to help him elect one that he enjoyed, which in this case was sand, and then trying to get him to understand that he could do things with the sand. This was a matter of his going into the sand box, receiving approbation for being there, throwing the sand all around as he desired, and receiving approbation for this; but, at the same time, the therapist tried to get him to realize that he was pushing the sand around, and this was reinforced by getting him to at least help hold the broom while sweeping up at the end of the session. He was not expected to sweep up and he was not expected to be clean, but he was made aware that sweeping up did have to occur as a result of his throwing the sand around. This was accompanied by the therapist calling him by name and trying to get him to respond to this one event. It was previously established that though he had been suspected of being deaf, actually he was not. The combination of his being permitted to do with the sand as he wished, and being reinforced in this fact by the realization that he had created a mess that had to be cleaned up, and thus that he had done something, as well as the therapist's naming him through the whole operation, eventually resulted in his responding to the therapist when his name was called. This was the first time that he had responded to his name, and the therapist was thus able to establish for him an identity which was his own through the conditioning process of permitting him free unstructured behavior but, at the same time, trying to produce cognition in the sense of his understanding that he had made the mess. Therefore, he had to this extent changed the milieu. In this very primitive case the therapist could go no further, and the goals of impulse control and living within limits were never established. Therapy was terminated shortly after because there seemed to be an inability on the part of the patient to move beyond this point. Unfortunately, this situation had to occur. It was recognized by the therapist that it only occurred because of her inability to conceive of the next step, though many things were tried to which the patient would not respond. The gains that were made, however, seemed to be fixed, and were still present when tested a year later.

Another history at a somewhat higher level concerns a group of three boys who came in completely unaware of themselves or each other, unable to play with the materials involved (it had been previously demonstrated in other settings that they were also unable to play with structured materials) but rather were so completely unrelated to their environment that the concept of play itself was essentially foreign to them. Here, the therapist spent most of the early therapy sessions trying to induce play, trying to induce some sort of association between the unstructured materials and some activity on the part of the patients. Though this was a group, there was no attempt at that time to develop group activities. Each patient was considered as an individual, and the function of the group was to limit the extent to which they were permitted to intrude upon each other, so that the concept that there was more than one person in the room was established and, in fact, the therapist at the end of one therapy session came in to his supervisor and stated that he had saved a couple of lives that day, because evidently the wooden blocks were thrown around very wildly, and he was able to keep one of the patients from getting hit. It was clearly indicated that these were wild and undirected throwings of completely free impulse usage but, since there was more than one individual in the room, there was a danger. The therapist thus devoted himself to eliminating this danger through the imposing of the proper limits, plus the constant attempt through the process of intrusion, of getting the three boys to deal with their activities at a cognitive level. Thus, the questions were asked on a very simple level, such as, "What are you doing?" and on a more complicated level, "What type of people do this sort of thing?" "What might result from what you are doing?" etc. Over a period of time, the questions relating to the child's activities and the attempt to get him to cognize and thus explain his activities, tended to produce the type of activity where the child made items with which he could play creatively through the use and development of imagination. It will be noted that the questions asked tended to be emotionally free; this deviates from some of the usual patterns of psychotherapy where the efforts are to derive emotional loading. Here, the effort was clearly aimed at not deriving emotional loading. Rather, the therapist was interested in only one thing, and that is that the child be able to express that he was doing something and that he was doing it, in a sense, because he wanted to do it. Once the child was able to express this kind of sentiment, the therapist then ceased intruding and began to support the activity, and the child thus gained recognition that some of the things that he wanted to do were acceptable or, in other words, that his desires were not all disastrous or destructive, that he as a person could be accepted, and that his behaviors could be accepted. The children thus learned that they were responsible for their behavior in conjunction with each other, and by the time this group was terminated, there was no longer any danger of flying blocks, but rather there was a very consistent type of group activity which, at the time of the termination of this phase of play therapy, ended with the whole group making a kite together and going outside and flying it. This, by the way, not only indicated a success in therapy, but also indicated that this particular type of therapy had to be terminated because the children themselves were demonstrating a need for a different type of therapy involving more structure.

These two examples should help indicate the types of procedures that the therapist uses. The key to the therapist's procedures is whether or not he has gained communication with the child. If he has not gained communication he has to keep trying through the processes of intrusion. If he has gained communication, he becomes supportive and thus conditions the child to expand his ongoing behavior. Again, the remarks and questions of the therapist must not be emotionally loaded nor seeking emotional loading. Neither should they attempt to establish reality, nor should they attempt to help the child establish insight. Establishing reality and insight is not being sought in this particular form of therapy. The only insight that is really wanted is the insight on the part of the child that he is responsible for his own behavior, and this can best be established as we have said above, through this type of conditioning process, rather than by trying to draw the emotional content out of the situation, as might be done, or as certainly is done in other forms of psychotherapy.

ADDITIONAL NOTES

100. Many of the ideas expressed in this chapter have already been published in the *AJMD*, viz. Leland and Smith, loc. cit.

101. Kahn, E. and Cohen, L. H., "Organic Drivenness, A Brain Stem Syndrome and an Experience," *New England J. of Med.*, 1934, 210:14, pp. 748-756.

102. Broadhead and Garrett, Cleveland, Ohio, make a "clay" sink needed for this type of playroom. Clay, sand, etc., clog the pipes very quickly and their "trap" eliminates the need for expensive repairs.

103. Another factor to be considered is the advantages of a setting where a child can completely smear himself with mud, finger paint, etc., as part of his primitive expression. This also involves dressing rooms, etc., and may not be feasible in every setting. See also: Morales, E. and Fueyo, A., *Mud Therapy*, (Mimeographed), Winfield State Hospital & Training Center, Winfield, Kansas, 1958.

104. Seguin, *op. cit.*, p. 219, makes this point in regard to the retarded. Many philosophers of education in the past have also referred to this fact, e.g., Froebel, F., *Education of Man*, D. Appleton & Co., N. Y., 1887 or Dewey, (1916) *op. cit.* However, recent writers seem to have neglected this point which we feel is unfortunate, since it is still extremely important.

105. Hollis (1962) *op. cit.*, points out that peers may deter maturation progress with profoundly maladaptive youngsters.

106. Boyd, *op. cit.*, cites various authors from the history of work with the retarded who emphasize the importance of the tactile sense, e.g., Condillac, Pereire, and Seguin.

107. Goldfarb, W., "Psychological Privation in Infancy and Subsequent Adjustment," *Amer. J. Orthopsychiatry*, 1945, 15:2, pp. 247-255, discussed this question of rejection from the social psychiatric point of view and, while we must disagree with many of his conclusions, his basic observations are quite valuable.

VI. The Method of Unstructured Materials with a Structured Approach (U-S)

DEFINITION OF THE U-S METHOD

This chapter presents the second of the four procedures, that which utilizes unstructured materials with a structured therapeutic approach. This is the method we have identified as the U-S method. As was pointed out in Chapter IV, the procedures of this method are not new to the therapeutic field since they are typically found in the activities of the Occupational Therapist, Music Therapist, Recreation Therapist, and other ancillary therapists when they apply their practices within a dynamic or psychiatric frame of reference. We are not trying to rewrite the concepts of O.T., M.T., or R.T. into psychotherapy, but rather to point out that these disciplines share many activities with psychotherapy. One major factor which must be remembered, however, is that for all practical intents and purposes, one of the differences between psychotherapy and something else which may also have psychotherapeutic goals, is the relationship between the patient and the therapist. Where this relationship is close and warm, the therapist is able to play the role of a model for the patient.[108,109] When the relationship, on the other hand, is more distant and, though possibly permissive and accepting, not based on an interchange of feeling between the therapist and the patient, but rather facilitates a setting where the patient feels safe to carry out his behaviors, this is usually described as the function of ancillary therapy, but is not given the specific title of psychotherapy. This is an oversimplification of the differences and certainly a definitive expose of the roles would be of use, but that is outside the scope of this book. We are not trying to claim psychotherapy only for the particular procedures or groups of procedures which we have described, but rather to state that the nature of these kinds of playroom activities tend to set up the warm, interpersonal relationship between the therapist and the patient, or between the therapist and a group of patients, which is required for psychotherapy to take place. The important factor here is the concept that the patient is able to translate his needs and desires into socially acceptable behavior by learning to anticipate what would be acceptable to the therapist. This prejudgment comes both from what he has ob-

108. Here, the idea of "functional" model takes a meaning somewhat different from the traditional usage. We are not implying that the therapist should serve as a prototype or standard for the patient to copy, but rather as a pattern of social and interpersonal behavior which the patient may adapt freely to his own needs. Viz. above Chap. II, "Cognitive stimulation."

served the therapist doing and what, based on previous experience and the amount of insight he has gained, he judged that the therapist expected him to do. Thus, the therapist functions as a representation of the more democentic aspects of society and becomes a model upon which the patient may test his behavior.

MATERIALS

As to the method itself, the procedure is one of utilizing unstructured materials in a slightly more structured manner than in the U-U method previously described. Though many of the same materials may be employed, the particular goals for which these materials are intended are more structured and more preconceived, just as in O.T. a piece of leather is conceived to become a belt, or a hunk of clay to become an ash tray, so in the U-S method of play therapy these unstructured materials may also be destined for a specific function. Here again the difference is in the relationship between the patient and the therapist as they approach this function. Actually, it should be underlined that the end product at no time is of great importance, but the general procedures followed by the patient in attempting to produce an end product becomes quite important. Thus, we might say that it does not matter how good a belt emerges from the piece of leather, but it does matter that the patient is able to sufficiently control his behavior, his impulses, and his general acting-out tendencies to the extent of actually making a belt. It is this factor of approaching a higher level of structure which seems to mark this form of psychotherapy and differentiates it from the others.

One of the underlying factors in this approach is our attempt to set up a play situation where the actual play occurs during the creative activity. We can best think of this if we remember the times a normal child goes out to play, calls it "going out to play," nonetheless gets a hammer, some nails, and a saw, and starts making something such as an airplane, a boat, or a scooter. If anyone were to accuse him of working he would think that they were silly. He feels that he is playing at the time he is making these things. He may even be daydreaming that he is a carpenter or a mechanic or something along this line, so that it is not only play, but also builds fantasy in terms of his self-reference. What is important here is that the activity itself takes on significance because he feels he is producing a product, but the efforts to create the product become a play effort which, in terms of our previous discussion of play in Chapter II, serves the function of play in terms of building imagination, helping towards creativity, improving understanding of the surrounding world, etc.[110]

Once the child has completed the object, he usually goes and plays with it. That is, if he makes an airplane, he will dab some paint on it if it is handy, and go flying around with his airplane. And it is in this frame of reference that the U-S form of play therapy should be approached. The whole situation is play; but certain creative activities are engaged in for the purpose of furthering the play though they may also, in a sense, be ends in themselves, because the activity which made the product possible is also a play activity. The child makes an item as part of play, he then plays with the item as a mode of self-expression and finally, as we will discuss below, disposes of the item when the expression of "projection" is finished. The items have no permanence and are not for display.

It should be recognized that the child who is brought into this particular form, probably already functions at a higher level than the child described in the discussion of the previous form. That is, he has already established recognition of self, he has already come to realize that his impulses can be controlled, and he has already become aware of the fact that there are boundaries in society. These realizations imply the structuring of some clearly defined cognitive controls. These are no longer mere primitive cognitions, but rather, more complex cognitions. This also implies that the child, because of the presence of these more complex cognitions, is able to communicate more freely. The basis of the ability to cognize at a more abstract or higher level is the inclusion of the ability of freer communication, though not solely speech. However, in terms of this particular therapy method, speech is probably the preferred means of communication. All of these factors tend to help the therapist select certain types of unstructured materials to be used. Thus, while the sand box may still be used, it becomes a means of developing roads and mountains and other sorts of relief map creations, for while the same materials are used, they become means towards an end rather than an end unto themselves. Again, wooden blocks are perfectly acceptable, but they rapidly should become automobiles and trucks, or structures of one sort or another, and again become means towards an end. The patient at this level tends toward rejecting some unstructured materials; he is less satisfied with leaves or twigs, or things of this sort, and demands items which can be converted into some sort of creation, either on an organized fantasy level, or on a realistic level. The therapist finds it incumbent upon himself to utilize materials or to introduce materials that have a potential fantasy or creative value. In short then, all of the materials previously outlined in Chapter V, are potentially acceptable with the understanding that their use is for the purpose of introducing a higher level of play rather than to serve as self-sustaining items which are sufficient for creating play without the introduction of either organized fantasy or reality.

Therapeutic Procedures

The introduction of reality demonstrates another difference, because with the U-S method, this becomes an important aspect of the psychotherapy. It becomes necessary that the patient not only know what he is doing, but also that he deal with some of the reality elements of what he is doing. Using an example that grew out of one of the successes of the U-U form, when the boy finally was able to say that clay was a hamburger, this was considered highly sufficient. The boy should also realize that he has made a clay hamburger, and that one does not really eat it. In other words, the actual reality dimensions of the play have to be slowly introduced. Part of this is involved in the structured approach, or the "S" portion of the U-S method, but part of it is also involved in the materials used, since the therapist must be totally aware of the potential successes and the potential dangers of introducing certain types of materials. The danger lies primarily in introducing materials in ways that do not lend themselves either to reality or to organized fantasy play, and thus actually serve to primitivize the child's cognitive behavior where the child, instead of progressing towards the more advanced goals, is actually regressing from them. Thus, for example, while the pounding of nails into a board may serve a useful play function at first, permitting this to continue without getting the child to make anything, will tend to break down the therapeutic value at this level. The therapist must literally have a preconceived idea of how the unstructured materials should be used, and thus try to induce the child to use them in a manner similar if not identical to his preconceived plan. The patient may be overly preoccupied with his skill or technique and lose track of the over-all goal of creating something. Here, the therapist must increase his intrusion in an effort to bring the child's attention back to the original goal. Further, it should be pointed out that some of the best unstructured materials for this level child are those which have a semipreconceived structure, such as erector sets, Tinker Toys, and things of this sort which lend themselves to certain specific types of design, which hopefully are already familiar to the child, in that he has seen them in toy shops, or with his siblings, or around the home, or in the home, or in the institution. In other words, the therapist begins to show the relationship between unstructured materials and familiar functional reality usage, and this introduces the patient to the idea that there are organized relationships within his own milieu.

For the above reasons, the approach of the therapist in this setting is much more structured or preconceived. The therapist plans at the beginning of the session what kinds of activities the child is going to be induced to carry out during the session. The types of activities are not left to free choice. Materials are made ready in the playroom before the child enters. If, for instance, the therapist has decided that they are going to work with clay, the clay is already on the table. The extra tools that are going to be needed are already there. The therapist then ushers the child into the playroom, sits down with him at the table, and they begin discussing the fact of using the clay to make something. At this point the structure ceases, because the therapist does not particularly care what the child makes, it is not an issue of making an ash tray or a Grecian urn, but rather that they make something, and the child may then begin making clay snakes or small balls. The therapist then discusses what these things are, and if the child indicates that they are clay snakes, there is an opening for a discussion on snakes, and whether or not the clay snakes he has made are like real snakes, and what his total feelings on the question are. It will be noted here that there is a slight reversion to the traditional individual therapeutic practices in that the therapist now is seeking emotional loading and feeling tone from the patient, rather than just the recognition that the patient is carrying out the activity. However, this should not be overemphasized since the therapist is still primarily interested in the patient's gaining sufficient confidence in himself to feel that he is accomplishing something, and the therapist's conversations concerning the activity should at no point become so probing that they actually force the stopping of the activity, because in this method, just as in the U-U method, it is considered that the activity has value unto itself, and if the therapist becomes too probing in the emotional area, he begins to be punishing where he actually should be rewarding. This probing is kept on fairly neutral ground, but nontheless becomes more exacting than it would have been in the U-U area. Along the same line, but also in terms of introducing greater reality constructs, the therapist will encourage the child to indicate the types of activities he would like to engage in, or the sort of things he would like to make. If the child indicates that he would like to make something more complex than the materials which are presently laid out will permit, the therapist then discusses with him what additional materials or tools would be needed and whether or not these additional tools and materials might be readily available. In this way, he begins to plan with the child for the next therapy session. The therapist can then either produce the necessary materials and tools, so the child may go ahead with his plans or discuss with him why they could not be carried out. Thus, the child is introduced not only to the reality of what things are made of, but also to the concepts of planning, or looking ahead, of recognizing that tomorrow may carry rewards that are not present today, or that the lack of immediate rewards is not necessarily punishment, and that sometimes aims must be postponed. These concepts become therapeutic values in their own right as well as permitting somewhat more "permissiveness" in the therapy session than if the therapist himself constantly prescribed the specific activities that would be carried out at each session. This same factor can work in a group setting where the therapist utilizes the round-table technique to stimulate the members of the group to agree that they all want to make something, and then discusses the types of materials that are needed. Thus, the whole group is then participating in the planning and becoming sufficiently involved in the project so that a group investment has been created. Groups do not, however, always end up with all members working on the same item. Thus, for example, one member may make a vase or another an ash tray, but all are working with clay. In this instance, the fantasy elements of play will be on a more individual basis, each child expressing his own associations.

Another factor present in the therapist's approach to the U-S type is that he becomes a much more active participant in the play activities. This represents another essential difference between this type of approach and that found in some of the ancillary therapies. Items which are being produced are essentially for play in the playroom, rather than merely aesthetic or practical functional creations which quite often result from activities in O.T., for instance.[111] Thus, the child makes something and the therapist helps him to make it, and after that the therapist and the child play with it. There will be times when the technical requirements of the project prevent its being completed in one session. Since, as discussed in Chapter IV, the "limit" of time is extremely important, it is necessary to find a stopping point when interest is still high and then carry the task over to the next session.[112] The play should always occur at the time the project is completed and therefore it is not a good procedure to finish an object at the end of a session when there is no time to play with it. An example of this type of play is when Tinker Toys are used to put together a teeter-totter and the therapist and the patient can put figures on the teeter-totter or use other Tinker Toys to represent dolls, and pretend that two people are teeter-tottering. If clay is used to make snakes, then the therapist will make a snake, and if the patient wishes, the two snakes will have a fight, thus permitting the patient to express some of the resentment against the therapist's intrusion in a socially acceptable manner, without violating the limits in terms of actually attacking the therapist. If finger painting is being done, the therapist, while he probably will not make a finger painting, will help the child make one in terms of the proper application of the paint to the paper and demonstrating how the fingers and whole hands, etc., can be used, and after this the therapist and the child will then discuss what has been painted, what the child thinks it is, and what, after the child has given it a label, the implications of this label are; therefore while they do not actually play with the painting, they can have a playful fantasying discussion together. This becomes a sort of verbal play which is valuable in this kind of therapy setting. Thus, the therapist actually at all levels participates with the patient when the behavior is acceptable. When the patient will not communicate or will not perform in an acceptable manner, the therapist again becomes intrusive, blocking, and thus punishing.[113]

113. Some therapists have found that a short period at the end of the session for the purpose of discussing and summarizing the events of the session with the patient is extremely valuable. This will be discussed further in relationship to the S-U method.

Here again the patient and the therapist must go along at about the same pace. The therapist must be very sure that he does not attempt to move faster than the patient, either in terms of the patient's intellectual ability to comprehend what is happening, or his emotional tolerance. This has, however, a worked-in safeguard because, if the therapist is constantly aware that he is working in a play structure and that the things being made are for fun rather than display, the patient is much more apt to be able to go along with him, and the therapist will get the usual warning signals that he is moving too fast when the patient is no longer having fun in the situation. Thus, when the situation becomes painful to the patient, and the therapist begins to feel that possibly he is unnecessarily punishing, he immediately stops, back tracks, and attempts to recoup the previous level of rapport and probably will stop the activities somewhere in that vicinity permitting the patient to synthesize whatever emotional feelings have been developed through the activity.

Therapy Setting

The playroom setting for this type of activity is similar to that of the U-U method. Since some messy materials are going to be used, an unadorned, crudely decorated playroom is preferable. Again the cement floor or a fire-proof structure is highly recommended because it is completely in keeping with this method that a patient build a fire and put it out, the difference being that this time it should be put out with a simulated fire truck and the whole process should become a fantasy matter of firemen putting out a fire, rather than just water putting it out. But beyond this point of introducing organized fantasy play, the activity itself should be permitted to occur in this setting. Again the playroom has to be the type of playroom that would support this sort of activity.[114]

Patients who are brought into this form of therapy usually have greater emotional endurance than patients in the U-U method (in which the time schedule was thought of in terms of short periods). Here the child is able to tolerate and utilize longer periods, so we would expect that a child in this setting probably could sustain a full hour of play therapy fairly well. It is even possible that such a child would be able to sustain as many as two of these play hours a week and still be able to gain insight and synthesize these insights in terms of the conditioning which is going on, so that the duration of the period is of less importance than it was in the more primitive area.

114. Here, as in Chap. V, the patient may be permitted to leave the playroom if the object which has been made can only be played with out of doors, e.g., a kite, but the majority of the session should be in the playroom with a procedure of making the kite in the room, flying it outside, and then discussing the activity back in the room.

Further, the limits which are introduced are also more structured in that they include not only the previously mentioned limits in relationship to person, but now also become limits which are set in relationship to things and activities. One of the initial limits is that the things created in the play situation are for play in that situation, and thus it is not permitted that they be taken "home to mama" to be hung on the wall; nor should they in any particular manner, shape, or form represent an aesthetic or artistic creation. They are strictly functional materials to be used for play and when the play is finished, it is discussed with the child that when he gives his consent the items are to be destroyed. It is thought by some therapists that the child actually prefers this type of play.[115] Therefore, one of the major limits that is imposed in this type of therapy over and above the personal safety limit, is that neither the materials nor the finished products leave the play session. In fact, the therapist is constantly de-emphasizing the finished product throughout all of his therapeutic efforts. In those instances where the object is a group product, the therapist must make sure that the disposal is also a group activity done with group consent. Additional limits are in relationship to the materials themselves. The child, of course, always has a perfect right to use up and destroy materials to the extent of his ability. This is one reason unstructured materials are used; in essence they cannot be destroyed or used up in the full sense of the word although the child does not have the right to misuse the materials in the sense of throwing them at the therapist, or at some other member of the group. Nor does he have the right to hurt himself with the materials, e.g., if the finger paints are in a glass jar and it breaks, the therapist must immediately intervene and make sure that he does not play with the glass. He is not permitted to eat or swallow the materials, and in the U-S method the therapist will actually block the eating procedure.--- The essential feature here is that the child must realize the reality of what the materials are, that they are not food, and that they are for play purposes. If the child proves himself to be of too low a functional level to comprehend this, then he should not have been brought into this type of play therapy in the first place, and he should be introduced or reintroduced into the U-U procedure.

The other specific limits which grow out of this method become defined as the therapy sessions themselves develop. The therapist will introduce limits relative to each particular material utilized. Thus, if leather is being utilized to make a belt where there are also sharp knives or pointed instruments involved, there will be special limits that would not necessarily

116. If the child seems to be one who constantly eats whatever comes to hand, the therapist in the U-U method may introduce other types of unstructured materials such as flour and water, or mashed turnips or something of this sort, thus permitting the child to become disgusted with his own eating habits.

be applied to the tongue depressors used in relationship to clay activity. Further, when this procedure is used as a form of group therapy, a very important limit that must be imposed is that all members of the group will, in one way or another, be engaging in similar activities. There will not be one child playing with clay, and another playing with finger paint, and a third one in the sand pile, but rather all will be working with clay, with finger paints, etc., and the child who will not cooperate is violating the limits and must be approached from that point of view. In this type of setting it is even conceivable that if the child insists on violating these limits, he will actually be removed from the setting in the sense that the therapist will so completely block his activity that he is no longer part of the group for that particular session, but is returned to his cottage or sent home with the recognition, however, that at the following session he may re-enter the group completely without prejudice.

INDICATIONS AND MAJOR CRITERIA FOR U-S THERAPY

The child who is most suited for this kind of therapeutic approach is aware that he is responsible for his behavior, but is not sufficiently aware of the manifestations or implications of this responsibility. He is still testing, or trying out his behavior in a sense of seeking his own power. The function of therapy in this case is to give the child opportunity to develop relationships with both people and objects which he can manipulate in a socially acceptable manner, and thus test his power, and come to know himself as a functioning person. The child who has not yet realized that he can be a functioning person is still too primitive for this type of therapy. The child that has full realization of this fact is too sophisticated,[117] but the child who is in between, who knows that he can function, but does not know to what extent or is unsure of what his social role could or should be, and is thus unable to express his emotional and behavioral problems because he is not quite sure as to their acceptability, is a child for whom this type of therapy is most clearly indicated. The child may come in with an outlandish level of aspiration, assuming that he can do a great number of things which, when actually faced with the task, he finds that he cannot do; or he may be a child who feels that he can do absolutely nothing, who when presented with the task and supportive help, finds that he can succeed. Both of these children properly belong in this type of therapy setting, so that their level of self-concept and reality can be united in a more socially usable manner.

GOALS

Improved Self-Concept. The first goal for this form of psychotherapy is the development of an improved self-concept. We have already established that the child has recognition of self, but this uniting of his self-image with objective reality in terms of his actual ability becomes a form of improving his self-concept by giving him self-confidence where it is lacking, or bringing it to the reality level where it seems to be distorted in the sense of delusions. This goal becomes extremely important if the child is to be able to live in the community at his level. We might point out here that the child we are discussing is most often the type who is also categorized as "brain damaged,"[118] or "organically involved," or is given some similar designation, and it must be recognized that this type of child must have a self-concept that will, on the one hand, be consistent with his ability and, on the other, will not be so self-depreciating that he cannot function up to his potential. Rather, it must permit him to recognize that there are many things he cannot do, but also that there are many things that he can do, and when this recognition has been established and accepted, it could be said that therapy in this area has been successful.

Improved Impulse Control. The second major goal for this type of therapy involves improved impulse control. Here, we have a child who realizes that impulses can be controlled. This knowledge may be a two-edged sword in the sense that he may still have a problem in controlling his impulses, though he knows that he can control them, and thus he may feel extremely guilty and upset because he does not. Again, we have a self-reinforcing process where the feelings of social uneasiness increase because the child is not doing something he knows he can do. Play therapy helps him to improve impulse control by increasing his understanding that the basic desires which his impulses are attempting to satisfy, can be satisfied in a socially accepted manner, that it is not the desires themselves that are at fault, but rather his knowledge of what to do about them.

Improved Social Interaction. The third goal involves the improvement of his ability to interact socially. The child, having learned that there are limits in society, has to learn further where the limits are imposed, how they are imposed, and the difference between major limits and minor limits in the area of social behavior. This is also related to social reality. The child's first impression on learning there are limits is that it is as great a crime to walk on the grass as it is to steal a neighbor's ball. Both are treated as equal sins, both are treated with equal daring if the child decides to be hostile to social limits. There is no effort on his part to differentiate between violating all social limits, opposing certain social limits, or conforming to all social limits. Actually, these three levels never seem to occur to young people who tend to be "all or nothing" in their approach.

The function of the U-S form of therapy is to help the child learn relative constructs in regard to limits, to help him understand that some limits can never be violated, such as striking the examiner or striking his peers in a group situation, and that other limits may sometimes be violated with permission, e.g., the instance where the ash tray that has been made may be taken from the therapy room under some very special circumstances, or where finger paint may have been thrown at the examiner in a mood of playfulness which was not considered aggressive, and therefore, accepted at its face value, rather than being translated into a heinous act. There are other limits which do not need to be imposed; thus the child can be angry at the examiner and even demonstrate his hostility in terms of using his snake to fight the examiner's snake and thus substitute his behavior for the desire to actually strike the examiner. In this manner, he learns the total pattern of imposed social interaction. This is further demonstrated at a higher level by group procedures where he also learns to be aware of the feelings of his peers and learns to modify his desires and feelings so that the group as a whole can reach some common ground. This is the highest level, yielding to cooperative and group interplay which again would be representative of successful therapy.

Individual Therapy

In judging whether or not the child in this setting should be brought into individual or group psychotherapy, a further set of considerations is necessary. Since all children have established a self-concept, the previously mentioned key point of emotional endurance is no longer an important one for deciding whether individual or group therapy is the best means of dealing with the situation. Rather, in this setting the question seems to be dependent on how great a need the patient has for a close one-to-one relationship with the therapist. This question can be approached from the point of considering how much about play the child actually knows. Does the child know how to play? Does he feel that he can, with safety to himself, fantasize, use his imagination for the purposes of increasing his knowledge of social reality, remembering as we stated in Chapter II, that play for the child is his way of working. It is his way of developing new skills, new techniques, new ideas. The question that we have to ask at this point is whether or not this child knows how to "work" in these terms. Is he able to utilize the materials and structure for the development of skills and new ideas, or is he highly constricted, impotent, unable to express himself along these lines? Remembering that this type of therapy is usually indicated for the child whose primary difficulty seems to be "organic" retardation, we are faced with a child whose expressions of self are generally impotent in the sense that he does not usually understand his feelings about certain things nor the source of his behavioral reactions.[119] We find that the child is a perplexed individual in the sense that he does not know what to do or how to react to stimuli from his environment, and further, he is unable to utilize his imagination to deal with the reality as the therapist is demanding. This child, we would say, does not know how to play, does not know how to use the cues and elements of his environment to broaden and develop himself. This type of child needs individual therapy because it is only through the guidance and imposed conditioning from the therapist that he will literally be taught how to utilize objects for the sake of his own self-improvement. The conditioning process has to be a very tight one, has to be as free as possible from outside interference, and has to be as closely centered on the specific activity and the specific objective as it possibly can be, so that the hyperactivity and the distractibility of the child will not interfere with the therapy goals. This type of child would best fit into the individual psychotherapy situation rather than group psychotherapy.

Group Therapy

Conversely, when the child seems to know how to play; when he seems to be able to deal with the materials in the manner in which the therapist is trying to guide him, but is unable to interact socially in terms of control of impulses, we would say that this child would work better in a group situation since the group itself can help the therapist impose the kinds of limits on uncontrolled impulses that the child needs to learn. The group may become a conditioning agent in that the child's peers may not let him get away with anything that in any way interferes with their freedom of behavior; in that sense each child in the group is a therapist, and with developing group consciousness should be able, in his own self-interest, to support the efforts of the therapist to keep the activity going on a group basis. Thus, the child whose problems center around learning that there are other people in his environment that have to be recognized and taken into consideration before he behaves in response to his desires, can best learn this through group therapy. The U-S method is uniquely suited for this purpose since projects using unstructured materials may, through group cooperation, result in a very satisfying activity, as in the example of the kite referred to above, where the group went out and flew it with the aid and support of the therapist. Other situations can be evolved where things that are too heavy for one child to move, or too awkward for one child to deal with, can be introduced into the therapy situation with the idea that if these objects are combined into, let us say, a house, they become handy toys with which the whole group can play, and this cannot be done unless they all work together in creating it. These are fairly standard nursery school or kindergarten techniques, but they lend themselves beautifully to this kind of therapeutic situation since they deal with unstructured materials, thus forcing the group to produce structure. The group, by being forced to produce structure, learns that structure is possible through cooperation, and each child within the group may learn how to behave in an improved manner in response to social impulses. In this particular area we may think of the therapy procedures as a progressive element in the sense that a child may be brought first into individual therapy, and after he has learned how to play and learned how to deal with the reality of structure, he may then be brought into a group to, in a sense, finish out the therapy goals. Thus, it is not necessarily true that a child should be brought into a group in the beginning, or be in a group the whole time, nor that he should be brought into an individual relationship in the beginning and remain in that the whole time. Rather, his placement should depend on how he was able to respond with the therapist toward the accomplishment of the major goals.

DISCUSSION

Practical Application of Some of the Theoretical Constructs

The particular theoretical constructs on which this form of therapy is based are not in any sense different from those already outlined in the U-U method. The child still needs to learn to develop cognition in the sense that he has to bring his behavior to a rational or thoughtful level; he must still through the process of reward and intrusion (punishment), be conditioned to behave in a socially acceptable or socially conforming manner. The factor that is present here that was not present before is that one must presume this child has had a greater number of life experiences before entering therapy than the child for whom the U-U method is indicated. Since he has had a greater number of life experiences, or at least since he has been able to absorb into his personality a greater number of associations, there is a much greater job of sorting to be done. Some of these associations have to be modified in the sense of a reconditioning process; some have to be built upon in the sense of a reinforcement process, and it is necessary for the therapist and the child to sort through these experiences in unison and find those which must be modified on one hand, and those which may be reinforced on the other. This sorting job, which is a matter of introducing higher or more abstract levels of thought and cognition, requires a much greater use of communicative skills, and one of the key theoretical constructs of this form of therapy is the major emphasis on communicative skills as a mode of conditioning. Thus, the child is not conditioned solely through either physical contact or through the therapist's intrusion in his behavior, but also through tones of voice, probing for the emotional content, involvement in historical references, etc., and the therapist's intrusion becomes one of social intrusion as well as one of actual physical intrusion. We realize in terms of usual therapy procedures with adults and with older children that verbal communication is usually the major if not the sole means of conditioning which is utilized. With children, the process of play permits the child to maintain a certain distance from the therapist, thus allowing freedom for an interaction, by making him feel safe, comfortable, or secure in his expression. However, this interceding distance makes the inclusion of verbal communication even more important, and therefore, communication between the therapist and the child becomes of primary importance in the conditioning process. Thus, while in the U-U method we talked in terms of "forcing the child to think," here we can talk in terms of "forcing the child to think about something." This is a higher level, it introduces a greater abstraction, and develops an ability on the part of the child to focus his thoughtful attention on certain specific areas relative to his personality.[120] Thus, we can say that we are still stimulating cognition, but we are stimulating it at a much higher level, and it has become more purposeful. Actually, the U-S method can be considered self-contained in the sense that if the child's emotional disturbance is primarily the result of his organicity, he can, at the successful completion of the U-S method, be considered ready to re-enter the community or to go into some specialized type of training program without having to consider further psychotherapy. We hope, under these circumstances, that he is then functioning somewhere in the vicinity of his potential, but, at the same time, this potential will be improved in terms of our definition of rehabilitation through the addition of training, and the psychotherapeutic goals can be maintained in the training shop, special education classroom, etc. Thus, we find that the function of psychotherapy here is to inhibit the maladaptive behavior which the child has developed as a response to the community's response to his organicity, and reinforce the more acceptable behavior which then permits him to become a contributing member of the community and an individual who can be accepted for what he is, and who can accept himself for what he is.

Indication of Gain in Play Therapy and Criteria for Termination

The progress towards the particular goals of the U-S method becomes a much simpler task of recognition than in other forms of psychotherapy. Since the goals are fairly specific, it is comparatively easy for the therapist to know when he has reached them. Thus, the child who does not know how to play, through the process of therapy, begins learning how to fantasize and learning how to use the objects in a playful manner. It becomes clear when he has gained this much knowledge. Furthermore, if in a group situation the child was totally unable either to integrate or to control his impulses in relationship to the other members of the group, and he begins to demonstrate that he can control his impulses and can take the other members of the group into consideration when making behavioral decisions, this again becomes completely clear to the therapist. Thus, the progress is not based on some abstract or unknown quality of psychological improvement, but rather on some very clear-cut, concrete behavioral manifestations which the child demonstrates. It becomes a very clear matter that before psychotherapy, the child did A, B, and C, and after psychotherapy, he no longer does A, B, and C, but now does D, E, and F. These are concrete factors and can be measured on a presence and absence basis and, therefore, make the therapist's job comparatively simple in terms of his ability to know when progress has been achieved. Of course, the therapist's job in achieving the progress is no simpler than in any other form of psychotherapy, and we do not want to create the illusion that this form of psychotherapy is any more successful in terms of numbers of helped patients than any other type, but if the therapy does work, if the efforts made by the therapist are successful, it will be immediately evident to him in the behavior of the patient.

A case in point is the patient who was brought into therapy at a time when it was known that he was able to communicate, that he seemed to have a concept of himself, and, in other words, met the usual demands or indications for the U-S method. But having been brought into therapy it was found that he would not participate in any of the activities, that he was totally withdrawn, that he would not play with any of the materials, but would just stand around and look at them. He was brought into a group procedure originally because it was felt that his major problem was one of group interaction, and since it was not convenient to move him out of the group, he was permitted to remain even though he would just stand and watch them play though he himself would do nothing. After a number of sessions, including an extensive amount of intervention on the part of the therapist, the patient began to play with some large wooden beads. This was mostly a matter of picking them up, shifting them from one hand to the other, moving them around on a table, but seeming in some way to consider them as toys. The therapist supported this activity, duplicated it himself, thus indicating that it was an acceptable activity, and helped the patient thus to raise the level of the activity. "Raising the level" at first took the form of sorting the beads, and then later of stringing them in various combinations and arrangements. During this phase of the therapy the patient began to discuss his activities with the therapist in nonsyllabic and simple word structures, but nonthe-less communication was established. After this the patient began to observe more carefully the activities of the other members of the group and in a slow, cautious manner interacted with them in some of their activities. Also, the therapist encouraged the other members of the group to interact with this patient and suggested that maybe they also would like to play with the beads. This two-way interaction developed group behavior which permitted the patient to feel that he was part of the group, and gradually he was able to give up his own activity in favor of going along with some of the group's activities. This developed further use of communication in terms of verbal discussion which finally resulted towards the end in the patient's saying that he was too big for this kind of play, that he should be doing more important things, things that older children do, and he then took the initiative of asking the vocational counselor to get him a job. This initiative was supported by the therapist and when the vocational counselor was able to get him a job, the therapy was terminated on the basis that the supervisor of the job would continue whatever counseling was required. Now this type of situation may not work out as readily in the community as it did in the institutional structure in which it occurred, but something similar can work in conjunction with special education or vocational rehabilitation services which the communities provide

CONCLUSION

We have presented here a method of psychotherapy which involves unstructured materials with a structured, therapeutic approach. We have indicated that this method seems to be most valuable with those children who, though they are emotionally disturbed, nonetheless owe their emotional disturbance more to organic disorders which have produced mental retardation, than to psychogenic cause. This is not to say that U-S therapy is only valuable for that type of child, but the child who behaves in that manner seems to be the most indicated for this type of therapy. The therapy procedures have been outlined with the major emphasis on the fact that in this type of therapy the development of fantasy, imagination, and social reality is emphasized, with the therapist developing as close a relationship as possible to the patient, and utilizing play as a binding element. The next chapter will discuss an alternative method which is useful with a more highly communicative, highly expressive child who also has a number of emotional problems which tend to retard his functioning.

ADDITIONAL NOTES

108. This note has been cited on page 90.

109. Chapanis, A., "Men, Machines and Models," *Amer. Psychol.*, 16, 1961, pp. 113-131, gives a very complete discussion of the mechanical concepts of models as machines or substitutes, "A model is analogy and no one expects an analogy to be completely adequate."

110. Dewey (1916), *op. cit.*, pp. 34-35.

111. Azima, H. and Azima, F. J., "Outline of a Dynamic Theory of Occupational Therapy," *Amer. J. of O.T.*, 13, 1959, pp. 215-221, makes a similar point from the frame of reference of an O.T.R.

112. Lewin, K., *A Dynamic Theory of Personality*, McGraw-Hill Book Co., 1935, pp. 242-247, "Zeigarnik effect."

113. This note has been cited on page 95.

114. This note has been cited on page 96.

115. Horst-Oesterhuis, C. J. van der, "Therapie figurative," *L'Evolution Psychiatrique*, IV, 1959, pp. 585-593, discusses this phenomenon and reports on this behavior, though he does it from a frame of reference very different from ours.

116. This note has been cited on page 97.

117. Viz. Chap. VII.

118. Strauss, A. and Kephart, N., *Psychopathology and Education of the Brain Injured Child*, Vol. II, Grune and Stratton, N. Y., 1955, pp. 128-143.

119. Horne, B. M. and Philleo, C. C., "A Comparative Study of the Spontaneous Play Activities of Normal and Mentally Defective Children," *J. Genet. Psych.*, 1962, 61, pp. 33-46, point out in a comparative study with normal children, that retarded children in their sample showed more interest in materials involving prescribed activities. These children were similar to those we are describing here.

120. Wallon, H., "Du Behaviorisme a la psychologie de motivation," *La Pensee*, Paris, 1961, pp. 3-6, discusses the essential role of verbal communication in humans and points out very vividly where the more orthodox "Behaviorists" seem to go astray.

VII. The Method of Structured Materials with an Unstructured Approach (S-U)

This chapter is a presentation of the third of the four methods of play therapy. This method, which involves structured materials with generally unstructured techniques and procedures, has been described by us as reflecting that method usually or traditionally found in psychotherapeutic play procedures. The contribution that we hope to make is the discussion of the application of these processes, in what is probably a nontraditional manner, to the functionally retarded child. In other words, while the materials, the approach, the indications for the psychotherapy and the goals may be similar, there are also important differences. As we have discussed before, the emotionally disturbed, brain damaged, retarded child presents problems and behaviors which are different from the child with normal intelligence, both because of etiology and because of the nature of the emotional disturbance.[121]

DEFINITION OF THE S-U METHOD

We would define this method as involving, as do the traditional precepts of play therapy, structured toys which have a preconceived construct as to their use and what they are, in a situation where the therapist has no preconception as to how he is going to approach the child or what he wants him to do. As will be noted below, the setting in the S-U situation is more narrowly conceived than in the usual play therapy room, and the toys are often more narrowly conceived, but, in general, the method can be thought of as one primarily aimed at inviting thematic play, and it is for this reason that we have described it in terms of the traditional precepts.

Materials

As to the materials themselves, this is a matter of dealing with the same materials usually found in a play therapy setting, but with certain differences established to accommodate the needs of the functionally retarded child. Thus, items that have to be manipulated, such as representative figures, should normally be somewhat larger than the figures found in the typical playroom, because the retarded child may have difficulty in handling them. As one of our therapists stated, "The patient, because of coordination difficulties with her hands, became so involved in trying to make a figure stand up, she never had sufficient psychic energy to play with the figure."

Figures that are larger, that are easy to manipulate, eliminate this kind of problem and permit the brain damaged child much more freedom by movement. Again, because of the difficulty that the retarded child has in making certain abstractions, it is expected that the materials should lend themselves more readily to consistent play activity. For example, if the play is with the doll house, it is found that much more effective and expressive play is achieved if the furniture available is furniture specifically designed for that particular doll house, rather than unrelated items which, while the normal child could make them fit into the doll house structure, for the functionally retarded child, create a special kind of confusion which again blocks the fluidity of the play themes. Other examples are related to factors of distractibility: too many of the materials should not be available at once, but rather should be segregated into categories and only certain categories should be available at any one time. It is noted that there are children, capable of thematic play once they are oriented by the therapist, who will wander around the room picking up every toy, looking at it, laying it down, not knowing what to do with any of them, primarily because the tremendous diffusion of toys makes organized thought on any one subject almost impossible. Conversely, the room should have a sufficient number of "exciting" toys to catch the child's imagination. The types of toys that either do not do anything or do only very complicated things after the child has gone through a very complicated procedure, present no interest to the retarded child, and regardless of his potential for play he will not play with them. Thus, the more basic, familiar toys are the bulk of our structured material.

The functionally retarded child is generally not well-developed in the area of discrimination. Surprisingly, however, he is often aware of the difference between, for example, a Ford and a Chevrolet car. Therefore, this kind of concrete awareness versus the more abstract awareness has to be taken into consideration in the selection of toys for the playroom in this kind of setting. We recall one patient who measured at an IQ of 55, who was quite disturbed that the Ford station wagon available in the playroom setting was not an exact replica of the Ford station wagon with which he was acquainted. This created another unfortunate example of where the therapist, hoping to continue the thematic play, made some remark about, "Well, that really doesn't matter," and found himself involved in a rather dialetic argument concerning why it did matter, and the play therapy session for that afternoon was finished as far as that patient was concerned. The important point of this illustration is that the patients become preoccupied with details and hang onto them very desperately because of their difficulty in generalizing, and if these details are interfered with, the therapist runs the danger of losing his patient. The materials then, should either have conscientious regard for details if they are going to be specific, or should be undetailed enough that the patient would not get involved in that aspect of the question. This rules out a large number of toys commonly found in a playroom setting. What is really involved here is a very careful selection, on the part of the therapist in furnishing his playroom, of toys that are either fairly exact in their duplication of what they are suppose to be, and these things should be fairly familiar, day-to-day items, or toys that are obtuse enough that there cannot be a really exact replication, and the patient will then accept them on their face value. Things in this latter category are wooden trains, play work benches, wooden trucks that disassemble and can be reassembled, etc. In other words, the lack of concreteness of the object can be compensated by the creativity which the patient must contribute in producing the final results. Here again, it must be emphasized that the objects should be large enough and simple enough to be assembled without the patient using up all of his psychic energy in figuring out how they go together.

With the above provisions in mind, the standard materials for this type of play involve trucks, dolls, guns, doll houses, telephones, hammering tools, bop bags (in this latter regard "bop bags" are far preferable to punching bags, because "bop bags" have faces and features which permit the child to take out aggression in the area where he is really aiming it, rather than encouraging abstract expressions of aggression), and general kinds of toys that have specific play function such as jig saw puzzles, dishes for tea parties, etc. Actually the list could be extremely long. We think the point, however, is fairly clearly made. Any item normally found on the counter of a "five and dime" is the kind of item we are seeking with the provision that it be large enough to be handled by brain damaged children, and simple enough that the complexities of operating it will not overwhelm the child, and thus negate the thematic aspects. Also, balls are generally acceptable, as are small sets of ten pins or something of this sort. One thing that we should emphasize here is that particularly masculine or particularly feminine toys are not the issue at this level since with the functionally retarded child any mode of expression is to be invited and elicited and if, for example, a 14 year old boy prefers to play with a doll because of his general maturational retardation, this is totally acceptable at this stage of the therapy.

As mentioned in Chapter VI, many of the unstructured toys can be utilized in a structured manner. Thus, sand can become roads and villages, finger paints can become a basis for producing a certain kind of thematic expression, water can be part of a fire truck apparatus to put out a fire, etc. These activities belong in the S-U form of therapy if they are organized in that manner. Also in this regard, higher level expressive play is certainly not to be ruled out. Certain patients have a great deal of facility, for instance, in dealing with hand puppets, or with other objects that require a great deal of manipulation. When the children demonstrate this facility, these items certainly should be part of S-U therapy since they are highly productive in the thematic area. Also, they provide sufficient distance so that the patient does not necessarily feel that he is doing the behaving, yet also permit sufficient closeness that full emotional expression can be had. Therefore, we are certainly not ruling out this type of play, but rather inserting a warning that the ability of the child to manipulate the material should be the guide post as to the type of play used, and if the child seems to be incoordinated, as so many brain damaged children are, he should be permitted to deal with objects that will not continually remind him of his coordination problems.

The question of the selection of toys, or the selection of activities for play, has recently been discussed by Ginott[122] and others with the conclusion that the proper selection must be made on the rationale upon which the therapy is being conducted. It is our usual practice that when a child is brought into play therapy, he is evaluated in terms of the therapy goals, and at that point the therapists may themselves go to a local toy counter and select the specific items which seem to be relative to this particular child's needs. The above listing of toys and materials is proposed as a guide to the types of materials to be used with functionally retarded children. Since the specific problems related to mental retardation and emotional disturbance involves both the present functioning of the child as well as his etiology, an all-purpose list of toys cannot be had.

Therapeutic Procedures

Regarding the approach of the therapist in this method, there is very little difference between this type of accepting, unstructured therapeutic approach and that used by therapists in most nondirective play procedures.[123] The major difference in the S-U setting is the fact that the therapist must, because he is dealing with a functionally retarded child, be more active. That is to say, he has to be constantly on the alert for activity producing meaningful associations on the part of the child, and must try to swing the child's behavior around the situation in such a way that the child can gain awareness. If he fails, the therapist must then be prepared for the kind of perservative, repetitious play in which the brain damaged child often engages until he is able to cognize, or until the therapist can insidiously direct him to it. Thus, we are not recommending that the therapist constantly be interpeting materials, as the retarded child has difficulty in forming meaningful associations, but rather, through quasi-interpretative remarks and leading questions, the therapist should try to get the child to gain insight, recognizing that the same ground is going to have to be covered many times before the child will make the necessary associations. Here, the therapist interacts very closely with the patients and, as mentioned in previous chapters, becomes part of the play, participates as actively as possible in the fantasies of the patient, and, in general, tries to conduct himself in a manner which in no way frustrates the efforts of the patient to intellectualize or organize the particular themas of the activity.[124] However, the therapist is somewhat more interested in reality play at this stage than in previous stages, and the conditioning takes the form of reinforcing those play fantasies and activities which are related to reality, and inhibiting those which have no relationship to reality; recognizing that by reality we do not mean the ignoring of the "reality" of fantasy material. The patient who re-enacts the television story, or a fairy tale, is certainly dealing with his reality and is to be encouraged. What we object to is where, for example, the father doll ate the baby doll and then regurgitated it alive. This sort of activity is not only contrary to socially acceptable behavior, but is disturbing in terms of the reality construct and, of course, would not be reinforced by the therapist. However, the idea of re-establishing life is a positive one and should be encouraged. While it would not be interpreted, it certainly would be probed in the sense that the therapist would stay with the subject, attempting to get the patient to explain the situation, to clarify it and, hopefully, to rationalize it along more acceptable or realistic lines. In this type of situation it is possible that the "punishing" instructions of the therapist will extinguish the bizarre behavior, and the child will either withdraw or make a substitution.

In view of the above, it can be protested that the therapist is not sufficiently permissive, not sufficiently nondirective, and does not give the patient sufficient freedom. This is a legitimate question, but with functionally retarded children, the type of permissiveness normally referred to in play therapy cannot be set forth. The fact that we are dealing with a functionally retarded child indicates the need for educative leadership, as it is not economic, in a temporal sense, to wait for a functionally retarded child to work out his own problems with reality, because this requires abilities which he has not yet, by definition, acquired. Thus, the therapist is always directive and always leading, but in an unstructured manner which means that he has no preconceived ideas as to the specific direction. Rather he takes his guidance from the free play of the child, picking up the cues and themas, and then working with them to try and establish the play patterns, but at no time could it be said that the child is enjoying free cathartic play. Further, the therapist is not able to act as the "model" in a manner required for the successful completion of the conditioning if he is withdrawn and not part of the active play situation.

THERAPY SETTING

As indicated above, the setting for this type of play tends to be much more highly structured than that for the play utilized in the U-U or U-S situation. Here, the setting is made to accommodate thematic play. There should be a

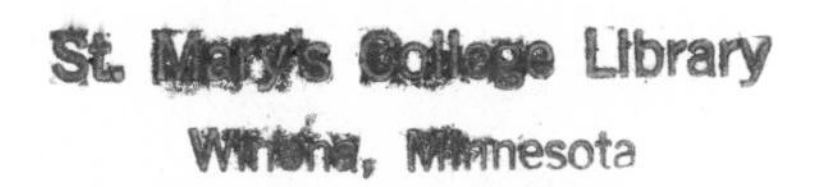

table and chairs where a tea party could be set and served. There should be space foı a doll house and material available to set up a doll play situation. There should be a place to run trucks and material available to put up roads, etc., but these are all fairly clearly defined, and if the materials themselves are somewhat unstructured, they are unstructured in a way that they normally lend themselves to the type of reality fantasy with which the average child engages in his play. The room may or may not be decorated, depending on the particular concepts to be followed, but it certainly should be painted, have colorful curtains, etc. It should be a comfortable room in which to work; the paint should not be an antagonistic color and should have a quieting but not sleepy effect. In this regard, it has been found that the lighter reds lend a very good color as do some of the greens. The brighter colors tend to be disturbing and intruding upon the brain damaged patients, and the pastel colors often tend to be too quieting and nonconducive to active behavior on their part.[125] This, however, is merely empirical observation on the part of the authors, and other writers may have had different experiences with different colors. The important thing is that colors which intrude on the patient detract from the thematic possibility of the play and from the intrusions of the therapist and should be avoided at all costs. A major recommendation is a blackboard. This permits the patient to draw his own pictures and becomes an aid to thematic expression as well as adding additional decoration to the room. In other words, this does not have to be the plain, bleak setting, previously described for unstructured play. The child, in terms of the limits of this type of activity, should learn to take a certain amount of pride in his playroom, and it should be recognized that if messy activities are to be engaged in, that they be done in the other playroom which is used for the unstructured materials, but which could be available to the patient in the structured setting for specific purposes such as finger painting, etc.

The limits of the playroom are tighter within themselves because, while the child can still break the toys if he so wishes, it is one of the limits of the play situation that if the toy is broken it is not replaced. Therefore, the child is faced with the fact that having destroyed a play object, it remains destroyed and does not magically reappear at the next play session, thus helping to build his concept of the reality relationship of life and death. The other types of limits regarding a child's relationship to things have to do with the fact that those things which the child produces in any sort of creative play can be protected for him, put aside and brought back at the following session. Those things which he destroyed, as was mentioned, remain destroyed; those which are partially destroyed remain partially destroyed, etc. A child is constantly reinforced in the concept that he is responsible for his own behavior and the things he does are lasting, and that he has done them. However, if the therapy goals indicate a need, a rational "rebirth" of the destroyed items can be provided. This should be discussed with the patients and new limits agreed upon. Also, the therapist should be less rigid if the destruction was clearly accidental. With this frame of reference, the limits of the play situation fairly readily define themselves in the sense that the child very rapidly imposes his own limits on his behavior if the consequences of his behavior have been made clear. Beyond this, the general limits still apply, the child cannot leave the playroom except with permission, he cannot, of course, physically strike either the therapist, or if he is in a group situation, the other members of the group; he cannot harm himself, nor can he harm any of the permanent fixtures of the playroom, such as the one-way vision screen, an air conditioner which is hopefully there, or other objects of this sort. Some of these limits are more demanding than in previous methods, but they are selected in view of the child's gaining proper respect and pride in his playroom to the extent that this becomes his world for the period of play, and it is the way in which he organizes this world which will help establish the way in which he lives in the external world.

The general question of the availability of psychic energy is not usually an issue in this type of therapy. The child may be seen for one or more hours a week, depending on the availability of the therapist's time. The child brought into this type of play activity is considered to have sufficient psychic energy to deal with the needs of the situation. The activities are his own initiation, but it is expected that the toys and materials in the playroom will, in many respects, define the activities. However, if the child wants to call a dump truck an army tank, he has a perfect right to do so, and the therapist is not so interested in reality that he would not go along with it, so that the child may adjust the toys to his own particular fantasies without any fear of reprisal on the part of the therapist. However, the therapist does want to clarify with the child the fact that they are merely playing that this is a tank, and that this is not a real tank, since the therapist in dealing with a retarded child, has also this peripheral teaching responsibility of not giving the child inaccurate information, even by accident.

INDICATIONS AND MAJOR CRITERIA FOR S-U THERAPY

GOALS

In discussing the indications for the S-U method, we have to think primarily of the characteristics which differentiate children for whom this type of play therapy would be indicated from those for whom either the previous types or the S-S method, which we will discuss in Chapter VIII, would be indicated. As we stated in the previous chapters, our efforts to work with the development and improvement of self-concept, the development and improvement of impulse control, and the development and improvement of social interaction are the distinguishing characteristics between the U-U and U-S methods. The child for whom the S-U method would be indicated is a child who has relatively adequate self-concept and impulse control but who, nonetheless, is ill at ease in his environment because of feelings of hostility or aggressiveness toward people or things as a result of an inability to build proper relationships with them.[126] There is a tendency to avoid interactions, because he is aware of his potential for destructiveness (he knows his power) and he is unsure how to create controls. Thus, his action is not entirely impulsive but rather a more highly developed conflict with misunderstood social mores. In other words, the avoidance would be either willful (rather than accidental) or as the result of fear. These avoidances grow out of major or minor misconceptions of the environment which have led to attitudes or behaviors which place additional blocks to intellectual development deriving from inability to abstract, inability to express oneself in a socially accepted manner, and inability to integrate the various cues which the environment provides into a reality oriented, organized, meaningful whole. Part of this may be due to the perplexity and impotency developed in organicity, part may be due to previous life experiences which have either set up a negative conditioning by reinforcing asocial or antisocial behaviors,[127] or have reinforced previously acceptable behavior which has now become unacceptable due to growth, but the retardate's maturational lag has kept him from realizing that the situation has changed. The aim of the S-U method is not to teach skills, although some teaching does occur, as we have mentioned, but rather to alleviate the feelings of hostility and frustration so that the child can come to accept himself and his environment as they really are. In other words, the aim is for the child to learn gratifying, practical, working relationships between himself and his environment. The important thing here is the introduction of objectivity and reality into his perception of himself in relationship to things and people, and thus he is helped to gain the opportunity to adopt various attitudes through the experience of play.

Building Relationships with Things and People. The purposes of the S-U method are *first* to help the child build relationships with people and things at the level of understanding that a more democentric and more expressive interaction of himself with his environment can be more gratifying than the egocentric, self-contained attitudes and behavior which he had previously adopted.[128] This is gained through the expression of himself in play, through the expression of the conflicts and hostilities which he feels, and through the associations which the therapist helps provide concerning acceptable means of expressing these feelings without destroying the environment or the interpersonal relationship.

Dealing with Social and Cultural Realities. Second, the purpose of the S-U method is to help the child deal with social and cultural realities in terms of the fact that while in the Taoist expression "neither heaven nor earth is particularly beneficial," nonetheless, the child is in a position to create some joy and gratification in his environment if he will learn to deal with the reality of society and the culture and thus not constantly be running contrary to their expectations or demands.

Evaluating Personal Goals. Third, the S-U method attempts to help the child evaluate his past experiences in the light of new attitudes and thus aids in his own development and in the establishment of personal goals of achievement, in terms of developing a realistic level of aspiration, a realistic consciousness of self and setting up aims and objectives which are consistent with a self-understanding of his ability and his potential. It may be argued that a retarded child with very little ability and very little potential is a preconceived failure in this kind of therapy. This is not necessarily true, because it is our experience that if a child is at a sufficiently high functional level to be brought into the S-U type of therapy, remembering the general indications required in terms of self-concept, etc., he has sufficient psychic energy and sufficient potential to contribute socially at various levels, and the understanding of what these levels are will only enhance his personality rather than increase the frustration.

Individual Therapy

The specific indications of whether a child in the S-U method should be brought into individual therapy or group therapy procedures are conceived in terms of the first purpose of this type of therapy, i.e., what is needed to build relationships with things and people. One might say as a rule of the thumb that, if the primary problem is overly-egocentric behavior on the part of the child so that he has either internalized his feelings in a withdrawn, self-involved manner, or is acting out his feelings of hostility and conflict by destruction of property, etc., then the primary need is for the development of a relationship with *things* in the sense of building a feeling that he may use the material as a sublimation for his hostility rather than as a mere source of expression in terms of destruction. This child would seem to fit most readily into an individual therapy setting. Conversely, if the primary factors concerning "respect of property" have been already established in the mind of the child, and his expressions of hostility and conflict are acted out against people, it may be that the group setting would be most conducive of the types of personality changes sought. To be more specific, if we have a child who seems to be totally unable to feel fondness for a toy or a person, the more primitive form of relationship is with the toy. This is seen in very young infants who quite often become much more attached to a glittering object or doll or teddy bear than they are to their parent or any person. This does not mean that one substitutes for the other, but rather that the two become in some way intertwined in the thinking of the child to the extent that he can only go to sleep with this particular toy, that feeding is often easier if the toy is clutched in his hand while the bottle or breast is in his mouth, or that other activities such as bathing become less disturbing if the toy is either a participant or sufficiently close at hand that the child can touch it or hold it when he feels the need. Thus, the more primitive, infantile form is the relationship with objects or toys, and the famous comic strip, "Peanuts", has carried this through to its ultimate in the form of Linus' blanket. This kind of object relationship is perfectly acceptable, the therapist does not want to fight it and, in fact, as we have discussed, where it is absent and has been absent in terms of a stage of maturation, the therapist hopes to induce it as a way of alleviating the maturational lag. Thus, in these situations the therapist finds the need to introduce the child to thematic materials in the hope that he can become sufficiently interested in them and dedicated so that he will begin to express himself in their terms rather than solely in his own egocentric patterns. This is essentially the role of individual therapy, and this particular function would probably be interfered with in a group setting. Thus, the child who has the immediate desire to punch the bop bag's nose, would find this need very severely frustrated if, for instance, he had to wait his turn.

Group Therapy

If the child has developed relationships with objects or is in a phase where he is able to express himself in terms of certain specific kinds of play, and his basic relationship with things has been established or shows that it had in the past been established, and that the child is no longer in need of this kind of expression, then it is felt that the child's problem stems from an inability to integrate fully with people. A group setting which demands this kind of integration becomes necessary. Thus, using the example given above, it becomes important to the child to learn that he must hold his hostility in check until it is his turn to hit the bop bag. He must learn, in other words, that impluses not only must be controlled, but that they must be held in check for periods of time while others are given the opportunity to express their impulses. This is essentially a new idea as far as the therapeutic procedures we have outlined are concerned. Previously we have been interested in getting the child to control his impulses and then when they are controlled, to express them in an acceptable, sublimated manner. Now he has to learn the additional factor that other people have the same impulses that he does, and that sometimes he has to wait his turn to express his while they are expressing theirs. This gives him knowledge of similarity between himself and other people, and presents the basis for eventually developing relationships with these other people because they are not "all that different" from him. This is based on the concept that relationships are easier between similar individuals than between totally different individuals.[129] This concept is based on an underlying feeling that one of the child's essential problems has been the fact that he has constantly found himself to be extremely different from his peers and from his environment, and that the iteration and reiteration of the fact that he is not "all that different" in all areas, becomes a way of establishing a more speedy road toward his general adjustment to the culture.

DISCUSSION

Application of Theoretical Constructs

The theoretical considerations for the S-U type of therapy are seen in the theories already expressed in describing the difference between individual and group therapy. The primary conditioning factor of this type of therapy is based on the concept previously mentioned of the therapist as a model. This is not the traditional concept of model that is used in the sense of transference. The therapist is not particularly interested in the patient's seeing him as an accepting person and therefore becoming an accepting person by behaving as the therapist behaves. We have no particular objection to the Golden Rule; we feel that it is a proper way of behavior, but it is not necessarily the most important therapeutic tool. What seems to be more important is the indication on the part of the therapist that he is acting as a model for society. In this sense he is like a model airplane, or a model train, where he is representing a reduced or miniature form of the larger reality—the larger reality in this case being the total of society with the therapist representing a miniature form of the attitudes and behaviors of the total society. The patient thus learns from the therapist that the total society can be accepting, that it can be rewarding, that it may under certain instances also be punishing, that acceptance and reward occur when behavior is consistent with the demands and needs of the society, and that reward is not forthcoming at those times when the child's behavior is not acceptable to the society. The therapist joins with the child in his play as he did in previous situations, and refuses to join when the play is bizarre or socially unacceptable. In this sense the conditioning process established by the therapist is very similar to those previously described, and we will not, therefore, go into any particular details at this time. The difference in this particular form is the fact that the patient gets the idea from the therapist of how people might react to him in situations outside of the therapy area. Thus, the child is conditioned to learn that people can respond to him in a variety of ways. This produces a real problem for the therapist, particularly if the child's family is rejecting, because the child becomes immediately aware of the contradiction between the playroom and the outside environment. The second aspect of the therapist's functioning as a model is then brought into play in terms of the fact that the child is helped to deal with social and cultural realities. He has to learn that in a sense there is selective behavior, and thus even though the therapist is sometimes punishing (he is not necessarily a "better father than the child's real father") the child learns that this other person behaves in such a way as to make life livable, rather than totally frustrating. However, even if the contradiction between the playroom and family is thus emphasized, the child still can learn that in some milieus things are fine and in other situations they are not so good, but there is always the potential that he will again find the fine milieu because it occurred once in terms of the therapist's behavior. The point that must be emphasized here is, of course, that completely accepting and never interfering or intruding into the child's behavior does not permit him to learn this very important truth, because the contradictions between the playroom and the home or community situation become so profound that the child is forced to disbelieve one of the two settings, and since the contact with the home community is greater than the contact with the play therapy setting, it becomes almost a matter of play therapy becoming a fantasy area which may not really exist, and the home and community becoming the real area, and the contradiction thus defeats the therapy. If the therapist is not always an accepting, permissive, nonpunishing type of individual, but rather by his intrusions refuses to accept certain behaviors, does not permit everything, and generally through this refusal to accept and the process of refusing to reward, actually punishes, then contradictions between the playroom and the home community are not so profound, the child can in a sense believe in both areas and thus, the conditioning which is being attempted throughout the whole therapy process becomes a realistic goal for the therapist, in that there are fewer counterforces which are interfering with the operation of the learning procedures.

Indications of Gain and Criteria for Termination

Here again, success in therapy becomes almost self-definable, except in this particular form of play therapy it is not quite as clear-cut as it has been in the other forms. Thus, it is not always readily known when the child has built a proper relationship with things and people, or when he is able to deal with social and cultural realities, or how well he is able to evaluate his past experiences and use them to develop new attitudes and personal goals. These things are somewhat abstract and it is quite difficult for the therapist to have a clear indication of when this has occurred. However, there are behavioral patterns which give some clues that something is being accomplished in these areas. An example of this type of situation is the case of a child who was diagnosed as Mongol *fruste*, who has various congenital anomalies, including a supernumery ear, and who is thus considered to be primarily retarded by reason of congenital maldevelopment. However, the behavior was also thought to be clearly psychotic and, for this reason, the child was brought into play therapy. This child had a long history of hostility which led to actual attacks on his peers, and these attacks had resulted finally in institutionalization. In therapy the child enacted, with an almost Broadway-like perfection, the various cowboy dramas that he had seen on television. During these sequences he would, in proper order, take the part of the sheriff, the villain, the hero, etc., and attribute proper actions and values to each of them. He did this to the extent of paying excessive attention to specific details of the performance, and someone watching him would almost have said that he was a well trained "method actor" going through the roles that he was playing. This was obviously the result of hyperacute observation of the television dramas that he had seen, and probably indicated a fantasy preoccupation to the exclusion of social reality as there was no creativity in these stories, just repetition of plots. Nonetheless they gave him a tremendous opportunity to express feelings of hostility and aggression both against his peers and authority, to take both sides of the question, and usually to permit the hero or the "good guy" to win. Although quite often the "good guy" that won was in the parlance of television youth, the "good-bad-guy" as opposed to the "bad-good-guy," but this distinction was very clear in his mind as it seems to be clear in the minds of most juvenile television observers. This is essentially an adult abstract attitude, and was not based on the traditions of our youth of the "white hat versus the black sombrero," but rather the more intricate feeling of emotional involvement which is found in the so-called adult western. All of these elements were expressed in this play situation, and during this period the acting out behavior towards his peers ceased and the play served as an excellent opportunity for this child to express himself. In this sense, success of therapy could easily be judged because the behavior outside the playroom became normalized, quiet, and the patient was thought of as becoming well adjusted; the general situation was considered good. The therapy was halted at the time that the therapist left the situation. The carry-over from the therapy remained for about one year; at the end of that time, however, the previously noted behavior began to recur—this time at a more intricate and higher level, so that an actual murder was attempted; but one would say that the play therapy postponed the feelings of aggression and hostility for quite a long period of time, and also produced an actual improvement in intellectualization, so that the hostility, when it finally did occur, was on a much more organized level. This may sound as though we are producing potential murderers or something of this sort, but if the therapy had been continued as originally prescribed, the patient probably would have been able to finally overcome his feelings in this area, and we would have seen a much more noteworthy success. In other words, even this obvious failure does seem to indicate a success for the general method.

Another positive example is a girl whose background is somewhat similar to that of the boy described above. That is to say, there were very tense feelings of extreme hostility against her peers. Most of these were fantasied rather than acted out, although there would be occasional explosions. The acting out quite often took the form of homosexual attack, and there was one particular peer who was usually subjected to this attack. Unfortunately, this other girl enjoyed being so selected and identified completely with the patient in question so that there was no extra force frustrating the behavior, except, of course, the adult who was able to forestall any serious consequences. The patient was brought into play therapy where she began by playing with dolls in an essentially female, acceptable manner. These dolls became immediately labeled and identified with peers, one of them being named after the girl who was usually the object of the patient's attack, another being named a wholly fictitious name, who became the attacking person, so that the patient was playing in effect that she herself never lost control, but this alter ego with another name was a very bad, aggressive girl who did all sorts of nasty things to people. She played in this manner for an extended period of time, and it was noted outside the playroom that as this type of play continued and as the therapist was able to support and try to help her work through what was going on, the antisocial, aggressive attacks ceased, although at this early phase they were replaced by attacks of self-mutiliation where she would bite her wrist or bite other parts of her body rather than attack one of her peers. This, though considered growth, was obviously equally unacceptable in the general run of things. However, as the play therapy continued, the mode of play did not change, because again the pattern of perseveration so often noted with brain damaged children occurred here, but the level of the play did improve and eventually the alter ego disappeared and the patient identified the aggressive doll with herself, so that there was a slow and increased realization that she was the one who was carrying out these behaviors rather than some fictitious alternate person. At this time the general communication with the therapist was increased, and the play sessions were divided into two parts, one where there was active thematic play, and a second where the therapist and the patient sat down and discussed it. This was originally introduced by the patient herself, not in those terms, but rather through the action of her saying that she was tired of playing, and "let's talk." This became a tradition for the play therapy, and over a period of time the talking sessions became every bit as important as the play sessions, and the patient was gradually able to express more and more in terms of verbal communication, and actually began to achieve certain insights of her own, such as the fact that when she got angry it would be better if she stomped her foot rather than bite her wrist or engage in some other self-destructive activity. Over a period of time the play began to be less and less important to the patient, and the talking session became more important, and the general pattern of progress which can be said to have then been achieved through the S-U method was the fact that it permitted the patient to get sufficiently out of herself that she could then begin to express herself at a level consistent with her intellectual potential which proved to be quite high. Here, we see that as the child is able to build a close relationship, first with the dolls representing her peers, and then later with the therapist who had functioned all along as the model of social behavior in not accepting her biting herself, not accepting the punishment that one doll was giving to another doll, but constantly accepting the girl herself throughout all of this, that she was able to use a relationship which permitted her to mature and to perform at a level more consistent with her actual potential.

CONCLUSIONS

It will be noted from the above examples that neither the materials nor the procedures are particularly different than any other case history of play therapy that you might read, and it is not intended that they be different. The authors do not feel that they are particularly contributing anything new to this area. What we are saying is that we are doing the same things but in a different tone of voice. That is, the procedures as such are essentially the same; the materials are essentially the same, but there are some slight differences throughout, which take into consideration the level of functioning of the child, the possible question of organicity and other general aspects related to a brain damaged, emotionally disturbed child, or a child of retarded functional behavior. These factors are the things we might underline for this chapter. Thus, it becomes noteworthy that the kinds of successes in the therapeutic case history which we have given, were obtained with retarded children who had an organic diagnosis. In other words, these are the types of case histories one usually reads in regard to normal children who are emotionally ill, and not in regard to the type of child who we have described. The fact that the histories can read in such similar manners and be developed on such similar lines indicates that the functionally retarded child is as good a candidate for this kind of therapy as is the child of normal intelligence.[130] In conclusion we have outlined a method which we have termed the S-U method. We have related this method to mental and functional retardation, and in this regard have made some general suggestions as to how the usual procedures might be modified through conditioning techniques to meet the needs of the functionally retarded child. The next chapter will discuss a more highly structured method to be utilized in readiness procedures for children who do not have sufficient controls in the emotional sphere to go right into a training situation, but who do have a very high training potential and who, through psychotherapeutic methods, can be made ready for training.

ADDITIONAL NOTES

121. Axline, Virginia M., "Mental Deficiency-Symptom or Disease?" *J. Cons. Psychol.*, 1949, 13, pp. 313-327, discusses some of the interactions between retarded intellectual ability and emotional disturbance as seen in play therapy.

122. Ginott, H. G., "A Rationale for Selecting Toys in Play Therapy," *J. Consult. Psy.*, 1960, 24, pp. 243-246; Lebo, D., "The Question of Toys in Play Therapy: An International Problem," *J. Ed. & Psy.*, Baroda, India, 1956, 14, pp. 66-73; ——— "A Formula for Selecting Toys for Nondirective Therapy," *J. Genet. Psy.*, 1958, 92, pp. 23-34, among others.

123. Axline (1947), *op. cit.;* ——— "Play Therapy Procedures and Results," *Amer. J. Orthopsychiatry*, 1955, 25, pp. 618-626; ——— "Entering the Child's World Via Play Experiences," *Progs. Ed.*, 1950, 27, pp. 68-75.

124. Bender, Lauretta and Woltman, A. G., "The Use of Puppet Shows as a Psychotherapeutic Method for Behavior Problems in Children," *Amer. J. Orthopsychiatry*, 1936, VI, pp. 341-354, demonstrate one of the ways that the therapist can become quite closely involved with the child's fantasy play without having obviously to depart from reality.

125. Knox, Beverly G., "Finger Painting as a Psychodiagnostic Tool with Mentally Retarded, Emotionally Disturbed Children," Unpublished Master's thesis, Kansas State College of Pittsburg, Pittsburg, Kansas, 1961, pp. 21-24, discusses and gives references to work done with the possible projective meaning of color and its possible emotional impact on the personality.

126. Rogers, C. R., "The Significance of the Self-Retarding Attitudes and Perceptions," in Reymert, M. S. (Ed.) *Feelings and Emotions*, N. Y.: McGraw-Hill, 1950, discusses relationship between self-attitude and adjustment.

127. Ayllon & Haughton, *op. cit.*

128. Rogers, C. R., *Client-Centered Therapy*, Houghton-Mifflin, N. Y., 1951, implies this approach in creating his "nondirective" therapy. While we deviate a great deal from his techniques, the basic, philosophical approach still seems to be extremely useful.

129. Rosenberg, S., Spradlin, J. E., and Mabel, S., "Interaction Among Retarded Children as a Function of Their Relative Language Skill," *J. Abnor. Soc. Psych.*, 1961, 63, pp. 402-410, found that children of similar language levels communicated, while those of different levels did not.

130. Axline (1949), *op. cit.;* Burton, A. "Psychotherapy With the Mentally Retarded," *AJMD*, 1954, 58, pp. 486-489, makes essentially the same point, but if one follows the literature, it does not seem to have been followed up and needs constant reiteration.

VIII. The Method of Structured Materials with a Structured Approach (S-S)

The fourth method of play therapy is that which utilizes structured materials with a structured therapeutic approach. This method we have identified as the S-S method. As was pointed out in Chapter IV, the procedures of this method are those which are often related to special education or other remedial programs where there is a definite group of materials and a definite way of utilizing them. From the point of view of psychotherapy, this method can be thought of in a number of ways. It may be thought of as a sort of finishing procedure, in the sense that certain specific areas may still remain problem areas after the completion of other forms of psychotherapy, it may be considered as a play mode of utilizing techniques often associated with guidance rather than specifically with psychotherapy, or it may be thought of in terms of a mode of treating specific symptoms without divorcing them from either the cognitive or social field of the patient.

DEFINITION OF THE S-S METHOD

The S-S form is partially based on the premise that the personality aberrations related to emotional disturbance are due in some manner to the child's being aware that he cannot function at a level equal to that of his peers. This basic assumption does not require a profound knowledge of the ramifications of the disturbance, which would be an obvious violation of Occam's Razor,[131] but rather, an observation at the behavioral level that he is not functioning in a manner equal to his peers, and that he is responding to his failure to function with some specific activity which becomes an annoyance to either his parents or in an institution, to the care personnel. Thus, it is conceivable that if a child feels that if he could only tell time, he could compete with the individuals who seem to be the major source of his frustrations, the S-S type of therapy may very specifically take time out to teach him how to tell time. Here, the therapist would not necessarily agree with the child that this was the whole source of the problem, but rather having taught him how to tell time, he would help the child understand that there was not much change and that there were still problems to be worked through, and that possibly the child could find better ways of working them through in terms of his present potential. This general question will be discussed a little later in the chapter when we get into the matter of goals, but every effort should be made to deal with specific processes rather than utilizing this highly structured technique to attempt to treat all aspects of the problem at once.

It is not our intention that this method should compete with special education. People in that field have their job to do, and as psychotherapists we feel we have ours. As we have already discussed in Chapter I, the function of the psychotherapist is that of a specialist dealing with a special form of teaching, and it is not really a matter of psychotherapy versus teaching, but rather that certain youngsters present problems in the sphere of social interaction which the special education teacher cannot handle. When this involves particular learning questions, or behaviors related to learning difficulties, it is logical that the psychotherapist integrate the teaching function into the therapy function, because often specific learning incorporated into a play or work teachnique aids in achieving the therapeutic aim of dealing with social adjustment symptoms.[132] Thus, the techniques involved in this type of learning process may or may not be the same as those in special education depending on the particular child's needs. When the immediate goal, for instance, is learning arithmetic, the emphasis should be on the longer range goal that the child learn about himself, his relationship to other persons and objects in his environment, and through this knowledge increase his control over the objects and people about him, while developing a meaningful interaction with them. That is, he comes to see himself as a person capable of learning arithmetic and thus, being like other persons in this regard, he can communicate with them concerning his knowledge. For this purpose, learning arithmetic has to become a play function so that the therapist does not become just a teacher, but is also free to inject guidance at the play therapy level. It becomes a play function using the techniques of arithmetic games, special counting techniques, or other devices of this sort, such as, for example, those suggested by John Locke[133] and other pioneers in teaching.[134]

S-S Materials

The materials utilized for this method are indicated by the questions we have already raised. They must be definite, highly structured, with an emphasis either on production of cognitive content or production of creative expression. The end product becomes important in the play situation, but the end product may either be improved cognition or actual creation of physical objects at an improved level. We will discuss below the different applications of these two ideas.

If the emphasis is on improved cognition, having decided that the child is ready for this approach, we seek increased verbalization or increased understanding on the part of the child, of his behavior in social situations. The major materials to be utilized in this aspect of play therapy are doll figures, puppets,[135] animal reproductions,[136] etc., in an effort to set the scene along the lines already familiar to those who have used psychodrama for social play and social reproduction of life situations.[137] This is described as an S-S process in that the situations are contrived and the patient does not establish for himself how he is going to play with the figure. The therapist sets up life situations surrounding the "spotlight" or symptom area and then tries to get the patient to play through the situations. The patient will learn from the interaction with the therapist, the proper mode of meeting these particular problems and, hopefully, will learn how to set up behaviors which will carry over to similar situations outside of the playroom. The materials should be as serviceable as possible, but still should be play materials because the child seems to need the distance of a puppet or a doll in order to project this kind of problem, and actual psychodrama or one-to-one contact between the child and the therapist, seems to become overly threatening to the retarded child and it becomes difficult for him to make the kinds of projections or to build the kinds of associations necessary to learn how to function in such a situation. Thus, both the materials and the approach are highly structured. The therapist sets the scenes, creates the situations, and makes it necessary for the child to work his way through them. In this instance many of the situations created by the therapist may include imposed frustrations, the therapist taking the form of the frustrating individual or agent and creating, at times, antagonisms in the child through the process of intrusion into the child's play, forcing him to make an adjustment and then giving him approbation when the adjustment has been properly conceived. This will be discussed below as we go into more detail on the therapist's role, the point here being that the materials are to be used exactly as they are labeled, e.g., if a doll figure is said to represent a father, it will be used only to act as a father; if some other person is required, then another doll must be acquired so that the very tight life structure of the situation will be presented to the patient who literally has no other escape than his own wits since he must figure his way out of the problems which the therapist has constructed for him. As nearly as possible, the labels should be consistent with the actual physical features of the dolls, remembering that a fireman doll can be a father, but only if the patient's father is a fireman. If puppets are used, this kind of strict adherence to form is not quite as easy. There is more flexibility, and this is quite often very useful for higher functional patients who can stand the extra bit of closeness which puppets permit over and above the distance of dolls. Conversely, a lower functional patient who cannot quite deal with dolls representing father or mother or specific figures, may deal with the situation a bit more freely if, for instance, animal substitutes can be made, thus introducing aggressive animals such as tigers or alligators, and passive animals such as rabbits and squirrels and permitting the child to play through the problems with these types of figures. Again, the therapist must make sure that the problems which are played through are conceived of in terms of their relationship to the problem area for which the child is in therapy.

On the other hand, if the program is aimed primarily at growth in specific knowledge areas, then the emphasis must be on specific creativity. The above reference to arithmetic falls into this second category where the games are partly a contrivance to add information. This would also apply to the use of other highly structured materials such as model airplanes or other items which have a definite kind of structure and a definite product. Here, the emphasis is on what the child is able to do rather than on what he is able to say, and the problem which is being worked through is one of his ability to utilize his assets to produce and thus become a larger person. This is done by providing him with success experiences, over a period of time, which have been associated with an approving therapist who helps him realize that he is having success experiences and thus helps him develop a feeling for success. This kind of success situation gives the patient a chance to work through "spotlight" problems where these problems seem to orbit around a generally poor feeling of achievement which the retardate seems to develop because of his competition with peers of higher intellectual ability.[138] Thus, we find that we are dealing with two types of symptoms for which two specific types of materials are required. The *first* type of symptom, which is specifically related to factors of social adjustment, uses materials which are highly structured play materials such as figurines, dolls, animals, puppets, etc., supported by trucks and cars to add life-like aspects to the situations.[139] The *second* type of symptom which, though still involved with social adjustment, is related more specifically to the ability of the child to use assets in creative growth and building success experiences, uses materials which are, for the most part, raw materials. They, nonetheless, have definite end products, such as construction models of one sort or another, or play activities which lead toward the learning of specific skills or the increase in specific knowledge, and the activities and materials utilized are considered highly structured even though as one approaches the play session their immediate appearance may not contain this structure.

S-S Therapeutic Procedures

We have already discussed the concept of a structured approach when we discussed the U-S form of psychotherapy, but even there the therapist is not as thorough in planning his approach as he is in the S-S form. Here, each

139. It has been found that standard table games with tight rules are also very useful in establishing the limits required in social living.

therapy session is conceived of in advance, and the therapist sets the scene with the patient, consistently making sure that he remains in the kind of situation which the therapist has contrived. The process becomes one of interacting with the patient very closely and calling his attention to ideations as they occurs in the sense of creating a major type of intrusion into the play activity of the child. Thus, for example, the therapist will permit the patient to enter into a particular type of play activity which has been defined previously in the play session, and when the child becomes tired of this particular activity, the therapist will then examine with the child why he is tired. He will offer him opportunity to cease the activity but only in exchange for a second opportunity to sit down and discuss the activity without the use of play. Thus, the major emphasis will be on the child's completing the activity, which is a matter of finding a solution to the frustrating social situation, or creating a completed object, and he will gain his reward in terms of approbation and therapeutic support while he is working with the object or working with the situation and, in a sense, will only "shake" the intrusion at the point where he succeeds in working through the frustrations or creating the object. This may take one play session, it may take a number of play sessions. If it takes a number of play sessions, the therapist maintains rapport and patient contact by constantly working with and participating in the play activities of the child, so that there is a semblance of the two of them trying to deal with the problem together rather than the child finding himself isolated. It is for this reason that the patient-therapist interaction becomes so extremely important in this form of therapy. At no time should the therapist merely set up a problem and then psychologically depart leaving the patient to work it out for himself. Rather, he sets up the problem and then together they attempt to work it through trying to find the kind of solution that is proper and thus permitting the patient to feel that he has an ally but not a servant, i.e., the final solution must come from the patient and not the therapist.

Procedures along this line involve a number of themes. For example, a patient was referred because she would not concentrate in class on one subject at a time. She was considered hyperactive and her behavior was typical of that of a brain damaged child.[140] The therapist constantly repeated to her during the therapy sessions that she had to do one thing at a time, and whenever she tried to change activities, she was again reminded of this until the first task was completed. When she wanted to play on the floor, the therapist got down on the floor with her, and the two of them sat there working through the activities. Consequently, the patient realized that although the therapist was with her every step of the way, he would not permit her to jump from one activity to another and that he insisted that the first activity be completed before the second was started. Over a period of time the therapist was eventually able to get her to understand the purpose for this controlled behavior and, while the therapy did nothing about the problem of "organic drivenness," it did raise the patient's cognitive level in terms of an understanding of her own behavior and she was then able to exercise greater controls.

Other situations might involve the therapist's setting up a roadway where two cars would be placed in such a manner that the patient's car could not move without the patient's first dealing with the therapist's car. The patient would then have to figure out how to handle this in a socially acceptable manner. If he decided to crash into the therapist's car, this would have to be worked through with the patient from the point of view of forcing him to explain why he did what he did, and what he thought he would accomplish from it. He will find that he has accomplished nothing toward achieving his end, but rather because of the therapist's structure in the situation, the end is even further off. Thus he will have to go back and figure a way to repair the wrecked therapist's car before the original goal can be achieved. In this way, the patient comes to understand that by dealing with the problem in an uncontrolled or thoughtless manner, he only creates new problems for himself.

Another situation along the same lines would be a contrived family where the therapist would play a number of parts representing members of the family that were creating problems in the patient's life, and the patient in essence would play himself and try to deal with these kinds of family situations in a manner which was acceptable to both the therapist and himself. If this is successful and he can adapt easily, one can use the usual psychodrama technique of switching roles, thus permitting the patient an increased cognition in terms of full understanding of the various aspects of the question. Other types of contrived situations can be built around a classroom or a downtown store, such as a grocery, in each instance building a problem which the patient has to solve in order to permit the situation to go forward smoothly.

On the other hand, where the therapist is attempting to develop creativity or increase the patient's knowledge in terms of a "spotlight" area, the emphasis must be on the end product. This is a major difference from the U-S form where the end product also had to exist, but it did not particularly matter, the major objective being that the patient produce something with which he could then play. In the S-S type, it does not matter if the patient produces something with which he can play, but it does matter that he produces something that is correct and that he becomes aware that he has produced something that is correct, thus raising his own conceptualization of his ability. The final item may even be a display item, and it is not necessary that it be played with or that it be destroyed. However, if the patient wishes to destroy it, he is free to do so, because he has earned the right to decide what will happen to the object by having created it, and thus having met the limits of the therapy situation. Of course, if the element is new knowledge, the question of destroying it does not arise. For this reason, only certain levels of patients can be considered as eligible for this phase of the S-S approach, since a lack of ability will block the therapy situation.

In S-S the therapist's approach is strictly formal with a "cards on the table" manner. He may even say to the patient that he has been told that there have been problems, that the school teacher has complained about certain things, or the mother has complained about certain things, and that the child is in psychotherapy at this time to try and correct these specific behaviors. He may further indicate that the child will remain in therapy until the behaviors can be dealt with, and that the two of them are going to try to work together to see how they can deal with the problems. An explanation is given the child as to the relationship between building a model airplane, for example, and the particular problems that he is having in terms of hyperactivity or self-control or whatever the spotlight problems are. If the patient is not intellectually able to deal with this kind of information, then other means have to be used, but the child must realize that he is here to work and play in the sense that the play must have a result, that it is not just "free" play, that he must do what the therapist wants, and that it will become more like play if he complies with the therapist's wishes, and less like play if he does not. This approach should be used, because cognition must be enhanced, and it becomes exceedingly important that the child have an increasing understanding of himself and his role in the situation as he goes along. From this point of view, it can be said that the S-S form of psychotherapy is really the highest form of play therapy, in that the child who is in this form presents less diffuse general problems, and more intensified specific problems.

Now in this regard, the specific problems do not have to be definitely related to the cause for referral, but they may be, as in the example we gave above. On the other hand, in the case of a child who was referred for psychotherapy because he was caught stealing, the psychotherapist obviously is not going to spend his time in the S-S session dealing only with the question of stealing. Rather, there will be an attempt to search through some of the bases for stealing, and some of the problems that set up the original desire to steal. In the particular case in point, the child stole because his allowance had been cut off as he had been failing in school. Although he was considered to be retarded as a failing student, his measured intelligence was high enough to indicate that this was merely a functional retardation. The parents took this to mean that he was lazy and therefore, the allowance was cut off. It was found through examination that an emotional disturbance and a serious memory disturbance were creating part of the difficulty, and the functions of the S-S play therapy were to deal with the memory problem as a way of alleviating the difficulty as well as to work through the question of his stealing which he related to his desire to get even with his parents. The therapist dealt first with the question of memory, and the play centered around the use of activity which could foster memory and exploration, thus letting the child feel that, to some extent, he was responsible for or master of his own destiny, and could then be responsible for his activities and potentially able to do better in school. School work did improve. It was also recognized by the teachers and the parents that the memory problem existed, and the whole situation was smoothed out. The child, instead of functioning at a retarded level as he had been, began to function at a dull normal level with a clear potential for normal functioning.

This approach illustrates the fact that even though we are treating behaviors, we are not necessarily only going to treat the specific external behaviors that brought about the referral to psychotherapy. Rather, we may treat certain less obvious symptoms which have produced the external behavior, and the answer to the question of what to treat depends on whether or not the behavior is the type of behavior that can be dealt with openly in a play session, or whether other activities have to be brought in.[141] The obvious point is that we might play marbles with children in attempting to cure enuresis, because by improving the child's self-confidence it is possible to deal with the problem of the enuresis. Certainly there is no pretense that marbles are directly related to enuresis, nor in a less satirical vein, that enuresis can be dealt with as such in a play session, except possibly by getting the child to recognize that he has this problem. But there certainly is nothing to be gained by making him feel guilty, and the purpose of the play session is to help the child mature at a more rapid rate hoping that with increased maturity, there will come increased control in the other areas. It is our feeling that the psychological child changes the physical child. That is, consistent with the idea that the hand is father to the brain, an activity which represents a delay in general maturation might be helped if behaviors are introduced which enhance the psychological aspects of maturation, e.g., emotional growth or cognitive development. Thus, enuresis which is related to the general development of the child may be eliminated if the child can be helped to achieve emotional control (it is assumed that there is no real physiological cause for the enuresis).

S-S Therapy Setting

The setting for the S-S form utilizes the structured playroom, as was utilized for the S-U form. This is a playroom which has very specific limits and where there are many things that the child cannot do. In this particular form of psychotherapy, limits reach their peak in the sense that there are often more things he cannot do than things he can do. However, some of the things he cannot do may become a reward for other activities. Thus, in the S-U form, the child may be permitted to play with the truck at will as long as he plays and develops thematic formulation around the play. In the S-S form, if the truck is not included in the therapist's plan, the child may not be permitted to play with it except as a reward for completing the therapist's plan. If the child successfully works through a problem or successfully learns the manipulations or information which the therapist had in mind, they may end the session by doing something the child wants to do in exchange for the child having done the things the therapist wanted to do, and at that point, what was previously a limit, may become a permission and the child can go forth and play with the truck for a stated time at the end of the session, having earned this reward for his previous activity. So that while there will be many more limits in this type of therapy—many more things that the child cannot do—the limits may at times be less rigid than they were in the previous form, in that there are legitimate ways of setting them aside through earned privilege. It is this question of earned privilege which becomes in itself instructional to the child since he learns how to cope with social frustration in the form of restriction which may be relaxed if he behaves in another manner. Some things have to be maintained more rigidly, however; time schedules, for example, must be quite closely followed. The child himself should know the time that his session starts, the time that it stops, and if he can tell time, a clock should be available in the session so that he may be aware when the time is up and not rely completely on the therapist to tell him that the session is over. The therapist may, of course, deviate slightly from set schedules, but the patient, as a matter of his own decision, may not. Thus, again, the restrictions of day-to-day living become a process to which the patient is conditioned.

In this instance, the playroom is always the setting, and the child never meets with the therapist as a therapist in any other setting; in certain instances it may even involve a specific area of the playroom, such as a specific table, or a specific corner, and the child is helped to develop an extremely compulsive attitude about specific aspects of the setting in order to impress upon him the importance of the activity. Thus, the child may use a certain corner of the playroom as a family corner where he acts out family situations. This permits other areas of the playroom to become a safe haven away from the family, so that if he is able to act through one of these situations, the therapist can move with him to another part of the playroom and provide some feeling of relief in the sense that the child has moved away from the family and can play in another area without having the family impose itself upon him. Thus, the setting should be one which will permit these kinds of limits on one hand, and alternative areas on the other which can serve as rewards for the child who seems to need them. It should be recognized that if the child does not require these kinds of rewards, but is perfectly happy to play through the whole therapy session in one activity, he should be permitted to do so.

Therefore, the setting, the limits, time schedules, etc., in the S-S form, have to be fairly strict, very highly structured as the form itself defines but, recognizing that the child may become quite antagonistic because of the extreme structure that has been imposed, the possibility of tangible rewards and the relaxation of limits may be worked into the procedures at the discretion of the therapist. Rewards may even be candy or something of this sort, so that the conditioning process can go forward. This should not be thought of as a form of bribery and it should be very definitely understood that the rewards occur only after the completion of the task. If the child, in other words, protests the kind of activity the therapist has defined, and through his negative behavior refuses to participate in any manner, we have to conclude as we did earlier, that we are ahead of him, that we have tried to structure him into a situation for which he is not yet ready; therefore, the whole activity must move back one step permitting the therapist to restructure at a level at which the child will work. We do not make the mistake of saying, "If you will do this, you can have some candy," or "you can play with the truck," thus presuming that he is only being negative but rather we have passed his present level and if he will help us, the candy or playing with the truck, or whatever reward the child feels is a reward, is then forthcoming. This difference is extremely important and is based on the concept of payment for work rather than special privilege. Thus, the incentives for improvement become the major prop in the conditioning process.

INDICATIONS AND MAJOR CRITERIA OF S-S THERAPY

In deciding what children are to be brought into this form of psychotherapy, there are two major considerations. The first is the criterion of the therapy, i.e., the goals, and the second is the type of individual.

Goals

As to the first, there are three general goals: *One*, the improvement of the level of social maturity through the development of improved cognitive function. *Two*, the development of understanding on the part of the child as to where he fits into his milieu in the sense that he has a place and can be accepted for himself. And *three*, the building of reality relationships leading to realistic levels of aspiration.

Improved Level of Social Maturity. The question of improved levels of social maturity has to do with an understanding of socially mature behavior, and through selective reinforcement a realization that rewards are best attained through this type of behavior. This is primarily a matter of improving the child's concept of himself as it relates to the rest of society, and further utilizes the premise already stated that as the child's behavior changes, so does his physical structure. The total child will be more able to understand and fit into the whole social complex. Thus, instead of having to feel that he is just a sore thumb in a situation, he can gain a feeling that he has worth, that he can assume social responsibility, and that he will receive approbation for socially responsible acts. This is defined in terms of maturation because it is more than the mere perception of the specific elements, but involves also a broader understanding of the implications of his behavior. For example, the socially responsible act might be making his bed when he gets up in the morning without having to be told; the social maturational elements involved might be a feeling that he is giving pleasure to his mother because of this, that he is contributing to the total peace of the family and, in general, that he is making a more useful place for himself in the family. These are high level thoughts which even normal children do not always acquire, but there are compensating factors for children of normal intelligence, because they are usually very active parts of the family unit without making these extra efforts, while the functionally retarded child must understand what his effort contributes, and this is done through understanding the total implications of his behavior rather than through the very limited knowledge that he has made his bed. This is equally true if we are thinking in terms of school achievements, or work achievements, or achievement in any other area which involves increased social responsibility. The goal here is one of improving ability to function through the understanding of the social reality of the situation. This is more than just gaining success experiences—it is also gaining a more mature cognition.

If this can be worked through along the lines of building mature knowledge, we will at the same time inhibit negative behaviors. If the child can be conditioned to understand that his mature behavior produces social rewards, then there will be carry over and he will learn to understand that his negative behavior produces punishment which serves no useful purpose since he can satisfy his desires in an acceptable manner. Thus, we have a process of his becoming aware of the whole forest and not just maintaining the egocentric preoccupation with himself as an individual tree.

Development of Understanding of Acceptance. The second goal deals with the other half of the problem created in the first goal, and that is looking at the tree as it exists in the forest. The development of understanding on the part of the child that he can be accepted for himself, is based on reality relationships. Even though there are many things that he cannot do, there are also many things that he can do, and he must learn that he can be accepted or be part of the social unit in terms of his specific assets or abilities to contribute, in spite of the fact that he cannot make the vast major contribution that he sees some of his peers or siblings making. This is one of the more difficult concepts to convey, because the child is constantly comparing himself with other individuals who, if they are normally endowed, will be able to make greater contributions to living situations than he. For example, the problem arising around the child who has three brothers, all of whom are going to college, getting advanced degrees with the potential of earning big money, etc., while he sees that he is not able to graduate from grammar school, creates within this child a definite feeling of mistrust of himself, of inferiority, and a total denial of self in the sense of a feeling of worthlessness and depression. Here, through play activities, the therapist must bring the child to realize that he is an individual, that as an individual he can do certain things, that the world is made up of individuals who do different things, that it would not be a very good world if everybody did the same thing, and that the things he can do are socially useful, socially necessary and he should learn to do them well. It is clear that this specific therapeutic approach would only be successful with the higher functional child who may be lacking in clearly defined assets. An emphasis can be placed on developing his ability to get along with people or on other factors of this sort, and the therapist thus has to become quite inventive regarding the specific assets the patient possesses. We can presume, and we have presumed, in terms of our basic feelings of human worth, that every child has some asset which can be built upon and be used as a base for building an acceptable level of self, even though it may not always meet the needs of the external environment.[142]

Building Reality Relationships. The third goal, relating to building reality relationships leading to realistic levels of aspiration, is very closely interwoven with the first two. Here, we find that the child can neither mature nor can he build a concept of personal worth unless he has some realistic knowledge of what he is able to do, and what he is not able to do. Thus, the realistic level of aspiration becomes one of the most important questions with which the therapist must be concerned. This, in a sense, is a matter of using the child's present level of aspiration, learning how to build in success experiences, and through these success experiences try to establish a more realistic level of aspiration. There seem to be two types of children with difficulties in this area. There are those who feel that they can do things which they may not be able to do. This, at first, is a source of disappointment if the

142. Here, as we will discuss in Chap. XII, there is a very definite role for parent counseling or case work to deal with the kind of environment that can accept the child with whatever asset he has to offer.

level of aspiration was too high, but on the other hand if the therapist can build sufficient reward into the level of achievement, the child can realize in a sense that a "bird in hand is worth two in the bush," and that the things that can be done are as important as the things that cannot be done.

The more usual situation, however, is the child who feels he is not able, because he has learned through competition over a period of time that he cannot achieve what he hoped to achieve. This child has, through the continually reinforced process of failure experiences, developed a habit of failure and has to find that he can have successes through his own behavior and his own creativity. Here, the therapist has to be very careful with programming his structured situation so that he can guarantee the child will have a success experience if he enters it, and the child having achieved a success experience, should receive from the therapist through either approbation or tangible objects, a clear indication of reward, so the fact he has succeeded will be properly reinforced. It is possible that the child's level of aspiration will be quite uneven. For example, he may consider himself a failure in his school experiences but may have come to believe that he has great physical strength and thus become a bully on the playground. This type of situation leads to the feeling that his physical strength is tremendous, but also to the feeling that he has no mental strength. Here, if the child can be brought to realize that rewards may be forthcoming in the school room, he will be more receptive to the idea of alternative behaviors being also possibly rewarding on the playground. If this can be accomplished, the child can develop an understanding of what he is able to do, and it is then possible for the therapist to work through the first two goals in terms of the role of the child in society.[143]

Individuals Who Respond Best to S-S Method

In deciding which individuals will specifically be indicated for this type of therapy, we have to consider the basis of the referral. We usually feel that children who have previously been in play therapy for a period of time and who have successfully completed the goals of the S-U or U-S form, or those who though they may not have been in psychotherapy previously, nonetheless present evidence of functioning at that level, are most suited for the S-S form of treatment. The usual child is brought into play therapy with a variety of problems and is introduced to one of the earlier forms of therapy. If having been through that he still presents certain specific areas of difficulty which his teachers or parents or care personnel bring to the attention of the therapist, he may be brought then into the S-S form of play therapy in order to deal with these specific areas of difficulty. As a rule of thumb, if the child has previously been in the S-U form, he is probably a child who has the kind of social adjustment problems that would lead one to bring him into that type of S-S therapy which emphasizes cognitive development in the area of social adjustment, and he would then go into a modified form of psychodrama or some other acting out type of behavior to deal with this problem. If, on the other hand, he has previously been in the U-S form, this would indicate that there was a major problem of self-concept and ability and he would be brought into the creativity aspects of the S-S form to complete his development in this area. However, this is not an absolute rule, and the specific behaviors presented by the child would have to indicate which type of S-S therapy was to be utilized. The important point is, however, that the therapist will already have had the child in a number of therapy sessions of a different nature before introducing him to the S-S form, or the child will have already learned how to adjust to various types of situations. Thus, many problems relating to rapport building and other kinds of relationship questions will not be as apt to exist with the S-S form and this fact is one which makes the form possible because such a highly structured form of psychotherapy would not be too successful if the therapist, at the same time, had to spend the usual amount of time building rapport, and gaining acceptance of these therapeutic procedures, which are so highly structured and so very demanding. Rather, the introduction of the S-S form comes along as the next step which the therapist can then explain to the child in those terms. As we stated, there is an exception where this form is used as a type of guidance, but here the child's disturbance has not yet fully generalized itself and, even though time must be spent with rapport building, it does not have to take the amount of time usually used and the S-S form can still be entered into, although not as quickly. To review then, we would say that the child goes into the S-S form generally only after he has been through another type of play therapy, and this form in a sense can be considered a finishing school in that it tries to deal with the problems left over from previous forms. The exception is the child who seemed to be already at that level before therapy was requested. Thus, the function is (1) to pick up whatever specific points the child feels concerned about, or (2) to pick up the specific points which the school or the parents feel need to be dealt with and, (3) to deal with these specific behaviors or developing symptoms on a highly structured guidance level.

Individual or Group Therapy

In view of the above discussion, there is a question whether individual or group psychotherapy should be the primary approach. At first glance it would seem that S-S play therapy would almost inevitably have to be individual therapy since these sessions have to be individually planned and project themselves around individual programming. However, some investigators have found that this is not necessarily true; for example, there are studies related to directive group therapy that indicate a tight structure will work with a group.[144] There are also studies that indicate that the group as a whole will benefit from the presentation of a single reinforcing stimulus.[145] These studies and others lead us to question whether or not a group approach to this S-S form might not be useful. However, this is an area for much more extensive research, since our own experiences do not specifically support this frame of reference. We would say, in short, that we feel that the S-S form of play therapy is primarily to be considered an individual play therapy procedure, but we would like to leave the door open for it to be a group play therapy procedure if further investigation reveals that this might be feasible, the main point being that if the emphasis has to be on social adjustment and realization of the social implications of behavior, a group form would be quite valuable.

DISCUSSION

Theoretical Constructs

In considering some of the reasons for establishing this particular form of play therapy, we stated that one of the major aspects of the S-S form was the treatment of individual symptoms or behaviors without divorcing them from the cognitive or social field of the patient. It is not sufficient to merely condition new behaviors to substitute for old behaviors, nor is it sufficient to merely try to inhibit old behaviors. It is our feeling that the efforts in those directions have led to the idea that treating symptoms only produces substitution. It is our contention that the error in the past has not been the treatment of specific symptoms or symptomatic behavior, but rather that they have been treated out of context and for this reason the desired results have not always been obtained. For, while the therapist is adding new behaviors and cognitive elements, society, at the same time, it is also adding new cognitive elements and, in terms of our previous reference to Festinger's findings,[146] this "dissonance" is producing competition between the behaviors produced in psychotherapy and the behaviors produced in the social field. This competition is extremely destructive if the primary goal is specific, concrete behavior on the part of the child. If, on the other hand, the goal is the child's learning how to integrate his behavior into the demands of the social situation, this competition does not have to be destructive. Instead the interaction resulting from the addition of new cognitive elements in therapy and the addition of new cognitive elements from the social field, can produce a new field for the child, a qualitative change in the whole pattern of behavior. Even if this change is not in a direction desired by the therapist, he can continue adding new cognitive elements at a rate somewhat faster than those being added by society, since those coming from psychotherapy are specific and based more concretely on goal directed behavior, while those from society are diffuse and therefore do not always hit the mark; he will thus, eventually create a cognitive field more consistent with that being sought. This is based on the even older premise that the difference between the normal child and the retarded child is that the retarded child fails to take from his environment sufficient indications and cues to lead him to understanding, and if understanding is to be achieved, it must be taught. Thus, we find that the therapist, functioning as a model, in relationship to this increased understanding, begins to carry more weight with the child than does the whole social field which is not taking time out to help him gain understanding. The difference between the S-S form and the other forms is that previously the therapist's function as a model was the prime element in the therapeutic effort, while here the whole therapy session becomes a phase of the patient's interaction with society, and it is no longer a matter of the therapist alone functioning as a model, but rather for the therapist, in conjunction with the therapy session and everything that happens in it, to seem to function as a model. Thus, the process becomes one of conditioning the child not only to behave in a certain manner, but also to have tested other forms of behaviors and thus have gained understanding of their failure as well as understanding of success or available rewards from the behavior which the therapist and the patient together can agree would be the most socially acceptable.

The therapist is called upon to set up situations very similar to those in the classroom areas to get the child to act through his behavior as it occurred in the classroom and also to act through various other ways of dealing with the same type of situation, remembering that the young child and the retardate need a chance to concretely act out the specific problem, that they cannot be expected to generalize on an abstract level. Thus, the therapist will lead the child to perform a problem and then point out the consequences of this behavior or, at the same time indicate the consequences of more mature behavior, thus giving the child the opportunity to have "been there once" and to gain understanding as to what was expected of him in that situation.

Once the child has begun to develop a new cognitive field, his response to his environment will cause the environment to make new responses to him and will begin, in effect, to reinforce the more positive behavior.

Indications of Gain and Criteria for Termination

With the above in mind, it becomes comparatively easy to identify exactly when progress in therapy has occurred, since specific symptoms or specific behaviors are being dealt with and when these symptoms or behaviors change, it is immediately clear. It is not quite as easy to know whether or not the child has achieved full understanding of the situation in the sense of retaining ability to meet new problems as they may arise in the social sphere, but since this form of therapy was established primarily to deal with concrete behaviors, the therapist does not have to worry whether or not he has provided for all future eventualities, what is important is that he has dealt with the present situation. Thus, if a child is brought in, to use our previous example, for stealing, and he stops stealing, the case is then ready for termination. That he may start stealing in the future, only indicates that a possible re-referral for short-term therapy to clear up whatever new problems have arisen, is demanded. The child is not retained in therapy because he might start stealing again, or because new symptoms may develop and the therapist has to watch for them. In other words, it is much more important to the child's self-concept that he realize he has made a success of therapy, that he has been terminated, and even if he later has to be brought back, it does not have to mean that he has failed in what he previously attempted to do, but rather that he could not quite succeed in the new effort, and that he needs help in developing a success in the new area, but that the previous success is still proudly under his belt, and can be something for the therapist to build upon.

CONCLUSIONS

We have introduced a form of psychotherapy which is more highly directive than traditional play therapy and is based on treatment of symptoms and symtomatic behavior rather than on merely permitting the child to play through a variety of problems as do the other forms. We have indicated the specific reasons for introducing this type of therapy and these center around the concept of a finishing procedure in the sense that certain specific areas still remain problem areas. This approach is seen as a way of dealing with specific symptoms without departing from the total social field. We have, on this basis, established goals around the improvement of social maturity, the development of understanding on the part of the child that he can be accepted for himself, and the building of reality relationships leading to realistic levels of aspiration.

ADDITIONAL NOTES

131. Newbury, E., "Current Interpretation and Significance of Lloyd Morgan's Canon," *Psych. Bull.*, 51, 1954, pp. 70-73, "entities must not be multiplied beyond necessity."

132. Kaliski, Lotte, "Educational Therapy for Brain Injured, Retarded Children," *AJMD*, 1955, 60, pp. 71-76, discusses some of these same elements and evidently utilizes similar procedures in carrying out what she calls "educational therapy." The emphasis she places on the use of sensory modalities is extremely important.

133. Locke, J., *Some Thoughts on Education*, cited in Ulick, R. (Ed.), *Three Thousand Years of Educational Wisdom*, Harvard Univ. Press, Cambridge, Mass., 2nd. Ed., 1954.

134. Drennen, Genevieve, "Numbers, Arithmetic, and Math, Part 2: Games for Teaching Elementary Arithmetic," *Exceptional Child*, 1957, 23, pp. 182-187, gives a large number of examples of this type of arithmetic game and poems.

135. Arnholter, Ethelwyne, "Social Drama for Retarded Adolescents," *Exceptional Child*, 1955, 21, pp. 132-134.

136. Creative Playthings, Inc., Princeton, N. J., makes useful doll figures and animals for this type of play.

137. Sarbin, T. R., "Spontaneity Training of the Feeble Minded," in Moreno, J. (Ed.) *Group Psychotherapy*, Beacon House, N. Y., N. Y., 1945, describes an attempt to apply psychodrama techniques to a retarded group.

138. Axline, Virginia M., "Nondirective Therapy for Poor Readers," *J. Cons. Psych.*, 1947, 11, pp. 61-69; and Bills, R. E., "Nondirective Play Therapy with Retarded Readers," *J. Cons. Psych.*, 1950, 14, pp. 140-149, both point out the role of psychotherapy in relationship to reading problems, and we have observed that a similar relationship exists with other academic areas.

139. This note has been cited on page 126.

140. Strauss and Kephart, *loc. cit.*

141. Levy, D. M., "Release Therapy in Young Children," *Psychiat.*, 1938, I, pp. 387-390, discusses dealing with specific problems on a short-term basis.

142. This note has been cited on page 134.

143. MacMillin, M. B., "Pavlovian Principles in the Treatment of an Unresponsive Seemingly Retarded Preschool Child," *AJMD*, 1961, 65, pp. 440-447, has demonstrated that understanding in no way implies that the child achieves insight. The specific attainment of insight is not necessary to success or attainment of goals.

144. Snyder, R. and Sechrest, L., "An Experimental Study of Directive Group Therapy with Defective Delinquents," *AJMD*, 1959, 64, pp. 117-123.

145. Azrin, N. H. and Lindsley, D. R., "The Reinforcement of Cooperation Between Children," *Jr. Abnor. and Soc. Psych.*, 1956, 52, pp. 100-102.

146. Festinger, *op. cit.*, p. 3.

IX. Play Therapy Techniques in Diagnosis and Evaluation[147]

One of the major by-products of play therapy is the wealth of projective and expressive material produced in a play session. Play therapy, while not specifically designed to deal with certain questions, nonetheless serves as an important adjunct toward answering them. Thus, we have situations where knowledge of how children play is necessary, even though they are not specifically in therapy as it is usually defined. Also, there are questions concerning the functioning level of the child; various types of research; the relationship of adjunctive areas such as O.T., M.T., or special education; the relationship with the specific milieu; or the work to be done with parents and care personnel. These areas are important to success in play therapy, and also the lessons we learn from play procedures may guide us and give us important help in understanding these other areas. Thus, play therapy procedures may be used for purposes other than therapy—one of these purposes is the use of play therapy procedures as part of an evaluation program.

PURPOSES OF PLAY THERAPY EVALUATION AND DIAGNOSIS

Many of the children evaluated in a setting for the mentally retarded or emotionally disturbed are not able to respond to psychometric or psychodiagnostic evaluation materials in the manner for which these materials were designed. There are various reasons for this failure. Sometimes there is a complete inability to respond to test materials because the mental level of the child is too low, or he is too disturbed to respond to the tests which are being used, i.e., he is unable to perform on enough of the subtests in a standardized instrument to provide information for a full evaluation. Furthermore, the extent of the emotional disturbance may be so great that he cannot permit himself to respond in a manner permitting clear-cut evaluation of his functional level, or to reveal the underlying factors related to his behavior. Or, the organic involvement may be so great that he is unable to deal with the subject matter at hand in any sort of controlled manner. Or it may be that the child is chronologically too young for the type of standardized test information being sought, or the test material normally utilized with children that young is not properly productive of that kind of information. There may be other reasons but, generally speaking, with the mentally subnormal, these are the main reasons why the usual standardized or psychodiagnostic materials are not used and the child is then quite often either described as "untestable" or the tests are described as being invalid for the estimation of the child's level of functioning. Furthermore, even when the examiner can use the usual instruments, it is often deemed valuable to gain the type of corollary information available through the observation of the child at play.[148]

Usually diagnostic evaluations, when done by a clinical psychologist, attempt to establish the present functional level of the individual being evaluated, to determine some of the psychological clues to the etiology of the condition, and to determine what recommendations might be made to aid in the correction of the condition, or what suggestions for rehabilitation might be derived from the test material. It becomes clear that a child who cannot take the tests or who, though he may take them, cannot give sufficiently controlled responses to give the psychologist material with which to work, has not provided the information required to complete these three basic missions of the evaluation. Since the general concept of projective testing includes the idea that all behavior is in one manner or another a reflection of the total personality, it is necessary to set up procedures which will help measure this behavior in a controlled setting. The various procedures of play therapy are admirably adapted to this particular idea.

This is not to imply that play therapy might produce an IQ, but as we will discuss in Chapter XI, the IQ as such is not a primary objective in this type of effort. Rather, when we are seeking an estimate of the child's present functioning, though the IQ is still a most useful medium, if it is not available, there are other ways of ascertaining the functioning level that do not involve an IQ. Thus, we find that many of the projective tests, such as the Rorschach technique and the Draw-A-Person Test, etc., even though they are not specifically developed to produce an IQ, nonetheless aid in the estimation of intelligence. Play therapy could be actually stronger than those devices because play therapy, if based on the four methods that we have indicated, produces both a free and a controlled environment in which the child may work, and the therapist then gets a better cross section of the child's ability, his fantasies and his social and personal understanding.

The techniques to be used for diagnosis and evaluative purposes are similar to those we have described for use in play therapy. The outstanding difference lies in the fact that instead of trying to create personality changes in the patient, the therapist is trying to learn as much as he can about the patient, and thus will use all of the techniques available to him without first attempting to select those most in keeping with the needs of the child. In this sense it is very similar to the general over-all evaluation techniques used with new admissions in many children's institutions where the children are exposed to all therapies for a short period of time before a case conference makes a decision as to which therapy they need most. Thus, diagnostic play utilizes all forms of play techniques in an effort to find which form receives the most response, or indicates the highest motivation on the part of the patient.

GOALS IN DIAGNOSTIC PLAY THERAPY

The goals in diagnostic play therapy could be stated as: (1) To determine the functional level of the child by comparing the manner in which he plays in the various areas presented to him, to such standardized measures as are already available. For example, the Vineland Social Maturity Scale, and the Gesell scales would be used in conjunction with comparisons to what would be considered "normal" play for a child his chronological age. Admittedly this process is quite subjective, but it also can be very informative as long as a specific IQ is not being sought. In other words, an attempt is made to estimate the behavioral age of a child in terms of the manner in which he plays, the things he says or does while playing, and his general attitude toward play. This cannot be conceived of as standardized, but there are standardized clues which can be used to help determine the functional level.

(2) To determine if the hyperactive, distractible behavior which may have prevented the psychometric evaluation from being completed is primarily due to organicity or to emotional disturbance. This is measured again on a subjective level in terms of whether or not the child plays in a manner typical of emotionally disturbed children, or whether the play pattern is predominantly due to organic driveness. Here, there are certain specific clues that may be followed:

> The emotionally disturbed child may (a) play in an egocentric manner not including the examiner in his play except when dire necessity forces it, and even then the examiner is not "included in," but rather becomes a mere means to an end; (b) not be able to play at any specific activity, but instead will have a single toy or a single piece of material which will preoccupy him without his investing himself in the material; (c) may present a number of auxiliary movements such as rocking or self-mutilation, purposeless sounds of an almost babbling nature; (d) not vocalize at all in terms of meaningful words, or if he does the words will not seem to be related to the subject at hand; (e) relate better to unstructured material, such as finger paint, clay, water, sand, etc., than he will to structured material such as specific toys or specifically planned activities; (f) have a general attitude and mein of opposing intrusion in the sense that he will seem to resent the whole procedure very strongly and in one manner or another will give indications of anger and antisocial or antiexaminer feelings; (g) in drawing activities have a tendency to make meaningless scribbles of a wild and aggressive nature, this being particularly true when finger painting or free drawing is used; and (if he

has usable speech) have a tendency to give violent names to the drawings in the sense that he may describe a war scene or a tornado or something of this sort; he usually will not try to describe specific parts, such as hands, arms, or legs; however, if the examiner asks for hands, arms, or legs, he will point indiscriminately to any of the scribbled lines.

These are some of the things which the examiner can look for, but obviously all emotionally disturbed children do not demonstrate these particular symptoms, as a great deal depends on the intellectual level. However, they are typical of certain types of emotional disturbance and usually two or more will be present if the child is primarily emotionally disturbed.

On the other hand, the child who is predominantly organic will have tendencies to:

(a) play in a dependent manner, still being egocentric by definition but calling upon the examiner for help, or hang around the examiner, though he will be unable to interact in the full sense; (b) jump "grasshopper" fashion from one activity to another, but in any single activity will demonstrate an ability no matter how short a time he stays with it, to play with the toys or to participate in the specific activity, (in other words the problem here is one of distractibility and hyperactivity, but if his attention can be maintained, he will demonstrate some ability to deal with the subject matter); (c) show a general absence of the stereotyped movements and babbling associated with emotional disturbance, but these may be replaced by rapid running around the room in a general type of hyperactive behavior which has not been localized in the specific sense of rocking or head pounding, etc., also he may get a great deal of pleasure out of pounding pegs in a pegboard or punching a bop bag; (d) be less apt to have speech ability, but the words he is able to command are usually fairly well controlled, and usually used in the appropriate manner or place; (e) relate better to structured types of playroom activity and to specific, well-defined toys and activities than to the loose, unstructured settings; (f) as was mentioned already in (a) not seem to resent the intrusion of the examiner, but will leave himself open to direction and supervision as a way of providing additional structure which seems to be the main element he is seeking; and (g) organize drawing or finger painting toward geometric form and short, abrupt lines or shapes, rather than open wild, meaningless scribble.

There is nothing in these two sets of symptoms to exclude the other. That is to say, the emotionally disturbed, brain damaged child may interlace symptoms, and some things from each list may be present. What we are pointing to here are the elements which seem to be predominantly demonstrated by the child whose overwhelming problem is in one or the other direction.

(3) To determine the extent of the disability; the goal here is to determine which of the reasons for not using test instruments seem to apply to this specific child. Here, it is not sufficient to state that the child appears to be organically damaged, or that he appears to be emotionally disturbed or severely retarded, because there are a number of emotionally disturbed, organically damaged, severely retarded youngsters who can be given a regular psychometric or psychodiagnostic evaluation. Rather, it must be indicated through the clues given in the play situation that the extent of these conditions and the underlying factors related to them are such that the psychometrics could not or should not be used. The reasons for this must, if possible, be determined through the play activity. For example, the child who comes into the playroom asking hundreds of questions about everything, may be an extremely insecure, anxious child who could not be evaluated properly with psychometrics because the level of insecurity and paranoid suspicion is so great that he could not permit himself sufficient thought to respond to the questions. Another child may come into the playroom and spend all of his time flitting from one thing to another, never settling down, and never in any way responding to the suggestions or commands of the examiner, and he is obviously extremely hyperactive, but he also may be too severely retarded to understand. Here, the examiner must differentiate between the extent of the retardation as such, and the organic drivenness in terms of children who may behave in the same hyperactive manner, but will respond to the examiner. These are just examples and not to be considered as diagnostic indicators, since obviously in the examples given, many more factors need to be observed and understood before a diagnosis of the condition can be produced. They are thus given only as the types of behaviors which the examiner must look for in order to make his final determination of the extent or type of disability.

(4) To give suggestions as to the possible corrective or rehabilitative procedures in the areas of management and care of the child, and in the training or treatment of the child. It is entirely possible that some treatment and training areas will have to be considered as almost completely inappropriate, and the major suggestion would be that the child was not yet ready. However, some suggestions should be made in each of the three areas so that planning can be done around the whole child. These suggestions grow out of the observations of the manner in which the child plays, the manner in which he responds to the various materials offered him, and the manner in which he responds to the examiner.

(5) To try to learn something about the adaptive ability of the child in order to determine the classification in terms of Adaptive Behavior. For, while the functional level leads to an estimate of Measured Intelligence, we must also think of an estimate of Adaptive Behavior. The difference is that the examiner is not estimating what the child knows or what he is capable of learning, but

rather what he is able to do with the knowledge that he has. Thus, a severely retarded, brain damaged child may, because of his extremely primitive knowledge of play, be considered at Level V as far as Measured Intelligence is concerned, but he may nonetheless have acquired a large number of social skills and graces at a less retarded level and thus would be estimated to be at Level III in Adaptive Behavior. This particular pattern is quite typical, for example, of a Mongoloid child, as we will discuss in Chapter X. Conversely, however, the severely emotionally disturbed child may demonstrate quite a bit of practical knowledge in terms of having a fairly rich speaking vocabulary, a fairly rich knowledge of how to work with finger paints or how to play with the toys, or how to carry out some of the other activities in play therapy but be completely lacking in any ability to interact socially and in any of the so-called social graces. This child might then be estimated to be at a Level II as far as Measured Intelligence is concerned, but at Level IV as far as Adaptive Behavior is concerned. Thus, this dimension must be given separate consideration in the final diagnosis of the child at play.

PROCEDURES

The procedures used in diagnostic play are very similar to those we have already described. The four types of play therapy U-U, U-S, S-U, and S-S are all utilized in this setting. The basic therapy procedure is to choose one of these techniques and to continue the play therapy program for a minimum of three months or more for the purpose of bringing about certain personality changes in keeping with the general goals. The procedures to be used in diagnostic play therapy consist of utilizing all four of the techniques in the course of the evaluation, but for only a short period of time. No more than one technique should be used in any given period. It is not necessary to switch off between the four techniques in any sort of rigid routine, but some time during the general course of diagnostic play all four of the techniques should have been attempted, and they should have been attempted a sufficient number of times to permit the examiner to gain a clear impression as to how the child responds in terms of the five goal areas of evaluation mentioned above. Thus, though the exact procedure cannot be outlined in a set form, the following is a functional outline which can be followed as long as it is not followed too rigidly.

First, the play should be set up for a minimum of eight hours. This may be organized in terms of one hour per week for eight weeks, or two half hours per week for eight weeks, or one half hour per week for sixteen weeks, or any other combination that seems feasible as long as we have a minimum of eight hours of diagnostic play. This organization of time is varied to depend on the amount of strength the examiner feels the patient has available. Usually one would not expect a child who is unable to perform in a meaningful manner on a standardized psychometric test to be able to stand a full hour of play of an intensive and intrusive nature and, therefore, we would say that most of the children coming into diagnostic play therapy probably should be scheduled one half hour at a time. However, there is certainly no objection to using this child two or three half hours per week if the therapist has the time to see him. Again, one would assume that more than three sessions a week would probably be excessive in terms of the child's ability to absorb the material.

Second, the session should be planned and the therapist should have a clear idea at the beginning of each session what it is they are going to do during that session. Any one of the four types of techniques may be employed, but whichever one is selected, must be continued throughout the whole session. Also, because the brain damaged child responds best to repetitive or perseverated activities, once a particular technique is elected, it should be continued for a number of sessions so that the full advantage of the technique can be demonstrated or measured. Thus, in a period of eight hours one would assume that each of the four procedures would be given two hours, and since we are considering half hour sessions, one would then consider four sessions with each technique. It is best if these four sessions are continuous. There is no particular rule as to the pattern to follow. The emotionally disturbed child is usually most responsive to shock surprise type elements and, therefore, the therapist may gain greater effect if he switches from a tightly structured situation to a totally unstructured situation and then back to a more structured situation, rather than going from a tightly structured situation through a less structured situation to an unstructured situation, however, with the organically damaged child this latter pattern may be more appropriate. Since the majority of the children will be some combination of the two, the therapist must judge for himself which seems to be the best pattern. However, all four techniques must be used and a preconceived pattern should be effected so that the child's responses to the pattern can be judged also, and some basis of comparison approaching standardization can be utilized.

Third, during the structured phase the therapist should make an effort to have the materials ready before the child comes into the playroom so the exact plan of therapy can be put into effect fairly quickly. This will provide an observation of how the child deals with expectations and whether or not he has memory, etc. However, during the unstructured phase we are interested in the child's ability to choose his own materials. Following this pattern we would say that in the highly structured period the materials should be ready on the table for the child when he comes into the room and these should be the only materials used during the session. During the unstructured periods the materials should be in the cabinets and the child should be guided to these cabinets, permitted to pick those materials which he wants to use, and then permitted to bring them out. Once he has brought them out, an effort should be made to keep him with them for a short period of time, remembering, however, that part of the nature of the unstructured program is to give him some latitude so if he tires or loses interest in the activity quickly, he should be permitted to shift. This pattern should be followed when unstructured media is used in the structured manner. For example, if finger painting is to be used during one of the structured or teaching phases of the therapy, finger paints should be on the table, etc., as indicated above. In other words, the nature of the materials alone does not define how they are placed; instead the nature of the therapy makes this definition. Thus, unstructured materials may be properly used in a structured therapy setting and in certain instances structured materials may be used in an unstructured therapy setting. However, the therapist must decide the type of setting he is introducing on this particular day and organize the materials accordingly.

Fourth, the therapist must also make a decision as to which therapy room is to be used for the session. In general, play activities revolving around unstructured materials should be conducted in a setting where cleanliness need not be considered. Also, when the effort is to have the patient use his own imagination, the distraction of toys, etc., is to be avoided. Thus, the furnished playroom should be used where furniture and equipment become part of the activity, and the unfurnished playroom should be used when the planned activities are to be freer or messier.

Fifth, regardless of the extent of the structure, certain general limits should be established at the beginning of the diagnostic play period, and these limits should run consistently throughout the whole eight hours. These limits should be fairly concrete, and once they are established, they should not be removed though new limits may be added from time to time. In this regard, the use of limits is very similar to that which we have already described. The major differences between diagnostic play therapy and regular play therapy are that the limits in the former may be introduced arbitrarily by the therapist rather than by waiting specifically for the situation to arise. Here, the underlying theory of limits is related to the improving of social consciousness on the part of the child. Since this is a diagnostic session, the basic limits usually used in play therapy do not necessarily apply as automatically because the therapist is also interested in seeing how the child behaves without limits. Thus, there may be some instances where the therapist will want to open the situation totally to some sort of free play of a totally uncontrolled or unlimited nature. This is something the therapist will have to decide for himself. Such play, however, may be quite informative and certainly comes within the definitions of the U-U type of organization, particularly when the U-U form is used with more intelligent children.

Limits are evolved essentially around two specific areas in diagnostic play and these are, first, the relationship of the patient to the therapist, and here the limits are very similar to those already described in regular play therapy and, second, the relationship of the patient to the materials in the playroom. Here, limits may be a bit more stringent than in regular play therapy since this is only a diagnostic session, i.e., the usual processes in terms of permission and acceptance may be made more controlled than in regular sessions. However, even under these circumstances, generally speaking, the patient should be able to destroy any of the toys or materials provided for him and thus, this kind of diagnostic session should not be confused with standardized testing where an effort is made to preserve the test materials for future patients. However, he has to be made to realize that if he has destroyed something, it will not be made available to him for future play; thus, there is an implied punishment here, and he should be only as free as the examiner feels he wants him to be.

After the limits have been explained and imposed, the patient will probably test them as in a play session, and the therapist should follow the general pattern of reexplaining the limits, pointing out that this is the type of thing that is not permitted. If the patient continues with the prohibited activity, the therapist must immediately cease the play period and return the patient to his living area, if he is in a residential setting, or to his parents, who should be instructed to return him to his home immediately,[149] if the examination is in a child guidance or other clinic setting. However, though this has some diagnostic value, this particular session should then be erased from the total number and an additional session within the same type of structure should be added. This may mean that in the process of getting the limits established, more than the eight hours originally prescribed may be utilized, but this addition to the eight hours would only be necessary if the child, because of his violation of limits, made structured play observation impossible. If the child persists in this violation of the limits, some type of punishment based on isolation or seclusion should be evolved.[150]

If the patient's activity is such that it has not violated a clearly defined limit, the patient will not be blamed for the activity, but he may be verbally corrected and a new limit imposed. Certainly, things related to leaving the playroom arbitrarily, arguing with the therapist, etc., may eventually produce limits, but should not be introduced as limits until they have occurred in such a manner as to interrupt the diagnostic observation. Finally, during the whole period of evaluation, the therapist will be under the supervision of a senior therapist and plans for the following session as well as the succession of procedures used in the present session should be worked out during these

149. The child should not be permitted, for example, to go down town to get an ice cream cone.

periods of supervision. This is just as important as it is in regular therapeutic procedures since the material being worked with is so highly subjective it is entirely possible, if not probable, that it will require this comparison of opinions before proper diagnostic evaluation can be had from the material at hand.

REPORTING

At the completion of each of these sessions the therapist will make precise verbatim notes. These notes should be as anecdotal as possible, of the "I said," "he said," then "I said," or "I did" and "he did" variety, and will include as much observational reporting as possible. They do not necessarily have to include conclusions or opinions, however, if the therapist feels that either he or the patient has achieved important understanding during this period, it should be included in the notes. These notes will be reviewed with the senior therapist during the supervision period and will become the therapy file for this patient. At the end of the play diagnosis, these eight hours of notes will be organized and condensed into a single therapy report, and this report should be similar to the usual psychological report in that it should contain case history material, present examination material (a review of the eight hours of therapy), a diagnostic impression, and recommendations. Recommendations should, if possible, include an indication of what the child might be capable of learning next, and what procedures might be used to facilitate this new learning.

The material for the "present examination" is derived from the verbatim notes, but does not have to contain direct quotations from them. However, to be of value it should lean as heavily upon them as possible. In other words, while the verbatim notes will contain a certain amount of the therapist's impressions if they are truly anecdotal, the final report will include the child's behavior in response to certain specific things which the therapist did, and it is this reporting of behavior which will produce the information needed for the final diagnosis. Also, in terms of the use of this method as part of the repetoire of a clinical psychologist, if the report is based more on reporting of actual behavior than on subjective impressions, it will be possible to compare the material from various types of play evaluations using this method, and a clearer estimate of mental age and performance can be had.

Thus, the process of reporting and the form utilized becomes important, and while we have not evolved a formal report form, we would suggest that the areas mentioned, e.g., background material,[151] present examination, diagnostic impression, and recommendations, be retained when play therapy is utilized as a diagnostic technique.

151. To be most useful, the background material should include case history data, a record of any previous evaluations and, if available, salient medical information.

CONCLUSION

We might mention here that this type of procedure has certain peripheral values in that it can be utilized in training students who are learning techniques of play therapy. Thus, because the procedures are comparatively short, only eight hours being required, and because the methods do not involve the seeking of personality change but rather the observation of present behavior on the part of the patient, it is possible to utilize relatively unsophisticated individuals as therapists—unsophisticated in the sense that they have not been formally trained in the procedures of either play or psychotherapy. It is expected, of course, that they will have had sufficient training with the tools of clinical psychology, and that they will be proficient in the use of psychometric and psychodiagnostic instruments, as well as having some awareness of the various comparative scales such as the Vineland or Gesell scales, which we have already mentioned. If the individual, however, has this awareness and this knowledge, but is not sophisticated in the techniques of psychotherapy, this particular procedure can be quite useful in teaching him how to function in a therapy setting, helping him work through his own problems in terms of accepting this level of child, working through his own understandings of the role of limits, (how to impose them and what their function in therapy is) and sharpening his ability to observe what goes on in therapy in the sense of maintaining control of the situation. We have found that one of the most disturbing aspects of play therapy to the unsophisticated therapist is the fact that there is a tendency for them to become completely swamped or overwhelmed by their patient, in that they are faced with behaviors which they did not predict and which they find they cannot change. This ability to stay with or ahead of the patient is something that comes with practice, as any other ability, but at least in terms again of developing a feeling of having "been there once," if the therapist has had the experience of going through these techniques in a diagnostic setting, he will have less of a tendency to be completely overwhelmed by his patient than if he had never previously had this experience. Therefore, diagnostic play therapy becomes an excellent type of training device for students of psychotherapy as well as an excellent manner of introducing all clinical psychologists to some of the ramifications of the problems present with brain damaged, emotionally disturbed, retarded children.

The procedures and outline of diagnostic play which we have presented in this chapter have been utilized to a limited extent in the clinic at PSH&TC, and we have found that the elements which we have reported are effective and represent a way of dealing with children who would otherwise be considered untestable or non-productive of useful test vaults. We have also found that there is some value in using this technique as an adjunct or confirming technique with children who are testable. When the child completes a test and the examiner has some question as to its validity, the sessions of diagnostic play may reinforce the examiner's opinions regarding whether or not the test is measuring high or low in terms of this specific child. It has generally been experienced that some children come into testing situations, particularly if they are on a "one-time" basis, and have difficulty establishing rapport with the examiner, or because of the anxiety created by the test situation itself, find themselves unable to perform in a manner in which other people who have observed these children, say they can. Thus, if the clinic could see the child for eight successive weeks for the purpose of playing with him, the diagnosis which is produced could be much more revealing in terms of the eventual treatment and rehabilitation of the child than that produced in the usual two or three hour testing session which takes a great deal out of the child and produces responses that may be the result of fear, anxiety, and fatigue every bit as much as the result of a low functional level. In other words, while we are not offering this as a method to substitute for the psychometric method, we are saying that this type of observation may give, in many instances, a much more accurate and much more useful picture of a child who is seeking rehabilitation. Our usual procedure in the institution is to utilize both, and we feel that community clinics would also benefit greatly if they were to adopt this procedure. Thus, it is not a matter of either diagnostic play or psychometrics, but rather a comparison of the two, and if the results tend to disagree, as they often do, it becomes incumbent upon the therapist to figure out the reason for the disagreement and if he is successful, he will probably also be successful in developing a sound rehabilitation program because the answer to the question of "how the disagreement occurs" usually contains the seeds for finding the means to correct the problem.

In this chapter we have briefly reviewed the use of diagnostic play therapy for those patients who are unable or unwilling to perform usefully in the regular standardized psychometric or psychodiagnostic evaluation situation. We have recommended that the various forms of play therapy be applied for the purposes of determining the information usually yielded from a psychological evaluation.

Diagnostic play is not to be considered a weaker or less efficient manner of evaluation than the standardized diagnostic procedures, and in many respects should be considered a stronger and more valuable manner of determining the functioning of the child. The disadvantages are the amount of time which must be consumed and the related delay in program planning, etc., as well as the fact that the conclusions are of necessity highly subjective and thus do not always have the validity of a more objective form of testing. However, the best test is generally not as good as intensive observation of a patient, in spite of the subjectivity of the latter, since the test situation itself produces certain problems which modify the patient's behavior. Play therapy also presents these problems, but since the child is given the chance to accommodate himself to the situation and the therapist is given an extensive opportunity to gain rapport, the specific difficulties can be mitigated and the over-all problem quite often is not as great. Therefore, diagnostic play is in many instances preferable to standardized techniques with younger children where the anxiety of the testing session is predominant over the value to be gained from it. This is a technique which can readily be used in the evaluation of kindergarten children and preschool children, even though there is no question of mental retardation or emotional disturbance or brain damage. It can also be readily used in child guidance clinics where mental retardation is not specifically the issue and, in general, we would say it has value as a diagnostic and evaluative instrument in any setting where a numerical IQ is not specifically required, and where the subjects to be evaluated are either extremely young children or youngsters who, because of psychological or physical disturbance, cannot be evaluated with regular instruments, and as we stated above, even where regular instruments are used, it has supplemental purposes in terms of either confirming or denying the results of this testing and thus producing additional information for the therapist.[152]

ADDITIONAL NOTES

147. The material in this chapter is based on the experience of the authors in training Public School Psychologists in a practicum program for Kansas State College at Pittsburg, Kans., and much of this material is cited from a class syllabus prepared by the senior author.

148. A number of authors have made this point; see, among others, Hamilton, G., *op. cit.*, p. 34-35; Jackson, Lydia and Todd, Kathleen M., *Child Treatment and Therapy of Play*, 2nd. Ed., Ronald Press Co., N. Y., 1950, pp. 59-61; Knoepfmacher, Juliani, *The Use of Play in Diagnosis and Therapy in a Child Guidance Clinic*, Smith College Studies in Social Work, Vol. 12, 1942, pp. 217-262; and Louttit, C. M., *Clinical Psychology of Exceptional Children*, 3rd. Ed., Harper Bros., N. Y., 1957, p. 4.

149. This note has been cited on page 149.

150. Boardman, *op. cit.*

151. This note has been cited on page 151.

152. Lederman, D. G., "Small Group Observation as a Diagnostic Technique," *AJMD*, 1958, 63, pp. 64-71, raises an interesting question concerning this kind of play diagnosis in a group setting. This should be investigated further.

PART THREE: INDICATIONS FOR PLAY THERAPY WITH SUBNORMAL CHILDREN

X. Adaptive Behavior in Reference to Play Therapy

The introduction cited the AAMD classification manual's description of a new dimension which has been called Adaptive Behavior.[153] Four levels are postulated, ranging from mildly maladaptive through profoundly maladaptive. We feel that this overlimits the concept of Adaptive Behavior in that it fails to take into account certain major considerations of the manner in which the individual "copes with the natural and social demands of his environment," particularly in regard to certain forms of orthopedic and physical handicaps, and generally does not quite serve the defined purpose. Therefore, in this chapter we are using a concept of Adaptive Behavior based on the underlying meanings of the dimension, but not tied to any specific number of levels. However, a "level" system is necessary for classification purposes, and our major examples will be drawn from our experiences with a five level system. The basis for this particular usage, as well as a general description of the intensions of the authors in regard to the different levels, is discussed at length in Jones (1963) and Leland (1964).[154]

Adaptive Behavior is described as relating to independent functioning, personal responsibility, and social responsibility to which we might add civic responsibility. Since every child who is able should be given every opportunity to remain in his own home and be aided in learning to live a happy, useful life, the problem of adaptation becomes both a treatment and training problem. That is to say, this is an area where correction is possible, where rehabilitation procedures may be used, and where the process of reversibility,[155] at least in terms of day-to-day functioning, may seem to be occurring because of improvement in Adaptive Behavior.[156]

IMPAIRMENTS RELATED TO SOCIAL AND CIVIC RESPONSIBILITY

Using this concept of Adaptive Behavior, we have divided the dimension into those areas which seem to best refer to the therapy needs of the functionally retarded child. Since the concept of Adaptive Behavior was not specifically established to deal with the needs of play therapy, but rather to help in prescribing rehabilitation objectives for retardates, it becomes logical that therapy needs might overlap, even though rehabilitation needs were different. Thus for example, the major rehabilitation objectives for one child might have been special education leading to prevocational guidance, plus sufficient psychotherapy to deal with those emotional disturbances that were present, and if he were in an institution, he would be apt to qualify for discharge. However, for another child the rehabilitation objectives might be special training, much greater emphasis on the prevocational guidance, because it was felt that he was presently at a lower level of adaptation and function and, therefore could not, for example, be expected to proceed in as unsupervised a manner as the other child, if he were in an institution, he would be recommended for further rehabilitation before discharge. These two youngsters in terms of rehabilitation are different, yet in terms of psychotherapy they may have many factors in common. They both may represent a major impairment in the area of social responsibility. *First*, there may be a general underlying failure to understand the responsibility of the individual in relationship to society. *Second*, there may be a general inability to understand the role of other individuals or groups in society. *Third*, there may be a general inability to develop proper social or civic understanding leading to acceptable interpersonal relationships. These maladaptations are shared in common by both youngsters, and the same type of play therapy can be utilized to try to meet their needs in this area.[157]

Social Responsibility of Individual

The problem of the child's understanding his responsibility in relationship to society usually involves the youngster who has made an otherwise fairly good adjustment. We recognize that children of all levels of Adaptive Behavior probably have some difficulty in understanding their individual roles, but the lower levels of Adaptive Behavior have so many more outstanding problems that the problem of responsibility never comes to the fore. However, the individual with a fairly high reality concept of what other people around him are doing, and how they respond to him, knows what he is not able to do. It becomes difficult for him to conceive of himself as a socially contributing individual. He feels rejected by society, feels that he is a useless appendage, and believes that there really is no place for him in the social construct. We will deal with this more completely in the next chapter when we discuss the relationship of intelligence to play therapy, but we mention it now because it is related to the individual's need to elect for himself a mode of behavior which will permit him to remain in society as an accepted individual. Here, psychotherapy has a primary responsibility of helping the individual gain understanding of how society expects him to behave, and how this behavior will serve the prupose of permitting him to remain as an accepted member of society. With the older child, who might conceivably be brought into a form of counseling psychotherapy, this particular problem could be dealt with in the more traditional way. In fact many of our readers may protest that this lack of understanding of the individual role in society is one of the profound difficulties facing almost anyone who comes into psychotherapy at any level. However, for the functionally retarded individual this takes on a new aspect because after he understands his responsibility, he possibly still is not going to like it. That is to say, he finds himself as an individual who may understand fully that his role in life is, in the old colloquial sense, to be a "ditch digger." He is sufficiently well adjusted to know that this is not the height of status in society; he is possibly also intelligent enough to know that ditch diggers do not get as good wages or other benefits; and the general underlying pattern is that he finds himself being stuck with a social orientation that is not particularly one which he would choose if he had freedom of choice. We find this, in the play therapy situation, reflected in fantasy play. Children become selective and choose figures such as nurses or doctor's in the hospital, or mothers and fathers, etc., immediately trying to replace themselves with the status figures ni their own life. The psychotherapy within the play situation becomes one of permitting the child to play out these fantasies, to find through the process of playing that he can find a niche for himself, that some of the fantasies which he is playing do not have a reality potential, and must be rejected or extinguished, while others may be built upon because they do have a potential reality. The types of play therapy which seem most in keeping with this particular element are both the S-U (thematic play with structured materials and an unstructured approach) and the S-S (structured materials and a structured approach). Those children whose main need is to work through their fantasy feelings and their feelings of rejection, anger, hostility, etc., would seem to fit best into the S-U area. Those children who need to have some idea of what they can accomplish at an acceptable level would fit best into the S-S type of therapy. Both of these groups have a major need to understand their individual responsibilities in society, and they have to have an opportunity to act out individual roles in a testing way to see how "society," that is, the therapist, accepts this type of behavior. Thus, it is through their testing and through their process of using the therapist as a model for society, that they can learn what roles are acceptable and what roles are not.

Group Responsibility in Society

The problem of understanding the role of groups in society is, in many respects, even more complicated and a more difficult thing with which to deal. Here, we find the child at the borderline or mild level of adaptive behavior to be actively comparing the model function of the therapist with all types of people in his environment who may or may not behave in a similar manner. As we pointed out in Chapter VII, this process of comparison is a necessary process. Hopefully, through the acting out of life situations in the S-U type of therapy, the child can work out for himself a rationale as to why the therapist seems to be behaving differently than, for example, his father; why other members of his therapy group can be friendly and giving while the neighbor children are prohibited from playing with him, etc. We are not assuming that the child is able to develop tremendous cultural-social insights into the workings of society, (which quite often even baffle your present authors) but rather that he has at least a working knowledge of what to expect; and he gains this working knowledge by playing out these situations through thematic play and seeing how model, the therapist, responds to him, so that he is in a sense gaining experience which he can then store away for further use when possibly a similar situation occurs in real life. In this way he prepares himself to meet his neighbors, to deal with his parents, to deal later with school teachers, employers, etc., since he has had the opportunity to "have been there once." Thus, we find that the understanding of the social responsibility of others in society as they relate to him becomes a matter of conditioning, and the child who has had the opportunity to go through the processes once is better able to deal with the stimuli the second time around, particularly if he has not been "burnt." This is an important aside, because we may presume in terms of what possibly has happened to the child before he came into play therapy, that he may have, through some of these experiences, already been "burnt," and thus be extremely afraid if not terrified by the thought of having to repeat them. Thus, the therapy has both the role of extinguishing previous feelings as well as adding new information in the form of new experiences where the child can go through life situations without this symbolic "burning."

Invisibility. This understanding is extremely important as it relates to the whole problem of "invisibility." Remembering, that the main element in social responsibility is the ability of the child to function in a socially acceptable manner with no more supervision than one would usually expect for a child his age, the retarded child can be judged to have best accomplished this when he no longer stands out as different. Thus, the child who may have a low IQ but a high level of Adaptive Behavior may be totally absorbed by the community and be considered, for all practical intents and purposes, a non-retarded individual in terms of community function; while conversely, maladapted children who are unable to function as the community expects will appear to be retarded or subnormal even if their intelligence measures within the normal range. This often makes the difference between the child who is institutionalized and the child who is able to remain in the community.

Civic Responsibility

Development of Relationship. The problems of understanding civic responsibility and developing acceptable interpersonal relationships is related to behaving in a manner consistent with the law and organization of the community. The point to underline here is that one of the elements which defines this level child is the fact that he has already strong ability to develop relationships, or his Adaptive Behavior would not be considered this high. However, there are still deficiencies in his ability relating to selectivity. This deficiency is the problem that most often brings the community and the retarded child into conflict. This is particularly true with the female retardate, because of the danger of pregnancy, but it is also true of the male retardate in terms of whether or not he will be "used" by a stronger personality or whether he might attack the neighbor children, or something of this sort. It is these kinds of fears which tend most to isolate the child in a community in terms of neighbors not permitting their children to play with him, or other people beginning to insist that "the child be taken care of in an institution or something." This becomes an extremely difficult area with which to deal in terms of interpersonal relationships, because the community is complaining about behavior in these children which is most like that of normal children. Here, we have the rather interesting contradiction that that which has set these children aside from other children is that they cannot behave like normal children, yet the community complains about behavior which resembles the normal, because certainly the sexual seeking, the neighborhood fights, the running in gangs, etc., is the behavior of many normal children, and is not necessarily a mark of either functional retardation or emotional maladjustment. The problem in this area boils down not to the behavior itself, although this is the element to which the community responds the most rapidly, but rather to the factor which we have introduced in terms of selectivity of relationships. This becomes an increasingly serious problem as the child grows older, and actually the child for whom this represents the greatest problem is usually already too old chronologically and functionally to be considered a candidate for play therapy, but we feel that if parts of this problem can be dealt with at the play therapy level in the younger child, then possibly by the time he is older he will have already developed abilities which will permit him to behave in a more selective manner, at least in the eyes of the community, and thus not present the kind of community problem that the borderline or moderately maladaptive child presents today. We realize that the community is not really attacking the child for behaving normally, but rather is attacking the fact that they fear he will not be able to handle the situation once he finds himself faced with it. Thus, a functionally retarded girl, who at this level probably looks like any other girl, (has no specific anomalies or disabilities that would in any way impair her social functioning) goes on a date and has a more difficult time saying "no" to an over-amorous swain than a more mature girl who has control of her behavior because of a stronger mental ability. We are not presuming that the retarded girls get into trouble, and the mentally normal or superior girls stay out of trouble—vital statistics of an average sized city would refute this claim immediately—but rather that the retarded girl deals with the situation in a much more awkward and more community-involving manner than the girl with the superior intelligence, probably because the retarded girl has a greater desire to be wanted or accepted and thus takes the first person who asks her. Thus, the problem of Adaptive Behavior here might almost boil down to the fact, in terms of interpersonal relationships, that the retarded individual makes the wrong kinds of relationships too easily, and has difficulty in finding what the right kinds would be. It becomes a matter for either S-S or S-U therapies to develop some sort of selectivity, some sort of ability to differentiate between proper and improper, or at least socially acceptable and non-acceptable relationships, so that he again will "have been there once," and will have some idea how this behavior, which admittedly is normal and admittedly is in response to desires which are normal, nonetheless may be controlled and so organized that the community will not become upset in the process. This is probably the hardest job the therapist has. Experientially, it is the most unsuccessful, but nonetheless the attempts that have been made do produce directional results which, in a sense, improve the child's concept of what he or she should be doing, and thus put some of the behavior at the cognitive level.

Thus, to sum up, we would say that these youngsters are most in need of the S-U and S-S forms of play therapy. The differentiation then depends essentially on factor two, that is, "their understanding the roles of others in society." If this is their weakest area then S-U therapy is clearly indicated, and since it will help also to accomplish the other two factors, this would be the type of therapy recommended. If the patients do not seem to demonstrate particular weakness in understanding the role of others, but do seem to demonstrate weakness in being able to realistically evaluate their own potential, then the S-S form is more indicated and should be utilized, but either of these two forms would seem to meet the particular types of problems that are indicated by these levels of Adaptive Behavior.

IMPAIRMENTS RELATED TO PERSONAL RESPONSIBILITY

A second group of youngsters differ from the above in that they are not as well adapted to their social surroundings, or to the interpersonal milieu as are the higher level youngsters. Therefore, while the three deficiencies which were indicated above are also present, there are three additional areas which make these children appear more poorly adapted than the children we have just discussed. These three additional factors are: *First*, the failure to develop a concept of personal responsibility; *second*, the inability to find acceptable modes of self-expression; and *third*, the difficulty in developing interpersonal relationships at their level. We are repeating the third factor because the development of relationships differs with each adaptive level and, therefore, the kinds of relationships that these children have to build are different than the kinds of relationships discussed above.

Concept of Personal Responsibility

As to the first factor, the development of personal responsibility, this in many respects is the major feature which distinguishes these children from their better adapted peers and conversely from their less well adapted peers. By personal responsibility we refer to the concept that the child, by his behavior, indicates whether or not he realizes that he is responsible for his own behavior. This basic understanding becomes the key to the various factors with which we have dealt in earlier sections of the book in terms of impulse control, recognition of self, and recognition of self in relationship to others. When the child understands that he is responsible for his own behavior, he is thus capable of impulse control, etc. If he fails to recognize this, it is very difficult for him to deal with the other social demands which have been translated by us into therapy goals. The child at this level seems to be a child who has sufficient understanding of himself to be potentially able to be responsible for his behavior. He, for example, is usually toilet trained, he usually feeds himself, dresses himself, obeys general commands, and from this frame of reference can care for himself in terms of body needs; this differentiates him from a child who needs one hundred per cent supervision. But, on the other hand, he does not have sufficient ability to assume responsibility for his acts in the social sphere, and has only a limited sense at this time of personal responsibility toward his behavior in the personal sphere. Thus, it is usually very difficult for him to make what we might consider logical or appropriate decisions regarding feeding habits, dressing habits, language habits, etc., and it is very difficult for him to apply information he may have gained in training programs, i.e., to generalize, to alternative areas that have not been specifically pointed out to him. An example of this in the area of Adaptive Behavior might be where he is told not to bang on the table with the toy gun, so he puts it down and bangs on the table with a block, making the translation that he is doing what he was told because he put the gun down. He is, however, still banging on the table, and it is difficult for him to realize that this is what is being criticized, and that the question of a gun or a block is not really the issue. This inability to make proper social translations becomes the major difficulty in teaching this type of child to assume complete and full personal responsibility for his behavior. It is the function of psychotherapy to attempt to do this, and those forms of psychotherapy most related to the development of creative ability and understanding of the consequences of one's behavior are best suited to this type of child. Thus, we have a child who would seem to fit well into the S-S type of structure, or at a more primitive intellectual level into the U-S type of structure. The need here is not for thematic or fantasy play, but rather the very concrete objective to enter the child into an action, have him follow through this action to its logical conclusion and become aware of the results of the behavior. This is one of the primary things that occurs in the U-S form; however, it may also occur in the S-S form, and thus the difference in intelligence becomes a consideration.[158] The important point being that the child needs that form of play therapy which will permit him to initiate action and become aware of the consequences of this initiation. In those play areas where the approach is unstructured, he does not have the full opportunity to become aware of the consequences of his behavior and, therefore, does not really "learn" to become a responsible person.

Acceptable Modes of Self-Expression

The second factor, the inability to find proper modes of expressing self, is related to the question of responsibility, because the individual with this problem has a great deal of difficulty in finding acceptable outlets. While he is searching for proper outlets, he experiments with certain kinds of behavior which, if they are not socially acceptable, immediately put him at war with the community. He is difficult to reason with, and any attempt to change this behavior or to correct it through punishment, often leads to anger, aggression, and other manifestations of the negative feelings which correctional procedures are likely to produce. On the other hand, the community cannot be permissive and accepting of his behavior, because it is often so completely out of line with community standards that it becomes most shocking and disturbing and thus disruptive of normal community relationships, e.g., the child who insists on masturbating outside on a street corner, or who insists on urinating on a neighbor's front yard. Another example might be the youngster who insists on picking up rocks and throwing them in all directions without any particular concern as to where they may land. All of these behaviors can be described as self-expression. They are unacceptable modes of self-expression, but the child's basic requirement is not to be told not to do it, it is rather to be told what he can do. However, since the community's major need is to stop the negative behavior, they do not have time to work this out with the child,

158. As we note in Chap. XI, there is no specific relationship between Measured Intelligence and Adaptive Behavior as such.

and using a process already described in the literature regarding reinforcement, there is a tendency for the behavior to actually be continued because it has been reinforced, even though the reinforcement has been negative. Thus, the community defeats itself in its attempt to stop the behavior. This produces greater punishment, greater negative feelings on the part of the child, and we find ourselves in an untenable bind where the child feels that he is not permitted to express himself in any manner because everyone around him is sure that it will be wrong and will have to be stopped. He thus begins either to behave without control or to internalize his feelings, both of which behaviors tend to produce further negative feelings, poor social adaptation, and greater community difficulties. Thus, the problem of developing personal responsibility, which we've already mentioned, is interwoven with the problem of finding the proper and socially acceptable modes of behavior. Here again one might think of an S-U form in terms of permitting the child to play out some of these experiences, but remembering that his feelings are on a comparatively primitive level, it is not actually a thematic expression that he is seeking, rather he is seeking a very primitive, primary expression of very primitive, primary emotions, as well as elementary limits. Thus, we find that the unstructured material is appropriate and the most ideal situation for a youngster here would seem to be the U-S method, although again we can remember that if there is a higher intellectual ability, he may be able to deal with structured materials, and the S-S method serves a function.[159] If, on one hand, the child can successfully take an unstructured material and produce something which is acceptable to his therapist and communicate this behavior verbally, even though this may have been done through acts of aggression and negativeness, he will begin to learn that some of his feelings are acceptable, that it is acceptable for him to express his feelings, and will then be started on the road to finding proper modes of behavior. If, on the other hand, through intellectual control, he has already learned to internalize much of these feelings so that he can deal with structured materials, then the same course may be followed utilizing his intellectual control to help him gain emotional control by learning socially acceptable means of expression in a training setting. Parenthetically, it is entirely possible that the child, by the time he comes to therapy, may be so completely wrapped up in the negative feelings that the community has created that he can do nothing more than scream and yell and fight back when placed under social pressure. At that point, of course, we would have to say that the U-U form of therapy is the most preferable for him. Thus, there is not at this level a specific therapy form which we would recommend, except to say that in dealing with the needs of finding proper modes of behavior one must ascertain what modes the child is using at the present time. If these modes are totally without control, then the U-U method would be the best; if there is some control but not enough to be acceptable at the community level, then the U-S method would be the best; if there are controls which might be accepted at community levels, but which have left the child a nonproductive individual, a "good child" in the sense that he doesn't bother anybody, but also does nothing for himself in a creative way, then the S-S method would be the best. Thus, the actual state of the child at the time he comes to therapy has to be the prime indicator of which of the three methods are called for at that point.

Development of Relationships

The third factor, the development of relationships, becomes a very broad question concerning peer groups for these children. If the child is in an institution, this is not particularly difficult, since the institution automatically creates peer groups through cottage placements, activity groups living areas, etc.[160] If the child is still at home, this may be a little more difficult since it is unlikely that there would be more than one or two children at this level in any given community area, and probably not more than one in a given neighborhood, so that the child has practically no opportunity to develop actual working relationships with his peers. The main problem of relationship development at this level is being with individuals who are going to be much superior as far as their maturation is concerned. It has been our experience that most retarded youngsters meet this problem by playing with children that are younger than they. This, however, again creates community difficulties with neighbors and we find a mother saying, "Well, I don't want your ten year old boy playing with my five year old girl." She probably feels that there is something unnatural in the relationship; and she becomes quite defensive of her five year old daughter, thus tending to further isolate the ten year old boy. This situation is repeated time and time again, and most individuals working with the functionally retarded have met it on an almost daily basis. We must realize, however, that the child, in seeking his own level, has found a proper solution. He has located another child at about the same level of maturity. When the normal child continues to grow and thus becomes more mature, the retarded child does not keep up, and the friendship is broken; the retarded child again seeks a younger individual who has not yet reached the older level of maturity, and the cycle continues. This is not too bad on a day-to-day basis if the neighbors can be understanding enough to accept it. However, it creates one additional problem in that it is totally impossible for the retarded child at this level to build any sort of lasting relationships, since all of his friends gradually mature away from him. Thus, the problem of development of relationships becomes a very complex one which really cannot be dealt with in a play therapy setting but, through the possibility of group therapy of the U-S or S-S type, it is possible for the child to learn to make his relationships as rich and as rewarding as possible. Thus, even though it will be broken off, at least each relationship will have its own values and the child will be aided by these so that when he enters into a new relationship, it can be at a higher plane. The role of play therapy here is not to deal with the social community problem as such, but rather to help the child get the most from the relationships that he is forced to make because of the nature of the community. Even if the child is institutionalized, the problem is not solved, although the difficulty of the lack of continuity is eliminated, these youngsters are all at his level and, therefore, they can offer very little to him he does not already have. He gets no opportunities for the enrichment and growth which having to deal on a friendly basis with slightly more mature youngsters will offer. Thus, the community relationships, if the maturity differences are not so great that they become frustrating and over-challenging, are of value to the functionally retarded youngster in that they tend to produce challenges for him which, in his effort to maintain the relationship, he will try to meet, and thus will be helped to grow, at least in terms of Adaptive Behavior. The institution does not provide this kind of challenge and thus it is very difficult for an institutionalized child to improve in Adaptive Behavior, except in a contrived milieu situation where the therapist has become aware of the lack of challenge and has purposely introduced challenge into the situation. Thus, the role of play therapy becomes clear in terms of trying to help the child gain as much from his milieu relationships as he possibly can.

IMPAIRMENTS IN INDEPENDENT FUNCTIONING

Another group of children are those who have problems of independent functioning. Remembering that Adaptive Behavior levels are based on the ability of the child to do things which society expects him to do, rather than on Measured Intelligence or his potential in terms of being able to do these things, we have to recognize that this last area is a very complicated one because for example, by definition a severely cerebral palsied child of high intelligence (75-80 IQ) or even possibly normal intelligence would, nonetheless, because of the extent of the cerebral palsy, be considered a lower level child. That is, he cannot do the things which society expects him to do in terms of behavior or adaptation to social needs. Thus, also emotionally disturbed children who may have comparatively high intelligence, but who because of the extent of their emotional disturbance do not function or do not communicate with society, may also be described as lower level children. Thus, we have a category of children with severely impaired Adaptive Behavior, for whom the potentials for psychotherapy have not been developed. This is not to say that they don't need psychotherapy; it is not to say that psychotherapy with them might not be effective under certain circumstances, and we will indicate those circumstances in a moment, but across the board, these children generally are those who are institutionalized, who are not placed into any form of therapy program, and who historically are considered untrainable or "custodial" types of patients. As we discussed in the Introduction to this book, we consider any child treatable in the therapeutic sense. However, in terms of availability of therapists, availability of time, use value of the procedures and, more important, the level of our present knowledge in the area, (our own retardation), certain very practical considerations unfortunately have to be made on whether or not psychotherapy should be indicated. With this in mind, there still remains a group of low level youngsters about whom it is felt that they could do much better or become much more adaptive socially if they could be brought into a therapeutic relationship with someone. This group are those who demonstrate: the possibility of development of motivation for growth; the possibility of development of interest in their personal well being; and the possibility of development of a sense of self (and a sense of others) for the development of relationships.

Motivation for Growth

In terms of the first element, the development of motivation for growth, we sometimes have a situation where the child's intellectual potential indicates that he could do a great deal more than he is doing. Or because of the etiology of the retardation we find a spotted area of success intermingled with a large number of areas of failure. Thus, we may find a child who is able to feed himself at the Vineland Age Equivalent five year level, though all the rest of his behavior is at the three year level.[161] We would say, in terms of a general rule of thumb, that success in any one area is indicative of a potential for success in most areas at the same level of ability. Therefore, this child potentially could be considered to be able to perform at a five year level. One of the factors that may be present in his inability to perform is that he is not really motivated to work any harder in those areas unrelated to his success area. This may be due to poor levels of aspiration; it may be due to inability to organize his successes so that he realizes that they are successes and thus think of himself only in terms of failure; it may be due to the fact that he just does not care; it may be due to a number of factors, and it is not our particular interest at this time to go into the specific implications of motivation. We merely mention this to illustrate what we mean by "trying to develop proper motivation for growth." The role of therapy is to attempt to get the child to realize that he is able to do more than he is doing, and that if he does do more, there will be some rewards which will make this extended effort more worthwhile. Further, there is a need for the patient to develop a higher level of aspiration, some feeling that he wants to do more than he is doing, and some dissatisfaction with his present lack of functioning. It is postulated by many therapists, particularly of the Rogerian school, that there is within the individual a "basic need for growth." Without going into that particular question, I think we can presume that most of the dysfunctioning or malfunctioning which we find in patients at this level is actually painful and uncomfortable to them. If they are the type of patient which we are describing where there is a higher intellectual potential, it is certainly distasteful or painful to them, and the only reason they put up with it would seem to be that it is less painful than the corresponding socially accepted behavior or corresponding growth motivated behavior and, therefore, they have taken the least painful of two evils. It becomes the function of psychotherapy to demonstrate to the child that the growth motivated behavior can, in the long run, actually be the less painful and that thus more tension will be relieved and greater feelings of reward will be felt if growth motivated behavior is utilized rather than growth retarding behavior.

Interest in Personal Well-Being

The second factor, the development of an interest in one's personal well being, is highly related to the first and to the process of the therapist functioning as a model. This development of interest in personal well being is related to a side concept that the patient should come to realize that somebody cares, that he is not alone in the world, that he does not have to work through all his problems by himself, without any help from anyone else. Thus, it is a social world, he is part of it, and there are people here who are very much concerned with what he does, how he does it, and what his general feelings in the whole area are. This recognition that there is somebody besides himself who wants to know how he feels about a certain issue or how he approaches a certain situation is, for the most part, quite a revelation to this level patient. The very fact that he is functioning on such an extremely low level in spite of a higher potential, is indicative of the fact that he is so totally self-engrossed in his own problems that he has completely neglected any awareness of the surrounding world. Therefore, it becomes almost a shock to him to find that there is someone who wants to protect him from the fantasied evils of that world, or who cares what happens to him in his "struggle." Conversely, the patient who, because of extreme orthopedic handicap finds himself in a similar incapacitated state, again tends to feel extremely sorry for himself, compares himself with his surrounding peers who can walk, who can use their arms, who have finger control, and finds an easy outlet into feeling a complete martyr and using his disability as an excuse for doing almost nothing, even though it would be possible with proper motivation for him to do a great number of things by exercising his intelligence. Here again, the indication to him that someone really cares, that he is not in this condition because people are mad at him or because people do not like him, but rather because of factors which neither he nor the therapist can control; and that in spite of these factors the therapist still can like him, can help him, cares very much what he does, what happens to him, also hopefully will give the child new ambition, new spirit, and permit him to utilize the assets he does have in spite of the severity of the handicap.

Concept of "Self" and "Others"

In keeping with this is the third factor, the development of a sense of self and others leading to building of relationships. This is the development of a very primitive understanding of the relationship between the individual and his environment; primitive, in the sense that one does not expect the child to understand the interaction between the "*moi et milieu*" with which we would hope more sophisticated adults could deal, but rather the very simple understanding that he is a person, that there are people in the environment, and that the two are dependent on each other for continued functioning. This is something that can develop through a patient-therapist relationship, and makes it possible for therapy to go forward at this level. Here, we lead directly into the question of development of relationships which is still a major factor throughout this whole pattern. We will not spend any time with it at this point, since we've discussed it very thoroughly above, but merely wish to underline here that it is again a very important issue in terms of developing peer group activity.

These three elements are all very primitive, they all deal essentially with the individual discovering himself, discovering the world around him, and the form of psychotherapy best related to this kind of primitive discovery is the U-U form. The material and the approach being totally unstructured, so that in a sense there is nothing there but the therapist, the patient, and various and sundry globs of materials, produces the situation that whatever comes out of the play is totally the product of the interaction between the patient, the materials, and the therapist. The therapist's function is to make the patient realize that the interaction did produce whatever was produced, that if the patient wishes more to be produced, the interaction has to improve, if the patient does not care whether more is produced or not, then he is going to have to face the situation of being constantly intruded upon, not being permitted to perform even at the primitive level at which he wishes to perform. This, hopefully, is a more obnoxious situation than one in which the patient makes some effort to produce, thus changing the psychological atmosphere. We have no particular guarantees this will work. Actually, this is probably the weakest area of the theoretical construct that we are presenting, and we recognize that at least nine out of ten patients at this level who are brought into play therapy will not demonstrate any positive changes that could be attributed to an indication of successful therapy.[162] However, if we can salvage the tenth patient, we feel it makes the whole effort worthwhile, and we want to emphasize that this can be attempted, particularly through the use of the U-U method.[163] Where this does work, it creates readiness in the child for a level of independent functioning consistent with his general potential.

We have throughout this chapter discussed some of the broad social implications of the different adaptive behaviors. In keeping with this presentation of the broader social implications, we have discussed improving Adaptive Behavior, because the rehabilitation concept with which we opened this book would imply that Adaptive Behavior is not a static, stable diagnostic category, but rather represents the functioning of a child at the point in time when he comes into contact with the examiner and is, therefore, often reversible. The things that the child learns in the psychotherapy program are things which we hope to be able to transfer outside of the therapy room, and in the process thus improve the community impression, and as the community's impression improves, his levels of aspiration should go up and there should be then an active interrelationship between raising Adaptive Behavior levels and integrating into more structured training programs in terms of special education.[164] In this sense psychotherapy can be considered as producing readiness for further training. We have discussed this in Chapter VIII, in terms of the major functions of the S-S forms, but as we have illustrated throughout this chapter, even the U-U as the most primitive, and certainly the U-S and S-U forms can play a role in this preparation in terms of helping the child become better adjusted socially, and thus better able to receive what society has to give in terms of improved training and higher levels of functioning. Essentially he obtains a smaller share of what the milieu has to offer because he is unable to utilize all of the material that is made available to him. With this in mind, it becomes evident that psychotherapy aimed at raising the level of Adaptive Behavior is, in a sense, raising the child's ability to take from his environment the good things that his environment has to offer, and also helping him to be more selective so that he is in a position to reject without frustration and without confusion some of the bad things that he finds in his environment.[165] The next chapter will further explore this general point in terms of the more objective elements of the child's behavior and thinking as illustrated in terms of psychometric testing, and as described here in terms of levels of Measured Intelligence.

162. The experiences with diagnostic play (Chap. IX) have led to the above conclusions, but this should not be considered a rule because there have been noteworthy exceptions.

163. As we discuss in Chap. XIII, ancillary therapies such as Recreation or Music are often better suited to deal with the needs of this level child than play therapy.

ADDITIONAL NOTES

153. Heber, *op. cit.*, pp. 61, Adaptive Behavior has been defined as: "The effectiveness with which the individual copes with the natural and social demands of his environment. It has two major facets: (1) The degree to which the individual is able to function and maintain himself independently, and (2) the degree to which he meets satisfactorily the culturally-imposed demands of personal and social responsibility." See also Chap. IV, p. 148.

154. Jones, J. C., "The Concept of Adaptive Behavior in our Institutional Setting," Unpublished Master's thesis, Kansas State College of Pittsburg, Kans., 1963, passim; Leland, H., "Some Thoughts on the Current Status of Adaptive Behavior," *Mental Retardation*, 2:3, 1964, pp. 171-176.

155. Gunzburg, H. C., "Therapy and Social Training for the Feebleminded Youth," *Brit. J. of Med. Psych.*, 1957, 30, pp. 42-48, makes the even stronger statement that "mental deficiency, defined as social inadequacy is curable."

156. Jordan, T. E., *The Mentally Retarded*, Charles E. Merrill Books, Inc., Columbus, Ohio, 1961, p. 271, presents very similar thinking under a different rubric. He and others feel that some such concept must be utilized if we are to serve fully the retarded child.

157. We recognize that these and other considerations throughout this chapter have to be taken as broad generalities since no attempt has been made to correlate these behaviors to an age-critical schema. The need for such a schema is apparent to the authors, but will have to wait for more complete research in the area of Adaptive Behavior. This need is well described by Scott, J. P., "Critical Periods in Behavioral Development," *Science*, 1962, 1938, pp. 949-958, and in child development situations by Lebo (1958), *op. cit.*, Ilg, Frances, "Developmental Aspects of Child Behavior," *Amer. J. Public Health*, 1961, 51, pp. 1847-1852, and Leland, H., "Conference on Measurement of Adaptive Behavior," (Mimeographed), PSH&TC, 1964.

158. This note has been cited on page 161.

159. Sherif, M. and Sherif, Carolyn W., *An Outline of Social Psychology*, Rev. Ed., Harper & Row, N. Y., 1956, p. 82, expresses a similar idea and utilizes the concept of structure in a very similar manner.

160. Stewart, Kathleen & Axelrod, Pearl, "Group Therapy on a Children's Psychiatric Ward," *Amer. J. Orthopsychiat.*, 1947, 17, pp. 312-325, describe working with those types of groups. See also Leland, H. (1964) *op. cit.*, pp. 9-11.

161. Doll, E. A., *Measurement of Social Competence*, Educational Publishers, Inc., N. Y., 1953, pp. 96, *et passim*. Doll's work is still the best single description of the "independent functioning" component of Adaptive Behavior.

162. This note has been cited on page 168.

163. This note has been cited on page 168.

164. Abel, Theodora M., "Resistance and Difficulties in Psychotherapy of Mental Retardates," *J. Clin. Psych.*, 1953, 9, pp. 107-109, makes the point that "if one can enjoy the individuals one works with . . . the therapeutic results may be not less effective . . . than with more intelligent individuals." Our feeling is that treating the Adaptive Behavior will increase the enjoyment of the patient.

165. Secord, P. F. and Beckman, C. W., "Personality Theory and the Problem of Stability and Change in Individual Behavior: An Interpersonal Approach," *Psych. Review*, 1961, 68, pp. 21-32, review a number of the theories in this area and conclude that the stability of structure is a function of the behavior of others toward the individuals in question. It would follow that the reverse could also be true.

XI. Intelligence and the Use of Play Therapy

THE MEANING OF THE IQ TO THE PSYCHOTHERAPIST

As mentioned in the last chapter, the problems connected with play therapy are not specifically related to the patient's IQ. In this chapter we will discuss this problem, in terms of the whole question of intelligence as it relates to play therapy, and more specifically as it relates to the procedures of the psychotherapist on one hand, and the problems which the patients face on the other.

Ability of the Mentally Retarded to Profit from Play Therapy

We have already discussed the use of psychotherapy with the mentally retarded and at this time, we only want to reiterate the underlying premise on which we are basing this whole work, that the mentally retarded can benefit from play therapy. This premise, unfortunately, is contrary to some of the opinions in the field. For example, one of the more recent books on play therapy indicates that the mentally retarded ". . . show little awareness of the function of each toy and no inventiveness or variety in its use, they do not see the potentialities inherent in toys and do not understand the purpose for which materials are intended . . . their failure to learn even a simple task in a play situation is significant, they show little profit from instruction and do not seem to learn from repeated demonstrations or from experience."[166] This position is shared by many in the field and is doubly unfortunate because, as can be seen from the examples in the earlier chapters of this book, it is not true. Even if it were true, these "facts" as presented, would not specifically rule the mentally retarded out of play therapy, but merely out of the more traditional forms. In other words, it is the responsibility of the therapist to find a manner in which he may do psychotherapy. It is not the patients' fault that they are ill or mentally retarded and while we agree that it is often not the doctor's fault, nonetheless, it is the doctor's responsibility to try to figure out what to do about it.[167] Thus, nothing is gained by comparing the play therapy behavior of the retarded child with the play therapy behavior of the normal child, and by saying the retarded child is more deficient. We have already said that, by defining him as a retarded child. Thus, in play therapy the important consideration is to learn what the retarded child can do. Here, we find that the IQ as a specific criterion is a very poor indicator. Using the previous citation, some children of low intelligence do not know how to use toys, other children with exactly the same IQ do know how to use toys, and to base the estimation that the child will not know how to use toys because he has a certain IQ or because he has been defined as mentally retarded, becomes a very dangerous and harmful procedure in estimating who will be brought into therapy and who will not. Conversely, many children with normal intelligence also will not play with toys because of the nature of their emotional disturbance, and they certainly would not be ruled out of therapy because they did not play with toys. Rather, the therapist would observe the situation and try to work through with the child some means of getting him to communicate his fears and anxieties. Thus, we find ourselves in the position of saying that if the child has a low intelligence and will not play, he should be dropped from therapy, but if he has a high intelligence and will not play, he should be maintained in therapy, with the premise that there is a basic relationship between therapy and intelligence.[168] Granted, there is a relationship in terms of factors of communication, but there is no one-to-one relationship between the intelligence of a child and his feasibility for therapy.

Expected Gains from Psychotherapy

One of the difficulties that produces the above state of affairs is a lack of agreement on what is expected to come from a therapy situation. Unfortunately, much of the literature which reports on the validity of psychotherapy with the mentally retarded, has utilized as its main indicator the fact that the IQ has or has not been raised. In other words, the implication has been that psychotherapy is useful with the retarded if it somehow helps diminish the retardation. This might be termed the use of psychotherapy for cure. People defending the use of psychotherapy with the mentally retarded have been some of the worst offenders in this area. The senior author of this book has published such an article, and although he feels it makes a contribution, it may also have been misleading in its implication that somehow psychotherapy will raise the IQ.[169] This is not, and never should have been, the main consideration for psychotherapy. It is not the intention for play therapy at any time to effect a cure of the disorder. The child will probably leave the play therapy situation in just as retarded a state as he was when he went into it. Certainly the brain damaged child will be as brain damaged. If the child's problem is derivative of various kinds of congenital anomalies, he will be just as anomalous when he leaves play therapy. These are not the areas where treatment is expected, and any such expectations lead to the totally erroneous conclusion that psychotherapy is not indicated in those cases cited because no cure is possible, and thus where the primary problem is neurological defect or cultural deficiency or some other irreversible condition, the irreversibility defines the child out of therapy.[170] This is a very unfortunate situation, not because it is inaccurate—obviously play therapy is not going to reverse irreversible conditions—but because it is based on the entirely fallacious goal of cure or raising the IQ which is not the major source of gain in psychotherapy.[171]

A better goal is one of improving the patient's ability to adjust or adapt to his level of functioning as we have discussed in the chapter on Adaptive Behavior, to develop readiness for training areas, and further to develop a generally more happy, more contented type of living situation so that the child will be a more pleasant person to be around, etc. We have made all of these points previously and only reiterate them now because they are the major answer to the bugaboo that if IQ is not raised, then somehow the psychotherapy has been unsuccessful. The main point is that the feasibility of play therapy should be based on the goal of helping the individual become a more adapted person and of supporting his right as a human being to make some sort of social contribution.

Generally speaking, a refusal to engage in play therapy with a maladapted child because he has low intelligence and because there is no expectation that the intelligence will rise is, in essence, a refusal to give this child an opportunity to utilize in the best way possible the functional ability that he does possess. Further, we would like to remind critics in this area that *results do not have to be perfect to be useful.* It is always the hope of the therapist that the patient will leave therapy a more socially acceptable and more socially functioning person. It is always the hope of the physician that the function of biological medicine will produce a physically whole person. However, it would be inconceivable for a physician to refuse to treat a patient because he did not feel that he could turn out a physically whole specimen, and it should be equally inconceivable for a psychotherapist to refuse to treat a patient just because he does not feel he can turn out a mentally whole specimen. Partial success, partial improvement in general adaptation, should be sufficient reward to the psychotherapist in the play situation to permit a very clear-cut claim that these patients were very properly given this service.

Availability of Community Services

At the moment, many community areas refuse to work with certain levels of retarded children. Here we find that the major meaning of the IQ to the psychotherapist is as a label or classification rather than merely additional information. Thus, if the mentally retarded child has difficulty in school for behavioral reasons and needs special help, suggestions are immediately made that he be institutionalized. If he does not have a low IQ, then special plans are made for some sort of therapy or special work to try to correct the situation. It is our experience, as we have already cited and as many others have cited, that the child with the lower IQ can also benefit from these therapies and special work. To decide that he should be in an institution is doing both him and the community a major disservice.[172] It is doing the child a major disservice because it is not permitting him to develop and utilize his potential. It is doing the community a major disservice because it is taking one more productive hand out of the community and putting it onto the tax rolls. Thus, this whole attitude actually becomes one of community blindness in the very area where the community as a whole could be of service to itself. These decisions are usually made in terms of the IQ, that is the numerical score, rather than the child's functioning. Thus, many states still have laws which exclude children from special education below a certain IQ, and which proscribe other services to children below a certain IQ, etc. This is extremely shortsighted and as we are pointing out, is extremely expensive to the community in the long run, because certainly full time residential care is much more expensive and a much greater drain on the tax resources of the community than partial services of a rehabilitative nature. This becomes even worse when the same criteria are applied by community mental health centers. Here we have a child who, except for an emotional disturbance, has been able to survive in a community and if this emotional disturbance can be handled in a corrective sense, he could remain in the community. Yet by refusing him service, the child will become more emotionally disturbed and even if he is then given the privilege of special education or other rehabilitative procedures, he will not be able to benefit as readily from them, and the whole process will break down. Thus, the problems of emotional disturbance and psychological maladjustment cannot be separated from the general question of mental retardation. The retarded child has as much right as anyone else to become emotionally disturbed, and he has as much right as anyone else to have these disturbances treated regardless of his measured IQ or the etiology of his condition.

Our responsibility is not to define him out of services, but to decide what particular special means or special processes can be utilized. Thus, for the present, measured intelligence has served the function of (1) permitting some psychotherapists to decide that many children were not feasible for therapy; (2) ruling out psychotherapy as a mode of treatment because the basic measurement of retardation, the IQ, was thought not to be affected by psychotherapy; and (3) using the measured intelligence as a way of differentiating between those to whom community services would be available and those to whom they would not be as readily available. These three distortions of the IQ have given the whole idea of measured intelligence a black eye in the minds of anyone who is sincerely interested in the rehabilitation of the mentally retarded, and have led to a continuous and often shortsighted bombardment of the IQ as being totally useless and extremely destructive of the retarded individual even to the extent of many forward looking workers stating that the IQ has no function whatsoever. The present authors feel that the IQ does have a function in the measurement of academic achievement and potential academic placement, and that simply because it has been misused in the area of mental retardation, does not mean that it is not a valid classification area for other processes. But, we must emphasize that the abuse of the concept of intelligence, particularly in the area of the treatment of emotional disturbance, has led to a tremendous waste of human resources and this should and must be corrected.[173]

MEASURED INTELLIGENCE AND ADAPTIVE BEHAVIOR

In discussing this element with less emotion, we have to look first at the differences between measured intelligence as a behavioral classification and adaptive behavior as a behavioral classification. Since both are presented in the *Manual*[174] on the classification of mental retardation, there is the obvious intention to consider them as separate and distinct dimensions. We find that it is most useful, at least in the treatment of the emotionally disturbed child, to continue to treat these concepts as separate and distinct dimensions, both having a role but also overlapping as separate parts of a single whole which we may call intelligence. In other words, it is our feeling that measured intelligence is merely one aspect of intelligence, that aspect which the tests measure, while adaptive behavior is another aspect of intelligence, that aspect relating to coping with environmental demands. It can be argued, and we would certainly accept, that part of the problem of coping with environmental demands is based on the elements measured by intelligence tests, and also that many of the processes relating to learning the material which a measured intelligence scale measures are based on the manner in which the child has coped; so the two concepts certainly interlock.

Distinguishing Measured Intelligence from Adaptive Behavior

However, there are differences in the processes. One of the most important differences to the person interested in rehabilitation and treatment is the fact that Measured Intelligence is based primarily on the average behavior of most children of a similar chronological age. As long as the child is behaving like an average child, this creates no difficulty. It does not even create difficulty if he deviates only slightly from the average, so that the amount of deviation can be absorbed by slight modifications in approach. But it creates a major difficulty if the deviation from the average is so great that he no longer resembles the average child. Here, the thought has been that if he has an IQ of 50, then he can do half as much as the average child or, if he has an IQ of 25, then he can do only a quarter as much as the average child. This may be true if we are thinking in terms of specific training areas, and certainly, measured intelligence is probably still the best single indicator of the potential success of a child in those areas of training which are represented by the qualities which the tests use to measure intelligence. Thus, it could certainly be fair to say that a child with a 50 IQ based on a vocabulary test knew only half as many words as a child with a 100 IQ based on a vocabulary test, and on down the line. And if the whole problem in training was one of training vocabulary, it would be fair to say that a child with a 50 IQ since he had not in the past learned as many words, potentially would not learn as many words in the future, all else being equal. If further, we have information that the reason he did not learn as many words in the past was because of certain physical or cultural factors which blocked and prevented his learning those words, and these physical and cultural factors could not be removed, we could be fairly sure that he probably would not learn those words in the future, and so if the whole question is one of learning a vocabulary, the IQ is a perfectly good measure. Thus, we can say very clearly that when we are defining a child in terms of the particular kind of training group into which we are placing him, the IQ measure is an important measure and one which should be known in advance so that the training in the group, whether it be college preparation for the gifted child, or job preparation for the retarded child, can go forward along the lines most fitting the particular training needs. However, since, as has also been discovered in working with normal children, the fact that they have the potential to succeed in a particular training area in no way indicates that this success will occur and thus, while the gifted child may at the age of ten potentially look like most college graduates, there is certainly no basis to predict that at an older age he will in fact graduate from college. Also, in terms of other predictions relating to training groups,[175] there is nothing in the IQ which would in any way imply success in the area, nor is there anything in the IQ which would in any way indicate how the child would be able to relate to other people or to cope with environmental pressures while a part of the training group. Now this becomes the function of the measurement of Adaptive Behavior. While it is also true that the level of Adaptive Behavior will not predict success in the particular area, it will give some indication as to how the child copes with his environment and it is hoped that a combination of these two sources of information will give us some indication as to potential success, again all else being equal.

Since Adaptive Behavior is related to coping procedures, we can say that Adaptive Behavior is also related to treatment, because the major role of psychotherapy is one of improving coping behavior. Thus, it becomes clear that the psychotherapist has to be less involved with the IQ of the patient, and more aware of his level of Adaptive Behavior. This means that while Adaptive Behavior and IQ have a relationship, they also have a difference and the psychotherapist and particularly the play therapist, is most interested in the Adaptive Behavior. We say particularly the play therapist, because the question of Adaptive Behavior with children seems to have more positive meaning at the moment than with adults. That is to say, with adults, normally the problem of independent functioning does not arise except with profoundly retarded or regressed individuals. However, the problem of independent functioning is a normal developmental question with children and is, of course, a major problem in play therapy as well as elsewhere because a child with extremely limited independent functioning creates difficulties in being able to do enough for the play therapy to go forward. Again, as we have pointed out, the U-U form is particularly contrived for this group but, nonetheless, this still creates difficulties for the therapist, which have to be overcome. Therefore, it is extremely important that the play therapist, in planning his therapy program, be aware of the level of Adaptive Behavior of his patient, but it is only of relative importance that he be aware of the patient's IQ.

In this instance we might say that measured intelligence, which by definition is the result of some sort of psychometric procedure, is based on objective reality from standardization procedures, while Adaptive Behavior, since it is based on popular reality[176] is more related to the types of information one would get from a projective device. Thus, we see that we are dealing with the usual relationship between therapy and testing, i.e., the utilization of projective information for decisions concerning therapy goals rather than psychometric information.

Finding Adequate Modes of Communication

All of the foregoing would seem to imply that in reality the psychotherapist has only a very mild interest in the measured intelligence of the child. There is, however, one specific area where he has to become more aware of intelligence as such, and that is in finding adequate modes of communication. It can certainly be accepted that a therapist has a major interest in the ability of his patient to communicate. The whole process of play therapy is based on an intercommunication between the therapist and the patient, so that the material with which the patient is playing can be brought to a level of under-

176. *Popular reality*, as we are using the term, refers to verbal and nonverbal perceptions by individuals in response to environmental stimuli as modified by cognitive processes. These perceptions are considered to be controlled as much by social and cultural conceptualizations as by the objective elements of the stimulus, e.g., an individual wearing vertical stripes looks slimmer than the same person wearing checks, although the objective size is identical in both instances. Thus, there seems to be popular agreement (though this may be based on optical illusions or other false sensory impressions) that certain "truths" are real as perceived, even though there is no objective basis for them. This fact leads to such conceptions as "psychological reality" or "social reality," etc., versus objective reality, and we have chosen to summarize these concepts under the rubric of popular reality, because they seem to gain their "realness" through some sort of consensus.

standing and cognition. Obviously, an inadequately communicating person[177] produces therapy problems which the high communicating person may not and, in terms of the therapist's preparation for play therapy with specific patients, measured intelligence is one of the potential indicators of the child's communication level. This is not to imply that children with higher IQ's necessarily communicate better than children with low IQ's once one reaches the retarded range, but rather that children with higher IQ's probably have a higher potential for communication at a verbal level than do children with lower IQ's. We would differentiate here between the high potential for communication at a verbal level and high potential for other forms of communication, because children with low IQ's may, in the long run, communicate just as well as children with high IQ's, but through the use of gestures and other substitute behaviors. One of the unwritten goals of psychotherapy is that the child should be brought to function at the highest level of which he is capable at that time. This is not to reintroduce the old idea of capacity which certainly has no place in any concepts of therapy or growth procedures, but rather to simply recognize that the therapist's responsibility in regard to the child is never to accept low functioning as an end product, but to be constantly aiming for slightly higher functioning. This again is not to indicate that the goal of psychotherapy is to raise the IQ, because as we pointed out, the areas of functioning with which we are dealing are most related to Adaptive Behavior which has already been discussed as a reversible dimension. Thus, it is possible that the child will be better adapted without in any way being more intelligent as the tests measure it. The therapist's job in terms of setting a goal based on raising the functioning level of the child is not one of finding ways to improve the IQ, but rather finding ways to improve the manner in which the child copes, and one of the major aspects of coping is communication.[178] Therefore, the problems of communication become part and parcel of the total problems of play therapy. This is particularly true of the forms utilized in this book, because so much is dependent on the patient's response to the intrusion of the therapist, that some communication based on "forcing the child to think" must be derived from each of the four forms. The therapist, however, must have some expectation as to the level of communication he should expect, and the best guide for this expectation is the measured intelligence of the subject.

Another factor in the same area is a matter of getting the child to utilize the particular aptitudes and abilities which he possesses in a manner which will produce more realistic levels of aspiration. The ability to deal with specific aptitudes or the knowledge of certain abilities is important to the therapist, and one of the best ways he can judge these is again through the level of intelligence of the child. Thus, we would presume that a child with a fairly high IQ would probably possess more aptitudes than a child with a comparatively low IQ.[179] There is no need to know what aptitudes specifically are possessed, as part of the function of the therapist is to derive knowledge of these aptitudes through the play procedure, but he does have a better idea of the type of thing he is looking for if he knows what the intelligence level is. Having this knowledge, however, and thus making his long range therapy plans, he no longer has any specific need to refer back to intelligence. Thus, we might say that knowledge of the level of intelligence of the child is extremely important to the therapist as he is developing his plans for the therapy program, but this loses its importance after the plans have been laid and the program has started. All of this is related to the more theoretical constructs which we have already offered concerning the role of cognition. Thus, we might say that intelligence for the play therapist can best be defined in terms of efficiency and versatility, recognizing also that factors relative to activation and reactivation of memory, (questions relating to environmental structure) are all part and parcel of the total process with which the play therapist is dealing.[180] These qualities, while not specifically measured by tests of intelligence, nonetheless are implied in the subtest patterns of those tests, which if utilized from the point of view of analysis of processes, provide a fair measure of the type of cognitive procedures of which the child is capable at this point in time. We recognize again that this data is not necessarily information, because ten different children each taking the same test and each having the same score, may have accumulated this score through a different relationship of subtests. Thus, merely looking at the IQ will not tell us that the ten children are different, have different cognitive processes, or have different thought patterns, but the subtest patterns and the manner in which the IQ's were derived, will give us a fairly usable picture of what these thought processes are, at least in the areas measured by the test. This becomes information as vitally important to the play therapist as it is to the person interested in training and rehabilitation. Further, since play therapy usually occurs during some of the critical developmental periods, if the therapist were to ignore the mode or cognitive style of his particular patient,[181] he would not only slow down the therapy processes, but more importantly, would tend to confuse the child, who would be under the impression that the therapist was expecting certain things from him which he did not quite understand, and was rejecting what he was offering, creating new failure experiences. Thus, for example, if the child's processes were related more to highly concrete fact orientation than to more abstract generalities and the therapist was constantly insisting on some sort of generality by his intrusions, the child might easily get the impression that his preoccupation with facts was not acceptable to the therapist and thus become further disturbed and disillusioned in the therapy process. But if the therapist understood that it was necessary to deal with highly concrete facts, and that if he wanted the child to generalize he was going to have to condition this process, then he could approach the child in such a way as to eliminate this disappointment and confusion and probably, in the long run, be able to achieve a much better therapeutic success. Thus, while it is said in a jocular vein that the psychotherapist tries to remake his patient in his own image, this is not always a joke. The therapist, functioning as a model, quite often has a tendency to reflect the patient's behavior in the light of his own personal experience and presumes that the patient will be able to respond to these experiences in a manner similar to the way in which the therapist responded to them. This is not an unhealthy or even improper expectation from a normal child given some amount of cultural continuity; however, it is a totally improper expectation from a retarded child because if the retarded child had been able to respond to stimulus cues in the manner in which the therapist had responded, the retarded child also would be on the road to becoming a Ph.D. Therefore, this tendency toward remaking the patient in his own image is one which the therapist working with the retarded child must completely eliminate from his thinking, and he must replace it with a concept of trying to find the particular cognitive patterns which his patients utilize best and then try to rework the situation around them, again aiming at the highest possible functional level within the current potentials of his patient. Since this is extremely difficult for the therapist because he does not have experiential guides (he himself has not been there once) it becomes even more important that he learn to put himself in the shoes of the patient and a greater emphasis must be placed on his ability to empathize, and to understand his patient's capabilities. Thus, measured intelligence becomes a tool which the therapist can use to provide information in an area where he has no personal experience other than the experience with similar patients.

POTENTIAL MEANING OF INTELLIGENCE TO THE PATIENT

Awareness of Social Differences

One other aspect of this problem which must be considered is the meaning of intelligence to the patient himself. Obviously the patient does not know what his IQ is and would not know what it meant if he did know; but the patient does have clear cut knowledge of intellectual differences and to him the problem of definition is no problem. That is to say, he is not faced with the question of what intelligence is and what aspect of it is measured and what aspect of it is not. To him intelligence is a simple matter of individuals who are able to do certain things and learn certain things in a similar manner versus individuals who are not able and cannot learn. In a school situation the child who gets his school work is intelligent, and the person who does not is "dumb," and it is almost that simple as far as the school child is concerned. That in reality, he may be emotionally disturbed, has no meaning to him. Thus, the fact of measured intelligence is not the issue; what is the issue is the behavior of the child in relationship to his peers; and the etiology of this behavior is not what concerns him, but rather how he looks to his peers and how his peers look to him in terms of peer groupings on one hand and social and adult expectations on the other. Thus, the first meaning of intelligence to the patient is translated in terms of what he is able to do, what he has seen himself do, what he has seen other children do, and how this compares. This is an extremely important meaning of intelligence to the patient, and for someone to say that this has no bearing, that the patient should not worry about whether he is intelligent or not, is in the sense of popular reality highly unrealistic, because the patient will only learn to distrust the adult since the adult is saying in effect, "I am not worried about your intelligence, therefore, you should not be worried about your intelligence," and the patient reads this to say that "I am not worried about the things you are worried about." Since the patient wants the adult to be worried about the things which he worries about, this becomes another form of rejection. If, on the other hand, the adult makes an overissue of the patient's intelligence, not in terms of any comparisons which the patient is making himself but in terms of adult comparisons, again the patient feels rejected because he feels that the adult is finding that he cannot do certain things, in other words, confirming his own observations that he cannot do certain things. Also, he feels that the adult is criticizing him for this failure and since he knows that he cannot do them, he feels he should not be criticized because this is not a matter of laziness or not trying, but rather that he just cannot do them. The important thing for the therapist to understand is that this aspect of the question of intelligence is extremely important to the patient; however, the therapist himself cannot make an issue of it without carrying on the criticism that the patient has already received in school or elsewhere. At the same time, he has to accept the patient's making an issue of it because it is an extremely important thing to the patient and the therapist must empathize with this. Thus, the process is not one of deciding "is the patient really that retarded or is he really something else," but rather a matter of the therapist finding out how intelligent the patient thinks he is and starting from that point to help the patient develop a better self-concept, a more useful intellectual functioning, and the two of them can work together for an improved relationship.

Problems in Decision Making

Related to the patient's concept of his own intelligence is the daily evidence that he has difficulties. The primary difficulty arises around decision making. Here, we again have different levels of function; there are some patients sufficiently retarded that they do not realize a decision has to be made and here the problem of intelligence is not one of making the right decisions, but being constantly annoyed by not having known that a decision had to be made and, therefore, finding themselves in bad social standing because a decision was not made. In other words, their constant plaint is that nobody told them, or they didn't know what to do, or something of this sort. The play therapist has a problem of teaching the child that there are such things as decisions to be made, and he must set up play situations which are constantly requiring the child to make decisions while at the same time not going beyond the child's ability to conceptualize. Thus, the therapist may be faced with a child who does not know that there are decisions to be made and he may have this child in a U-U or S-U form of therapy. He obviously is not going to introduce decision making at this stage but will postpone it until he has completed the goals of this therapy and then entering into either the U-S or S-S form, will introduce structure requiring decisions. However, eventually it is part of the goal of play therapy to deal with decision making factors since the questions of discrimination and selectivity are all part of the Adaptive Behavior of the child and this is one of the treatment responsibilities of the therapy situation. Beyond that, however, is a major problem of a child who knows a decision has to be made, but has not learned how to weigh social cues sufficiently to make a decision and, therefore, finds himself hung up on various possibilities. This problem is illustrated by an experience the senior author had with a group of children from an institution for the mentally retarded who were taken on an excursion to a large city. As part of the excursion they were brought to a cafeteria for lunch and for the first time in their lives were faced with a problem of more than one main dish to choose. This became a major trauma to some of the patients who stood and stared at the variety of food without being able to even look like they were going to make a decision. Other patients, knowing well that a decision had to be made and feeling the extreme social pressure of other individuals in the cafeteria line, tried to deal with the question by taking something of everything, which is, of course, another way of not making the decision. Part of this is the effect of institutionalization where the child can live twenty-four hours a day without ever making a decision, e.g., he is told when to get up in the morning, what to wear, what to do at each stage of the period, when to go to breakfast, he is handed the food that he is to eat, he is told at what speed to eat it, and when to return to the cottage, where to go after that, etc., and the child can survive if he desires on a complete day by day basis without ever having made a decision. This leads to the phenomena which has been described as overinstitutionalization, and one of the major problems in play therapy in residential settings is to introduce decision making to the overinstitutionalized child in an effort to break down this additional separation from the outside community and thus make him a more feasible rehabilitation candidate. This clearly has nothing to do with the actual intelligence of the child, as anyone in contact with an institution knows that some of the most over-institutionalized patients are those who fall into the mild or borderline retarded group, but have over the years become staid institutional workers and cannot conceive of life anywhere outside of that protected environment. Our function in working with children is to prevent this from occurring and, therefore, the whole problem of the child's inability to make decisions which is by implication a feeling on his part that he does not have the intelligence to make the right decision, is something that the therapist must help the child overcome.

Problems in Planning for Future

The final aspect of the effect of intelligence on the patient himself is based on his ability to plan for his own future. He may never have really thought about this question and it may even come as a shock to him that anybody would raise it. As most psychologists have experienced in evaluating retarded children, the question of "What do you want to be when you grow up?" usually produces either the ambiguous kind of answer, "I don't know," or "I haven't thought about it," etc., or the usual fantasy answer such as a "fireman," "policeman," or a "nurse" or "doctor," but very rarely does it produce any answer which the child has thought out. No one expects a child at the age at which children are usually brought into play therapy to have thought these things out. That is no one would expect a normal child of eight, nine or ten to have thought out what he wants to be when he grows up. However, a normal child is usually, when asked this question, able under prodding to give the problem some thought and it is thus fairly simple to move from the declaration that he wants to be a policeman to a question of what his father does and would he like to do the sort of thing that his father does, or would he like to do something different, and it is not at all unusual for the child to decide that he wants to be like his uncle or his father, or someone else with whom he identifies and then to pick an actual trade or profession different and more realistically oriented than the fantasy answer which was first elicited. However, the retarded child is not usually able to make this kind of transfer and will remain either with the fantasy answer or will become extremely confused and extremely disturbed if the fantasy answer is in anyway challenged or questioned. Not only does this failure to plan apply to long-range goals, but, even in terms of the child knowing what he would like to do tomorrow, there is again this type fantasy production which produces disturbance and annoyance if it is in any way challenged. This is further contaminated by the situation in the institution where the child may seem to give a very logical and well thought out answer because his answer for tomorrow is based on today, and since the institutional routine is set, he may readily say that tomorrow he wants to go swimming because tomorrow happens to be swimming day, and has been swimming day for the last six months. Thus, it would seem that he had actually planned for the future but in reality the planning had all been done and he had simply learned the schedule. Thus, again the effect of low intelligence on the patient is to limit his ability to conceive or cast himself beyond his present reality and since the whole process of coping with the environment is dependent both on the patient having been there once and also on his being able to predict what may occur, this planlessness has to be dealt with to some extent in the play therapy situation. We are not pretending that the child is consciously saying "I don't have the intellectual potential to plan," but he is in a sense saying to himself that anything that he has wanted to do has failed, and that he has never been able to really achieve what he wanted, so what is the point of trying. It seems to make more sense, in terms of his previous experience, to simply take things as they come, and this having been well conditioned into him long before the therapist ever sees him, the usual result of the therapist's attempt to get the child to plan is one of drawing a complete blank or a reaction of anger or disturbance. The therapist again must know how intelligent the child thinks he is, he must know what the child thinks he is capable of, and then starting from that try to demonstrate to the child that things which the child plans for in therapy either are able to be brought about, or the reasons why they could not be brought about must be made sufficiently clear to the child that he feels that he participated in the event not occurring, and thus helped plan the outcome. Thus, the therapist by utilizing the intellectual level at which the child thinks he is working, is able to get the child to feel that he has a stake in the future, that he has something to say about how the future is brought about and that, therefore, there might be some point in trying to plan for the future.

In this chapter we have attempted to describe some of the relationships of intelligence to play therapy, we have been highly critical of previous positions taken by many individuals concerning the role of intelligence and play therapy, particularly in regard to the feeling that low intelligence is a counter indication for the use of play therapy. We have also discussed Measured Intelligence and Adaptive Behavior as two separate aspects of the total quality of intelligence, and tried to demonstrate how they are different on one hand but related on the other, and how the play therapist has a use for both in working through his program.[182] Finally, we have discussed the potential meaning of intelligence to the patient. It is this last aspect which is the most important consideration for the therapist, because regardless of how intelligent the patient actually is, it is how intelligent he thinks he is which defines what will happen in the therapy situation in relation to problems of coping or decision making and of planning. While these three areas are not specific goals in any single form of play therapy, they are nevertheless implied or subsumed goals in all forms of play therapy and therefore are of extreme importance to the therapist in terms of his developing an understanding of his relationship with the patient.

ADDITIONAL NOTES

166. Ginott (1961), *op. cit.*, pp. 45-46.

167. This concept should be considered the underlying basis for all play therapy. The therapist assumes the responsibility of seeking entrance into his patient's world, rather than saying, "He is not part of my world, therefore, I won't try to treat him." This idea has been best expressed by Virginia Axline (1950), *op. cit.*, pp. 68-75. "Play therapy is a safety zone where a child can try out his self."

168. Many workers in the field have previously reached a similar conclusion and, in fact, this approach goes back a number of years as can be seen from the span of the references we selected here. (We don't know why this is still an area of controversy, but we suspect that it is related to the general neglect of the problem of mental retardation which only recently has become an area of national concern.):

Glassman, Lillian "Is Dull Normal Intelligence a Contraindication for Psychotherapy?" *Smith College Stud. in Soc. Work*, 1943, 13, 275-298; Miller, Helen F., "Play Therapy for the Institutional Child," *Nervous Child*, 1948, 7, 311-317; Kanner, L., "Emotional Interference with Intellectual Functioning," *AJMD*, 1952, 56, 701-707; Wilcox, G. T. and Guthrie, G. M., "Changes in Adjustment of Institutionalized Female Defectives Following Group Psychotherapy," *Jr. Clin. Psych.*, 1957, 13, 9-13; Boston, J. A., Jr., "The Defective Child, His Family and the Use of Child Guidance Clinic," *Amer. Jr. of Public Health*, 1960, 50, 799-802; Gallagher, J. J., "Developments in Psychological Theory and Knowledge Relevant to Mental Retardation," *AJMD*, 1961, 65, 644-647; Chess, Stella "Psychiatric Treatment of the Mentally Retarded Child with Behavior Problems," A. Jr. *Orthopsychiat.*, 1962, 32, 863-869; Schachter, Frances F., Meyer, Lucille R., and Loomis, E. A. J., "Childhood Schizophrenia and Mental Retardation: Differential Diagnosis Before and After One Year of Psychotherapy," *A. Jr. Orthopsychiat.*, 1962, 32, 584-594.

169. Leland, et al, (1959) *op. cit.*, also typical of this approach is the still useful study by Ricciuti, Florence B., "A Study in Differential Diagnosis Using a Modified Play Technique," *Training School Bull.*, 1954, 51, 135-145.

170. Sternlicht, M., "A Theoretical Model for the Psychological Treatment of Mental Retardation," *AJMD*, 68, 1964, pp. 618-622.

171. Though not referring specifically to the mentally retarded, Hobbs, N., "Sources of Gain in Psychotherapy," *Amer. Psych.*, 1962, 17, 741-747, outlines the areas of "gain" as follows: 1. Therapeutic relationship, i.e., sustained experience of intimacy with another human being without getting hurt; 2. Helping divest verbal and other symbols of their anxiety producing potential; 3. Transference relationship; 4. Opportunities to practice decision making, to learn to be responsible for himself; to develop a concept of himself . . . ; and 5. Cognitive processes.

It is clear that these apply equally well to play therapy with the mentally retarded as we have defined it.

172. Schachter, et al, *op. cit.*, includes a discussion by Spotnitz, H., where he stated that "The need for institutionalization of children with mental and emotional conditions will

eventually decrease, I believe, as we continue to develop our skills in psychotherapy," p. 594-595.

173. Zazzo, R., "Qu'est-ce que la débilité mentale?" *La Raison*, Paris, 16, 1959, 5-18, gives an excellent discussion of this question and puts tests and the IQ into a more appropriate context.

174. Heber (1961), *op. cit.*, pp. 55-56.

175. The difficulty in coming to grips with this question is best represented by the highly inconclusive article by Bayley, Nancy "On The Growth of Intelligence," *Amer. Psychol.*, 1955, 10, pp. 805-818.

176. This note has been cited on page 176.

177. Spradlin, J. E., Assessment of Speech and Language of Retarded Children: Parsons Language Sample, *J. of Speech and Hearing Disorders*, Mono. Suppl. 10, 1963, 8-31 & 32; also, Spradlin, J. E. and Rosenberg, S., Parsons Project Working Paper No. 18, 1959 (unpublished) Bureau of Child Research, Lawrence, Kansas, discusses different levels of verbal communication and some of their possible relationships to rehabilitation. Also, Zazzo (1959), *loc. cit.*, cites a letter from Luria which underlines the fact that the intelligence of the retarded cannot be considered globally, but must be seen as different functions existing at different levels.

178. Milgram, N. A. and Furth, H. G., "The Influence of Language on Concept Attainment in Educable Retarded Children," presented annual meeting AAMD, N. Y., 1962, (mimeographed) underlines the importance of speech development in cognition.

179. There is no intention here to imply that the retarded IQ is permanent or unchangeable. The classic studies of Clarke and Clarke have already refuted that error. We are merely saying that if conditions are equal, the differences in IQ must be considered to have some meaning. Clarke, A. D. B. and Clarke, A. M., "Cognitive Changes in the Feebleminded," *British J. Psych.*, 1954, 45, pp. 173-179; and Clarke, A. D. B., Clarke, A. M., and Reiman, S., "Cognitive and Social Changes in the Feebleminded . . . Three Further Studies," *British J. Psych.*, 1958, 49, pp. 144-157.

180. Mark, H. J., "Elementary Thinking and the Classification of Behavior," *Science*, 1962, 135, pp. 75-87. The authors consider this an extremely important article in setting a theoretical framework for the relationship of intelligence and behavior.

181. Hurtig, M. C., Merlet, L., Santucci, H. and Zazzo, R., "An Experimental Examination of the Concepts of Mental Deficiency," in *Proceedings of the London Conference*, Vol. II, 1960, *op. cit.*, pp. 650-658, discuss the relationship between IQ's and "growth rhythms" as part of development. Also, Solley, C. M. and Murphy, G., *Development of the Perceptual World*, N. Y., Basic Books, Inc., 1960, present a well worked out table listing the contributions of Piaget, Werner, Lewin, Schilder, Bleuler and Rappaport to the "developmental stages in cognition," pp. 132-133.

182. We have not attempted an exposition of the whole question of intelligence, and we suggest that the reader who is interested in a more thorough analysis of the broader aspects of these problems refer to some of the following: Hunt, J. McV., (1961), *op. cit.*, Inhelder, B., *Le Diagnostic du raisonnement chez les debiles menteaux*. Thése #102, Delacheaut and Niestle, S. A., Neuchatel: Switzerland, 1943; Piaget, J., *The Origins of Intelligence in Children*, International Universities Press, N. Y., 1952 (Margaret Cook, trans.) Wallon, H., *Les origines de la pensee chez l'enfant*, Presses Universitaires de France, Paris, 1945, 2 vols; Woodward, Mary, "The Application of Piaget's Concepts to Mental Deficiency," *Proceedings of London Conference*, Vol. II, *op. cit.*, pp. 437-443; Zazzo, R., *Le Devenir de l'Intelligence*, Presses Universitaires de France, Paris, 1946.

XII. The Relationship of the Child in Play Therapy to His Milieu

When the child is brought into a therapy situation, regardless of the origin of the referral, he has to be considered a "captive patient." That is, he has not come voluntarily. We do not expect young children to come knocking at our doors saying, "Doctor help me, I'm sick"; they have to be brought by their parents. Often they are quite negative and quite often they are protesting at the "top of their lungs." The parents themselves, not having been trained in the processes of therapy are also often negative. They want to know what is going to go on, what is this "peculiar" thing that has been recommended to them. They often feel that whatever has happened with their child is considered their fault. They have read the various articles in popular magazines, newspapers, etc., which indicate that there is no such thing as a sick child, but "only sick parents," and so their bringing the child to the therapist is a tacit admission, in their eyes, that they are "sick." The therapist may develop a type of relationship with the parents which, to some extent, may even reinforce this projected feeling. This is unfortunate, but since we must consider the child in his total milieu, the parents have to be part of the picture.[183]

CHILD-PARENT RELATIONSHIPS

The first aspect that has to be considered is the basic relationship of the parent to the child. The treatment cannot go forward unless parents have some understanding of this relationship.[184] When the relationship of the child to his milieu is such that he has to be brought into therapy, one has to presume that this has also had an effect on the parents. Not only have they felt guilty, as indicated above, but they may have been criticized by teachers, neighbors, inlaws, relatives, etc., and so, from certain standpoints, they have been made to feel more guilty and more resentful by this criticism than by the child's actual behavior. They are defensive, not only toward the therapist, but also toward the child. The child's behavior becomes self-reinforcing because the parents expect him to behave in a particular way. He finds that this is the way he gets attention, and he may even find that this is the way he gets the parent's indulgence. Since they may have read a book or an article which indicated that they are never supposed to be "rejecting," they may have become overly loving or overly indulgent when the child acts in a particular way, because they are afraid that if they spank or discipline him, they will be "rejecting" and he will get worse. This results in his becoming "worse" because, if he is given approbation and love for what he knows is disturbing behavior, his confusion will be increased and he will be driven to more extensive tests in an attempt to resolve his confusion, while at the same time he continues behaving in ways which have proven to be rewarding. Parents who have become confused and uncertain, also have a tendency to move from one extreme to the other in dealing with their children's irritating behavior so that the emotionally disturbed child may find that a behavior will produce a slap and the next time it will produce a piece of candy, or a bribe, or a kiss. A child with normal intelligence in this situation becomes conniving and often extremely successful at figuring out ways to earn the candy and avoid the slap. A child who is functionally retarded becomes increasingly emotionally disturbed because he is not successful at earning the candy and avoiding the slap, and thus this tendency toward increasing confusion overrules the fact that a couple of times he came out ahead.[185]

Here, we will consider that group of children who have some degree of functional retardation. Regardless of measured intelligence, their behavior, whether in the classroom or in the neighborhood, is something less than the teacher or the neighbors would want. Parents of these children frequently say, "My child isn't retarded, he's emotionally ill," as though there was some sort of special blessing to being emotionally ill rather than retarded. On the other hand there are parents who say, "My child is not emotionally ill, he's just mentally retarded." Usually this second group of parents have been in a community where there has been an education campaign concerning the nature of mental retardation, and they have responded in this manner. The parents not only say this to the therapist, but the child himself is also made aware of the parent's attitude, and feels that he is regarded as "dumb" or "crazy." Thus, there is the necessity of getting the parents to shift their attitude in regard to the child so that the function of therapy, regardless of what form is used, may go forward fairly freely with some possibility of success.[186]

Casework with Parents

Work with parents is another form of psychotherapy, though it would fit into the category of counseling therapy.[187] However, the concept of casework is preferable over the more general concept of psychotherapy, because in working with the parents one is not dealing directly with the patient's own problem, but rather with the parent's relationship to the patient's problem. That problems centering around the parent's emotional life may break through during the casework sessions certainly cannot be ignored, and when they do the caseworker or therapist has the responsibility of dealing with them. But this casework, nonetheless, is based primarily on working with the parents in terms of the day to day needs of the child rather than specifically with their own emotional needs. However, by casework we do not mean to imply that only the social worker does it. Certainly, a social worker may do it, and in many of the traditional child guidance centers, etc., the social worker is expected to do it. However, there is no particular reason why a psychologist or a psychiatrist or any of the other trained personnel working with children cannot do it, and the term casework is used, to emphasize that the orientation is toward the child rather than the parents.[188]

Part of the casework should be trying to help the parents understand the child's relationship to them, and part should be trying to help the parents understand their relationship to the child. This includes a vast area. There are some investigators, for example, who talk in terms of bringing a whole family into psychotherapy if one member appears sick.[189] The logic behind this is essentially that mental illness, as defined, is a relationship of the individual to his milieu, the child's most specific milieu is his family, if the child's relationship to his family is a "sick" relationship, then the whole family must in some way have contributed to this illness and, therefore, the whole family probably needs help. There is an implication that the family may even need to have a sick member present as a scapegoat for their own difficulties, because as long as one member of the family can be sick, the rest can remain well, taking out their traumas, problems, and fears, etc., on this one member. This is one extreme.

The other extreme is the feelings of some people that you only treat the child and forget that he has parents. In fact we hear the statement, "I could do a great deal with this child if he just didn't have any parents," or "It would be so wonderful if I didn't have to deal with the parents." This particular attitude is probably most noted in certain educational circles, but it also is found in some therapeutic circles. Also, there are those who feel that work with parents is unnecessary, but that it might speed the process and thus be of some help.[190] Somewhere in between these two extremes is the position that parents have a role in life, that children are not really just stuck with their parents, but rather, on one hand are a reflection of them and on the other, represent individual personalities that are not necessarily like their parents. Thus, insofar as the child is a reflection of his parents and their milieu, the parents need help in understanding and accepting this behavior; insofar as he is an independent personality having his own difficulties which have developed either from certain organic problems or certain sociogenic problems, etc., regardless of source, the child has to learn to deal with these difficulties, and the parents have to know how the child is learning to deal with them. This last point is important in terms of any type of therapeutic plan. It is obviously absurd for the child to follow a therapy plan or to work through with the therapist certain experiences, and then have this immediately cancelled out by the behavior of his parents. This can be forestalled through proper casework so that the parent is aware of what the therapist is doing and can learn to react accordingly. Further, it must be remembered that many of the child's reactions, particularly in the early days of therapy, may actually produce a worsening of the condition, and the parents have to be prepared to deal with this. These two major aspects of the situation are interwoven, and the caseworker must carefully discover which is most pertinent at this point in time.[191]

Sharing Information with Parents

Further, much of the work with parents may center around an area which can be described as parent education. That is to say, there are certain things along didactic lines which parents have to learn. They certainly have a right to know what is wrong with their child and, to the fullest extent of the therapist's ability to explain, they have a right to know how this illness or disorder functions, what its origins were (if known) and what can be done to correct it. These things should not be hidden but should be shared with the parents. They should be in a position to know what the therapist is doing and the therapist should feel free enough in the total relationship to be able to say that he does not have all the answers. Particularly in the areas of psychotherapy with children, this last condition is the most prevalent, and the average play therapy situation tends to be experimentation every time the child comes in. This, by the way, is not necessarily an evil, recognizing that each child, regardless of his difficulty, is an independent personality, it makes sense to expect each therapy plan will have some independence and in some respects be unrelated to other therapy plans, presuming that the underlying techniques and philosophies are fairly consistent. Now this does not mean that the parent has to be given a Ph.D. program in psychology in order to bring his child into psychotherapy, but it does mean that insofar as there are certain things to be noted about the child, the parent certainly has a right to know them. However, harm can be done by merely giving the parent information cold without taking the time to explain it or to work through its implications. This reminds us of the cartoon where a mother was calling a doctor and said, "Doctor, Johnny just came home from school with an IQ of 110, shall I put him right to bed?" This particular type of parent education is to be frowned upon by all therapists, because it only leads to more confusion and produces in the parent a feeling of frustration. However, with proper education on a straight didactic level but in a casework atmosphere, the parent can understand the nature of the therapist-child relationship, understand the reasons why the therapist is doing certain things with the child, why the parents themselves are, in a sense, treated as though they also had problems, and how they can be brought to play a specific and important role in terms of the whole child and his treatment. That is, the parents are patients in effect alongside of the child, but they are working through their child's problems rather than working through their own problems, and the thought is that the child will be able to work through his problems much more rapidly if the parents also have been able to work through their own.[192]

Relationship of the Patient with His "Family"

We have mentioned before that it becomes almost absurd in terms of the child's adjustment, for example, to return him as a highly flexible, easily moved individual, to a family that is highly compulsive, obsessive, and has a very set and strict way of doing things. Parents with such a child would find themselves in even greater conflict than they did before he was brought into therapy, so the therapist has a responsibility to understand the parents and the parental adjustment to their milieu every bit as much as to understand the child. It becomes the caseworker's responsibility in this regard to transmit this information to the therapist, and this requires a relationship between the therapist and the caseworker which lets all psychotherapy procedure go forward at a more rapid pace. Further, the caseworker has a responsibility of trying to work out with the parents the relationship of the patient with the rest of his family; and the family may include, besides the immediate family, uncles and aunts, grandparents, and putative aunts and uncles in terms of best friends that drop in and are expected to have this relationship with the child.[193] These individuals have a special relationship to the child. They sometimes are very cruel, e.g. Johnny may be sitting in the middle of the living room floor playing quietly when an uncle comes in and his first remarks are, after having properly greeted everyone, "Well, is Johnny still breaking up everything in the house?" and so Johnny stops whatever he was doing and proceeds to go break up something because this is what his uncle expects him to do. Now this is not intentional cruelty on the part of the uncle, it is merely solicitious feeling for the parents, but the one thing they do not need is "solicitation." Many children's problems have been increased tremendously by the fact that the external family feels so sorry for them that they exude sympathy, but at no time give support of any sort, and the child begins to feel more and more of an outsider in his own family. These problems also have to be worked through in the casework structure. It is obviously impossible and usually undesirable under most circumstances to bring the total family of the patient into any sort of casework or psychotherapy relationship, so that the next best thing has to be an understanding on the part of both the patient and his parents as to what their attitude will be in response to the "family," and this is a matter of the parents and the child presenting a mutually accepting attitude to the rest of the world.

It is very difficult to get parents and children to present this kind of attitude. The retarded child has difficulty adapting himself to the needs of the situation; if he did not, he would not be in therapy; therefore, the parents have to make the major adaptation, so that when we talk in terms of a mutually accepting attitude, we mean specifically that the parent has to learn how to let the child know that he is accepted.[194] Further, it has to be remembered that there are going to be many people in the child's external "family" who will have no contact with therapeutic settings, will not even know if the child is in therapy, will only know that the child has been a difficult person for one reason or another. Thus, for example, the corner grocer who may have had experience with the child stealing something or knocking down stacks of tin cans or rows of cereal boxes, may tend to shudder when he sees the child come into the store. The mother, being highly defensive, jutting out her chin and saying, "I have a right to bring my child into your store if you want my custom," intensifies the problem because the child, in a sense, knows the mother is putting up a fight for him and this pleases him; he also knows that she has to put up a fight for him and this displeases him. The ambivalence between knowing that the mother is willing to make these extra efforts on his behalf, and knowing that these extra efforts are necessary, tends often to increase the disturbance, and if the play therapy has not yet reached the point where the child has learned to play through these activities and thus learn responses to them, there is a genuine difficulty which will interfere with the process of therapy. Thus, in this final area the caseworker has a responsibility to try to get the parents to understand the situation well enough that they will adopt a fairly blase or laissez faire attitude in regard to other people (never in regard to the child, of course) in the sense that "this is our business and we are taking care of it, and you go on about your business." If the child can be made to understand that this is the attitude the parent takes, then he will begin to feel that he is part of some sort of a game, that it might be fun, that his mother really loves him and is willing to include him in this game, and we then establish the feeling of acceptance of his behavior which he must have if the therapist is going to be able to do his job.[195]

The Relationship of the Child and Care Personnel

The situation in relationship to the child in play therapy who has already been institutionalized, is somewhat different. Here, we have to remember that the child has already experienced the major rejection. He has been taken out of the home, he has been placed in an institution. Without going into a discussion of the level of child that can be accepted for psychotherapy, and not at home. That is, he may not have been able to clearly define in his own mind, because of his age, limited experience, mental retardation, or other factors, that the mother hates him and thus put him in the institution. It may not be that clear-cut, but nonetheless he does have the feeling that someone with whom he had a very close relationship is no longer there, no longer has that relationship with him, and that somehow or other he must have deserved the change. That is, he must have done something that brought it about. Now this means that he immediately begins setting up testing relationships with the care personnel in the institution. Long before he ever comes into psychotherapy, the problem of the emotional attitude of the care personnel, the aides, etc., in relationship to the child has to be thought of in terms of the establishment of life situations. In this sense, the care personnel in the institution become foster parents in the eyes of the child. Now this does not go into the question of the different institutional attitudes concerning the relationship of care personnel as foster parents. We know that some institutions make this their primary aim, and they set up cottages with cottage parents who are called "mothers and fathers," and they try to remake the whole home for the youngsters; while other institutions will not permit the care personnel to establish any sort of identification with the patient. This latter is accomplished by transferring the care personnel in a very rapid fashion from one cottage or one ward to another, by making sure that they are called Miss, Mrs., or Mr., by making sure that the child is seen on only a cursory basis for functional purposes, etc. However, there is a need to develop a relationship which will permit the child to identify with the care personnel and to receive a certain amount of the emotional experience and training that he has to have for his maturation but, at the same time, not to identify with them so much that he will actually begin to think of them as his parents and thus completely cut his ties with the community.

Patient Oriented Conferences

The way to accomplish this double objective is to bring the care personnel also into some form of supervision. This is impossible in large institutions because it would mean that the whole work force would be spending a great deal of their working day away from the patients. But certainly in terms of those children who are in psychotherapy in the institution, there is a need to develop patient oriented conferences with the care personnel. This means, just as in clinics outside of institutions, there must be some casework done for the purpose of speeding the psychotherapy processes, getting the care
I think we can presume that if the child is in play therapy, he is of a high enough level of emotional maturity and intellect to have made some sort of personal conclusions regarding the fact that he is living in an institution

personnel to understand the problems of the patient, the changes that the therapist expects to effect, and to understand their own emotional relationship to the patient. This certainly does not mean that the therapist brings the care personnel into psychotherapy; it is a very important principle that within an institutional structure you do not do psychotherapy with your colleagues or with your employees. But it does mean that on the basis of a patient oriented program, the processes and emotional feelings of the care personnel towards the patient have to be worked through or they may undo everything that the therapist is trying to accomplish.

In-Service Training Needs

Now again, some of this may have to be thought of in terms of didactic education. In the institution this means the expansion and extension of the inservice training programs, and thus in many respects becomes a pattern similar to working with parents. In an institution this inservice training aspect becomes even more important in terms of the psychotherapy program, because we have to recognize that a single member of the care personnel staff may have under his care as many as thirty or more patients, and he has a need to understand the emotional problems of each one of them. Thus, while the parent has only a small number of children to understand fully,[196] a member of the care personnel staff of an institution has a large group on her ward who are in various forms of active psychotherapy, and it is necessary that she recognize the emotional reactions of each of them. Much of this can be accomplished through inservice training relating to understanding interpersonal relationships and should include an attempt to give elementary understanding of the processes of psychotherapy and emotional disturbance, particularly in terms of low functional behavior, thus permitting the care personnel not only to know what is going on, but to understand the reasons and to bring the therapy in the milieu setting into something close to a 16 waking hour basis instead of the one hour a week that the child spends with the therapist.

Another extremely important factor is that, once the child is institutionalized, a major step in his whole life has been taken, and we then have the additional problem of getting him back to the community. Thus, the child in the community does not need psychotherapy 16 hours a day, 7 days a week, because he is already at home and the major problem is not to get him there, but in a sense to merely keep him there; the child in the institution finds himself in a situation where in addition to his emotional disturbance, in the institution must try to maintain itself as a therapeutic community, which means that the role of the care personnel may also revolve around setting

196. We might also note that in reverse, the patient is going to have many more "mothers" to whom to adjust than his community counterpart.

up certain types of activity within the cottage area. In other words, certain of the activities which the play therapist will carry out in the playroom, have also to be carried over to the cottage area, not for the purpose of specifically augmenting the activities of the play therapist, because this becomes too great a load for the child to carry, but rather to help the child work through at a more rapid pace the technical difficulties in play therapy in terms of knowing how to play, knowing what to do with certain activities, e.g., how to put the train tracks together, how to wind up wind-up toys and things of this sort, so that when he comes into play therapy the therapist will be in a position to spend more time in the actual interpersonal relationship aspects of the therapy.

Role of Care Personnel and Play Therapy

This need to get the child home is further emphasized in terms of the fact that problems in the institution are different. We have emphasized, in terms of the child's relationship with his parents, the development of a mutually accepting attitude which, in a sense, means that the child is at peace when he is at home. In the institution this is not actually what is desired, since a child who is at peace in the institution is no longer in a sense "fighting to get out," is no longer trying to work his way back to his home, and becomes what is described as "over institutionalized," so that the effort in relationship to the child in the institution is not one of developing mutual acceptance, but rather, one of getting the child to understand that he is accepted but that he would be more accepted if he could behave in such a way that would permit him to be returned home. Thus, it is not enough that he merely do what he is supposed to do, remembering that as most institutions are conceived today, a child can live twenty-four hours a day without ever having made a decision, but rather that he be motivated to try to do a little bit more than he is supposed to do, even if these decisions are contrary to the more rigid management patterns of the care personnel. Thus, the care personnel have a tremendous teaching role in relationship to the child in that they have within their jurisdiction the power to introduce management procedures, and if these are introduced in an incorrect manner, they will tend to eliminate the creative forces within the child and to further discourage independence of thought, decision making, etc. The play therapists wish to encourage these creative activities, and they have to work through a clear understanding with the care personnel as to what can be done in each area so as not to interfere with each other, and still work in the best interests of the child. Thus, the care personnel have to try to set up situations on their wards where the child can or must make some decisions. They have to set up situations where the child finds his unacceptable behavior is not accepted, even though he personally is not rejected. This means that he may have to be permitted at times to identify with certain staff personnel, even though the overidentification will later require that a separation be developed, or it may mean that a favorite child on the ward has to be treated a little bit more strictly than the ward personnel would like, so that the "teacher's pet" aspects of the treatment will not mitigate against other patients on the ward. These are all situations not too different than those found in the community, except that it is important that they be emphasized here because of the underlying factor that the child will never be able to get back to the community if the institution is not careful how it handles him in those situations.

THE RELATIONSHIP OF THE CHILD TO THE COMMUNITY MILIEU

The problem of returning the child to the community raises another question in the relationship of the retarded child to the community milieu. We have pointed out some of the general aspects of the child's relationship to his parents, but we must recognize that different community structures establish different types of community problems. It is certainly obvious that a child who originates in a large, urban community is going to have to understand a different kind of milieu than a child who originates in a small, rural community.

Understanding Patients' Milieu

The problem here is essentially one which is of extreme difficulty for the therapist, because more often than not he has to lean on his own knowledge of the milieu, and if the child originates in an area different than that of the therapist, there will be difficulties in communication. The therapist may be able to utilize the information derived from the child's play to gain better understanding, but there is a problem also of developing a process of misunderstanding because the child may not, as would be expected, be playing with complete objectivity or complete accuracy. More important, is that the type of casework processes discussed in the early part of the chapter be utilized to find out exactly what the impact of the child in his home community actually is. This involves the impact of the child on the family, how the siblings react to this child: do they feel that having him in the family lowers their social prestige; if there are older children, do they avoid bringing their dates to the house; if there are younger children, are they teased; what actually goes on in relationship to the child in his community and further, what does the community actually expect of him? Does the community have the ability in terms of their own social stability to absorb this kind of youngster, or are the social and economic factors of the community so tense that any additional pressure of this sort only sets off an explosive situation? We must not think of the retarded child as being something apart from the rest of the day-to-day occurrences within the world, and the question of the total impact of this child upon his family, neighbors, and the rest of the community has to be thought of in terms of the social and economic factors present in the community at the time the child is being treated. It is extremely important that the therapist know and understand these things. Obviously, there will be a different kind of play structure set forth with a child whose father has been unemployed for a period of time and a child whose father has had regular employment. The whole question of how the play is going to work is involved in this difference. The child's general feeling of stability within the home or the home's general stability in relationship to the child is affected by this, so that it is extremely important that the therapist not assume, as has so often been the case, that the home situation from which his patient is derived follows the usual mores and practices of the so-called average, middle class American family. He must make some effort to find out for himself or, hopefully, through the social worker doing casework with the parents, exactly what the standards and mores of the particular community setting from which this child derives actually are.

Changing the Milieu

Also, there may be many things in the milieu which are actually anti-therapeutic—not in the sense used by different schools of psychotherapy, but rather in the sense that there are things which need to be changed if the therapist is going to be properly able to make the necessary changes in his patient. It has to be remembered that the retarded child cannot be thought of as the source of mentally healthy behavior for the rest of the family, or for the rest of the community. That is to say, one cannot fight the problems of the community on the back of the patient. While the therapist may have been able to successfully develop his patient in terms of improvement in Adaptive Behavior so that he is able to leave therapy demonstrating a fairly high level of social responsibility, we still cannot consider that this behavior will become a model or a demonstration to other members of the family or other members of the community. The retarded child cannot be expected to teach social responsibility to others, because he is still mentally retarded; the very problems which are related to his learning and his ability to take from the community and his environment the necessary cues to continue learning, are going to interfere with his being able to function effectively even after successful psychotherapy in any but the most general types of predictable occurrences, and he will still have a great deal of difficulty in making any kind of acceptable adjustment to occurrences that are totally unpredictable and totally surprising to him. Thus, it may be necessary for the therapist to actually make or attempt to make some very specific changes in the milieu of his patient in order to reduce the number of unpredictable occurrences. This may mean that the success or failure of psychotherapy may depend on the patient moving from an urban to a rural community, or vice versa. It may mean that the child would be more accepted in a home other than his parent's home; it may mean that a special kind of training has to be instituted which would require that the child be entered in a special type of schooling. In other words, the therapist should not hesitate to attempt to make necessary changes in the milieu of the patient if those changes will make the patient's adjustment to a community easier and more permanent. He should not try to manipulate the milieu merely for the purpose of easing the patient's lot, because that type of manipulation is bound to be temporary and will not create the kind of milieu which gives any type of permanence to the therapy gains. Thus, it is much better if the therapist insists that the patient use his own resources to deal with his peers rather than suggest that the parents or supervising personnel step in and settle all disputes. This kind of manipulation would be very destructive to the eventual treatment of the patient but, as we stated above, if the manipulation can create conditions whereby the patient is more apt to be able to predict on a long term basis the situation within the community, then the manipulation is called for and will probably be therapeutic.

Long-Range Goals in the Community

The final consideration in regard to the child and his community has to be the long range goals. In a sense, why are we bothering to do psychotherapy with this youngster, what are we hoping to accomplish from the point of view of the community? This is a difficult question to answer because it requires a certain amount of crystal ball information. However, we can make one or two assertions based on present information. In the first place, there seems to be no question but that, given the usual amount of prosperity and social and economic success within our national community, there is a good possibility that a comparatively well adjusted retardate will be absorbed by the community as a useful citizen. It is true that this retardate will still probably be one of the first individuals laid off in the face of any economic change, it is further true that he will have a great deal of difficulty adjusting to any sort of technological improvement or change. But beyond that factor there remains the situation that he probably will be able to deal at some level of adequacy with most of the job requirements available to individuals at his level if his adjustment emotionally is within the minimum standards of the community.

Now we might, from the point of view of crystal ball observation, state that one of the oddities of the present technological developments within our industrial community is the fact that there might be an increased role for the adjusted retardate in an industrial function. This is obvious today in terms of one of the new functions of sheltered workshops, where the retarded individual can play a useful industrial role by completing, correcting or salvaging the mistakes of the machine. Thus, an item that is produced in a factory on a machine basis often needs additional hand polishing or additional shaping, or some other minor changes to make the item conform to original specifications where, for some reason, the machine did not do the job properly. These items can be sent over on a contract basis to a sheltered workshop where the retarded or handicapped individual can make these minor adjustments and thus keep products on the market which otherwise would have had to be considered waste. This role of the sheltered workshop is increasing as the technological changes within the nation increase. Further, most individuals who are sufficiently self-controlled and maintain a sufficient level of individual and social responsibility, can be accepted by their community even on a noncontributing basis if they are able from time to time to make small or general types of contributions. Thus, again the retardate fits very well into service jobs, such as delivery work, helping with loading and unloading, moving of goods from one area to another, running service elevators, dishwashing, and the retarded or handicapped individual can actually aid the business in question by taking these jobs out of the transient category so that the business does not have to wonder from day to day where they are going to get somebody to do this particular job. In other words, some service occupations are remaining in spite of technological changes. As we pointed out, some of them may actually increase with technological changes and, in general, there is a definite place for the retarded individual who is otherwise sufficiently well adjusted in terms of a high level of adaptive behavior.

ADDITIONAL NOTES

183. Friend, M. R., The Historical Development of Family Diagnosis, *The Social Service Review*, 1960, XXXIV, pp. 2-18, reviews the history of this type of approach to the problem; in brief, the child is a product of his environment of which the family is the major aspect.

184. Pollak, O., A Family Diagnosis Model, *The Social Service Review*, 1960, XXXIV, pp. 19-31, attempts to set up a systematic method of evaluating interrelationships between family members and indicates some of the causes of aberrations in these relationships. Also, Pollak, O., Design of a Model of Healthy Family Relationships as a Basis for Evaluative Research, *Soc. Serv. Review*, XXXI, 1957, correlates maturity with capacity to give and tries to show what "healthy" relationships would be.

185. Hirschberg, J. C., "The Meaning to Parents of Retardation in Their Child," in *New Trends in Mental Retardation*, "*The Family*," 1963, (Leland, Helen, Ed.), Kansas State Board of Social Welfare, Topeka, Kans., 1963, pp. 18-20, outlines various types of parent reactions to this problem. See also Bryant, K. N. and Hirschberg, J. C., "Helping the Parents of a Retarded Child," *A. J. Dis. Child*, 1961, 102, pp. 82-96.

186. Kanner, L., "Mental Health in Child Rearing," *Child*, 1953(b), XVII, pp. 116-117, discusses effects of parental attitudes and fact that parents are usually more confused than rejecting.

187. Goldberg, B., "Family Psychiatry and the Retarded Child," *Canadian Psychiatric Assoc. Jr.*, 1962, 7, pp. 140-146, points up the fact that families who bring retarded children to outpatient clinics often have psychiatric problems of their own, and that dealing with these problems makes it easier to help the child. See also, Harley, A. J., Jr., "Group Psychotherapy for Parents of Disturbed Children," *Mental Hosp.*, 1963, 14, pp. 14-19.

188. Beck, Helen L., "Casework with Parents of Mentally Retarded Children," *A. J. Orthopsychiat.*, 1962, 32, pp. 870-877, sets up a guide for casework procedure. See also, Bennett, Daphne N., "Therapy with Parents of Handicapped Children," *Exceptional Child*, 1957, 23, ppl 154-159, and Kanner, L., "Parent's Feelings about Retarded Children," *AJMD*, 1953 (a), 57, pp. 375-383.

189. Bowen, M., "Family Dynamics" in *Etiology of Schizophrenia*, (D. D. Jackson, Ed.) Basic Books, Inc., N. Y., 1960, pp. 346-371, discusses the concept of the "family unit" or "family as a single organism."

190. Axline (1947), *op. cit.*, p. 68.

191. Mandelbaum, A. and Wheeler, Mary E., "The Meaning of a Defective Child to Parents," *Social Casework*, 1960, discusses some of these factors under the heading "defense patterns."

192. Bryant and Hirschberg (1961), *op. cit.*, pp. 87-90.

193. Farber, B., "Perceptions of Crisis and Related Variables in the Impact of a Retarded Child on the Mother," *Jr. Health and Human Behavior*, 1960, 1, pp. 108-118, also Farber (1962), *op. cit.*

194. Or as Kanner (1956) *op. cit.*, has said, "any child has a good chance for satisfactory mental health . . . if he is accepted as he is," p. 116.

195. Bryant and Hirschberg (1961), *op. cit.*, p. 82.

196. This note has been cited on page 193.

XIII. Play Therapy as Related to Other Treatment Modalities, Diagnosis and Research

In Chapter XI, we discussed some aspects of the problem of expected gain in play therapy. We pointed out that various types of diagnostic entities have been excluded from play therapy because it was thought that the therapy could not affect the cause of the problem. Therapy is certainly not going to change malformations or encephalopathies, and if this were the goal of play therapy, that would be the end of the road. However, to reiterate, our main problem is how the child adjusts to his defects, and this is a role for play therapy in any kind of setting.

PLAY THERAPY IN REFERENCE TO MEDICAL DIAGNOSIS

Defects, Malformations and Encephalopathies

One error that seems to be made fairly universally by psychologists and psychiatrists alike, dealing with behavior problems of retarded children, is to assume that a particular type of diagnosis is somehow descriptive of the child. Most diagnoses in the area of mental retardation are of etiological origin.[197] They are based on the premise that certain types of defects, malformations, or encephalopathies have caused the retardation or are related to the processes which have caused the retardation. It is presumed further that many of these causes are a result of various types of congenital or prenatal processes or insults, that others have a genetic basis, and that others have a postnatal or paranatal traumatic basis.[198] This leads, as we say, to a major problem in terms of the function of the clinical psychologist, psychiatrist, or psychotherapist, because of the unwritten presumption that a child, having been given this diagnosis, will function in a certain manner and, in this sense, the etiological diagnosis often serves, particularly in residential centers and institutions for the mentally retarded, in the same way as the IQ diagnosis. Thus, it is presumed that an acroephalic child will behave in a certain manner, or a Mongoloid child or a post-encephalitic child, and these children are thought of as groups; in some institutions they are placed together on the same wards with the presumption that they are the same type of child, and the general approach is often one of grouping children in terms of their diagnosis instead of grouping them behaviorally.[199] This is even truer in terms of secondary conditions, and it was not too long ago that we had whole hospitals dedicated to epileptics, for example, and there are still cerebral palsy centers and other centers of this sort which presume that the etiologic or basic physical diagnosis unites the children in some manner, and that behavioral aspects should follow from this etiologic or medical diagnosis. This position is not entirely false, but psychologists have to learn to observe children, not only in terms of the medical diagnoses, but also in terms of the psychological functioning of the child, and here we find that there are new groupings which open themselves to us. Thus, on one hand it is found that most phenylketonuric children demonstrate behaviors which make them appear very similar to childhood schizophrenics. If they are profoundly or severely retarded, these behaviors resemble autism; if they are mildly retarded, they resemble simple schizophrenia, but most individuals with this diagnosis have many behavioral characteristics in common with the schizophrenic individual at different levels.[200] Or again, we find with certain types of kernicterus that the child's behavior more often resembles that of the emotionally disturbed child than it does the brain damaged or congenitally defective child. However, this is not to say that this is universal, and again, we cannot make the error of presuming that all children with kernicterus will behave this way, but a sufficient number do for the clinical psychologist or psychiatrist to look for that type of behavior with this diagnosis.

Conversely, all Mongoloid children are not pleasant, happy-go-lucky little individuals; many of them are extremely disturbed, many of them act out in an angry and aggressive manner, and the old universal concept of Mongolism certainly is not borne out as they are seen as individuals. Thus, we find that the medical diagnosis as such does not give us much information in terms of specific treatment modalities. Diagnosis at any level has relatively little value if it is not a guide to treatment, and knowing the child is suffering from Down's syndrome has no particular importance to us unless we know how to treat Down's syndrome. This is not to say that we do not want that information, it is not to say that we do not seek that information, but having it should not become a basis for feeling that we know something definite about the child from the behavioral point of view. Thus, the play therapist has a responsibility of evaluating the child regardless of his diagnosis, seeing what behaviors are present which can be corrected, and going forth in the therapy process to attempt to correct them. Thus, we would make a plea that no child be excluded from play therapy merely because the etiological or medical diagnosis offers no treatment possibility.[201]

Another problem is related to the questions raised previously in discussing Adaptive Behavior. Many of these youngsters function at a level which would make them excellent candidates for sheltered workshops. However, there is the additional problem of their developing proper work habits, proper attitudes towards work, proper motivation, etc. The play therapist can be of service here to the rehabilitation team, because if these children can learn proper play habits and proper attitudes towards play in the sense of controlled play in a therapy situation, it will be much easier for them when they are older to transfer these habits into work situations. Since many of the youngsters with the more clear-cut types of diagnoses are the ones who make the best candidates for sheltered employment, it would follow that there is a very definite need not only to not exclude these youngsters from play therapy, but to make a point of trying to bring them in, in an effort to make prevocational and vocational readiness a more systematic part of their training. Thus, while the medical diagnosis has limited meaning to the play therapist, the meaning it does have is that these youngsters have special needs to accept themselves, to learn the meaning of organized, controlled play so that when they are older they can learn the meaning of organized, controlled work, and thus we can help insure that their right to make a contribution is maintained and preserved for them.[202]

Functional Disorders and Cultural Deprivation

One group of mentally retarded youngsters, however, fits very closely into the play therapy program because of their diagnosis. This is the group which is described essentially as "retarded with functional reaction alone manifest." This includes those who are considered retarded for cultural-familial reasons, for reasons of deprivation, retarded in terms of primary psychogenic disturbance, major personality disorders, or adjustment reactions, etc. This group is primarily a psychiatric population in the sense that they need treatment for personality or adjustment disorders. Here, we are faced with another area where the community at large has not quite caught up with some of the thinking of the people working in the field. Essentially, if an individual is sent to a hospital because he has broken a leg, the hospital will treat the broken leg. If this individual happened to have only four fingers, the hospital will discharge him, having treated the broken leg, and not wait for him to grow a new fifth finger. Yet children are sent to institutions, schools, and community services for the mentally retarded on the basis of various types of functional reactions but, more often than not, after they have been treated for these conditions they are not released from these hospitals and institutions until somebody is able to say this person is less retarded. This is an absurdity; that is not why the child was sent there in the first place, and the reversible process is related to the use of his brain, not the growing of a new one. In terms of various kinds of prevalence surveys and counts that have been taken in mental retardation, it has become highly apparent that there are many more retardates in a community than ever would see a hospital. This is particularly true of children, where we have figures as great as ten per cent of the school age population in some areas being indicated as potentially mentally retarded,[203] at least as defined by psychological tests or teachers' ratings. The difference between this large group of youngsters who might be considered retarded and the extremely small group of youngsters who finally make their way into the institutions[204] is usually based on the behavior, or as we indicated, the adaptive behavior of the youngster, and it is this which the institution must treat because this is why the child was hospitalized.[205] The fact that he was also retarded is coincidental to the hospitalization, since there are many more individuals in the community with similar intelligence levels who do not need to be hospitalized, because their level of adaptive behavior is sufficiently high that they can survive in the community in terms of community expectations.[206] With this in mind, it becomes patently absurd to bring a child suffering from cultural-familial retardation of psychogenic origin into the hospital, and then refuse to treat him as though he were a psychiatric patient. The whole process of deprivation and psychogenic disturbance has evidently been such that this has separated him from his home community and it becomes the responsibility of the hospital to give this child psychotherapy, to treat him as it would any other psychiatric patient, and, when this treatment has been completed, to return him to the community with no great expectations regarding the level of retardation except that he must also receive special education and rehabilitation services relative to his critical growth period. Thus, any child who is diagnosed as suffering from mental retardation due to functional manifestations alone, should be given a very high priority for play therapy because the whole process which has brought this child to the attention of the hospital or clinic is one of emotional disturbance or maladjustment, and this can and must be treated. The medical diagnoses, which used to be called familial or idiopathic and which now have been broken into subparts giving evidence of some of the psychogenic and cultural-familial origins, should be almost automatic indicators for the consideration of this child as a potential candidate for play therapy.[207]

Sensory Handicaps

The third aspect of play therapy in relation to diagnostic entities is really more of a parenthetical mention of things than a separate idea. This has to do with the problems relating to sensory handicaps. The reason that we consider this parenthetical is because it has such an involved and well worked through role that the specialists who treat these areas usually use play therapy techniques in their treatment, and the bringing in of an additional therapist would become redundant. Thus, where we have a speech and hearing defect, the speech pathologist more often than not uses techniques which would be entirely familiar to a play therapist as part of the regular speech therapy program. It would, of course, be foolish for the speech pathologist doing play therapy to send the patient to another play therapist to do play therapy; we run immediately into the "too many cooks" situation, and it is much more important that the speech pathologist, who is also treating the sensory defect, do the whole job. If he needs special help, he will seek consultation from a specialist in psychotherapy, but purely on a consultative basis. There is certainly no question in our mind but that the speech pathologist or other such specialists can do the therapy job every bit as well as one trained specifically to do play therapy. Thus, we find that many of these areas of disorder, e.g., hearing, sight, speech, etc., involve the conversion of sensory disabilities into handicaps along the lines of rehabilitation goals,[208] and the disciplines trained to deal with them used play therapy techniques in treating the child. We find that not only must the handicap be handled, but also the child's attitude toward it, and play therapy techniques help the child accept himself as a handicapped person on one hand, and accept the treatment which the therapist is trying to offer him on the other. We would like, at this time, merely to underline the fact that what has proven so successful in the areas of speech therapy, sight saving, hearing therapy, etc., can prove equally successful in dealing with other disabilities of a congenital nature (we will speak in a moment of the special problems related to orthopedic difficulties), and even those malformations, defects, etc., of which we have already spoken may be generally less disabling if the same kinds of procedures can be applied. Thus, we have a great deal to learn from some of the other disciplines which have been successful in treating patients because they have discovered, what we should have known all along, that the emotional or adaptive aspects of the child are every bit as important as the training or rehabilitative aspects. The process being sought is one of compensation, i.e., we are trying to get the child to utilize the qualities or assets which he has available in place of the qualities which he has lost or never had gained.

Here, one of the best approaches is that utilized in the U-S form, where the child learns to take materials that have no particular identity and to give them an identity of his own creation. It becomes easier after he has learned this particular technique to take a sensory stimulus which he feels has no particular identity and convert it to meaningful and useful elements. We recognize that most of the disciplines treating sensory handicaps use something more similar to the S-S form, and we would like to suggest that they might consider some of the qualities of the U-S form as being possibly more appropriate.

---

208. Here again it is recognized that therapy will not "cure" the disability, but rather modify it so that the individual, though still "handicapped," can nonetheless learn to function with it.

PLAY THERAPY AND OTHER TREATMENT MODALITIES

The above should not be taken to imply that the psychotherapist has no need to be conscious of the situation in regard to medical treatment or medical problems. Certainly there should and must be a very close relationship between the psychotherapist and various rehabilitative medical disciplines because of the specific needs that many handicapped children show. In thinking about the role of play therapy in relationship to various types of problems and treatments, we have to deal generally with three areas. One, the role of play therapy and psychiatry; two, the role of play therapy and physical rehabilitation; and three, the role of play therapy in general patient management. As to the first, this may sound like gilding the lily. That is, play therapy is one of the usual tools of psychiatry. However, the psychiatrist has other major tools and there is a tendency for him to utilize a single treatment process at a time. Thus, it is not unusual for a child to be put on tranquilizing medication or electroconvulsive therapy or antidepressant medication without any further efforts to introduce other psychotherapeutic techniques. There seems to be the feeling that if the child can benefit from psychotherapy or play therapy, he should not need the medical measures and also that if the other methods are used, they are doing the job and additional therapy is considered extra. It has been our experience in the area of the mentally retarded that the psychiatrist tends to give a prescription for medication or shock treatment, or something of this sort,[209] and not combine this with other forms of therapy.

Play Therapy and Psychiatry

It is not our intention at this time to challenge psychiatric processes or prescriptions. We certainly do not want to add fuel to the hopefully dying fire of conflict between the clinical psychologist and the psychiatrist. We would like only to point out that one does not isolate a child from learning experiences while treating him for a psychiatric disorder. This is probably the heart of the question. It may not matter with an adult who has already completed his basic learning if he is put on a single treatment that does not involve new learning; however, with a child the psychiatric role also involves training, because the child is in the crucial period when learning must go forward, and the psychiatrist or the treatment personnel have to continue to deal with the learning problem.

With the above in mind, let us examine some of the factors relative to the special therapies. First, we must consider electroconvulsive therapy. This particular treatment is not too common among the mentally retarded, though some psychiatrists feel that it is very effective and should be utilized.[210] However, without engaging in that aspect of the question, we have found that the retarded, brain damaged child receiving ECT goes through a period of disorganization which is extremely profound and generally makes him inaccessible to any type of therapeutic program. However, after the completion of the ECT, there is a period of reorganization which could potentially synthesize at a level somewhat higher than the initial preshock level. Whether or not he will synthesize at this higher level could depend very much on the kind of program in which the child is placed at the completion of the ECT series. Generally speaking, it is impossible to put this child back into a special education area because of the disorientation, etc., and the only really feasible type of program is regular play therapy which will permit him to develop learning. This particular relationship has given some indications that it might be effective.[211] The general function of U-U therapy aimed at developing increasing consciousness of self and increased ability to cognize, seems to be ready-made for bringing orientation back into a situation where, in a sense, ECT has cut it out.[212] This is an example where play therapy procedures, as we have described them, could serve a very useful purpose to a psychiatrist.

The child who is receiving psychopharmacological agents presents different types of problems. Most of the research work done in relationship to retarded children and this type of medication in learning situations has indicated that it is overused and, except in the very rare occasions when the medication is used to deal with a clearly defined behavioral difficulty, it seems to have no specific effect. To the contrary, it is found that it is impossible to determine which group of children are receiving medication and which are not in a behavioral situation;[213] it has also been found that youngsters on placeboes do every bit as well as youngsters on tranquilizers[214] and that, in general, the over-all pattern of behavior of children on tranquilizing medication, even though they exhibit initial symptoms for which the medication was designed, does not differ or show any real improvement over youngsters who are on no medication or on placebo.[215] This leaves us in somewhat of a quandary concerning the continued use of tranquilizing medication, particularly in terms of learning, because one of the features which seems to be present throughout most of the studies with the mentally retarded in this area, is that learning is not enhanced, from the schoolroom point of view. There is increasing evidence that most of the psychopharmacological agents utilized to produce calm and tranquilization, produce blocking of ability or an "I don't care" kind of attitude which makes learning more difficult and the child less accessible to teaching efforts. However, in the area of patient management the tranquilizer is prescribed because it is needed, i.e., the child's behavior is such that it calls for tranquilization. There is a pattern of behavior either on the ward or in the home which has led the psychiatrist to the decision to introduce this type of management device in an effort to control the child's behavior and made him more "livable," but even though the medication is necessary and invaluable from the management point of view, we have the learning needs of the child to consider, and the child does not learn as readily in school or in other areas where learning is a major emphasis. Nonetheless, the child can progress in play therapy. The reasons seem to be related to the fact that he is receiving more individual attention. It is postulated that one of the reasons the tranquilizers seem to work at all with the retarded is because of the individual attention that they imply. Further, it may be that the processes of cognition are not actually blocked or slowed down, but rather, the child's initiative or desire to explore, to learn, has in a sense been slowed down and the play therapy procedure of creating instrusions is forcing him to wake up this process even though he does not particularly want to. This latter assumption can be made since one of the reasons the tranquilizer is recommended in the first place is that it tends to inhibit the hyperactivity of the child, and this hyperactivity is generally considered to be a combination of a drivenness and an uncontrolled exploratory behavior where he is "in and out" of everything. Thus, it might follow logically that if this is successfully controlled, those aspects of exploratory behavior which are necessary to new learning will also be controlled, and this might explain some of the results which seem to show an inhibition of learning. Active, one-to-one, intrusion may activate this area even though it is "tranquilized." However, that being as it may, youngsters on tranquilizing medication who are brought into play therapy show success similar to those who are not on tranquilizing medication, even though the procedure may take a little longer and the process require a little more general effort on the part of both the patient and the therapist.

In short, we have tried to indicate how psychiatry can be expanded through the use of play therapy techniques. This is not a particularly new idea and individuals working with children on psychiatric wards have already raised this possibility.[216]

Play Therapy and Physical Rehabilitation

The next area has to do with physical rehabilitation therapy. Here, the role of play therapy is clearer and more traditional. The major problem is that the child learn how to adjust to his physical handicap. Thus, play therapy has long been considered an adjunct to orthopedic treatment, treatment of various specific handicaps, and treatment of handicaps relating to debilitating diseases such as rheumatic fever, polio, etc. However, there is relatively little in the literature concerning the child who, besides the other handicaps, is also mentally retarded.[217] The retarded child is usually quite aware of his physical handicap, he knows that he is different from other children and this difference becomes a very clear-cut thing to him, and he is often highly motivated to affect a change. Thus, we have seen multihandicapped children work extremely hard in various therapies because they felt that they were somehow diminishing the differences. In terms of the play therapy techniques, there seems to be a relationship between children with physical handicaps and specific play therapy approaches. Taking first the child with the orthopedic handicap, this child usually has a program directed by a physical therapist or an orthopedic physician. The problem has to be centered on those elements which the physician or P.T. have found to be impeding the child's progress over and above his physical condition.[218] The role of the play therapist is both to maintain a learning pace, as we discussed above, and to work on the spotlight areas which have been indicated to be factors holding up more rapid or better progress. Thus, a modified form of the S-U or S-S therapies would seem to be called for. The S-U form is needed for the child to work out his actual feelings concerning being "crippled" or orthopedically handicapped and the unstructured approach gives him an opportunity to introduce thematic material which will permit the therapist to work through with him the real meaning of the handicap. But, because of the problem of dealing with spotlight areas, the S-S approach may also be quite useful and the major decision on the part of the therapist must be which would be the most productive in the shortest period of time. Here, the level of intelligence may be a factor, the higher level child being able to perform, in this instance, a little better in the S-U area since he is more capable of developing fantasy material, while the lower level child may respond best to the more complete structure. But in either case, the child can benefit greatly from play therapy if, as we indicated, the physical therapist feels that psychogenic processes are interfering with the physical processes.

Another area has to do with the therapy needs of the child who has suffered from a debilitating disease, has need of a prosthesis or is currently involved with a chronic disorder. The thing most of these conditions have in common is that they usually affect an individual who has previously functioned at a higher level, but is now functioning at a lower level because of the disorder. Thus, we would not treat an amputee the same way as a child with a congenital orthopedic handicap, unless the amputation occurred at such a young age that he had no memory of proper physical functioning. There are variations of this; the polio child could probably belong in either area, and much depends on the age at the time of the disability and on his present psychological attitude. If he does not seem to have a profound sense of loss, we would treat him as we do the cerebral palsied and congenitally handicapped. If he does seem to have a profound psychological sense of loss, then he should be considered in the group with the debilitating diseases.

We might also say that the problems in the use of prosthetic devices for the individual with a whole mind are different than for the retarded and are a very special area for play therapy. In essence, the individual with the whole mind can be taught to use prosthetic devices on a mechanical rote basis by instructing him how to use them, so that over time can become quite expert. The function of play therapy here would be a matter of conditioning the child to want to use the device. This is a matter of the milieu no longer reinforcing negative behavior, but beginning to reinforce only the hoped for behavior. Thus, if the child is not carried, but forced to use his artificial leg, he will use it more quickly than if he is carried from place to place. The play therapy can set the model for this and other types of behavior by having the child work through the problem and his feelings about it, first, in play.

However, with the mentally retarded, additional problems exist in that they cannot always be taught to use these prosthetic devices by the book. They have to be given long, involved demonstrations, and one cannot always be certain that they are clear in their mind as to what is supposed to happen and when. Here, play therapy can combine the training in the use of the device with the conditioning of the child to want to use it. Because the training usually is a long, tedious process, there is a tendency for the retarded to become quite frustrated, to give up the struggle, and the long, involved training, instead of becoming productive of efficiency, may actually result in a lower level of performance than in the beginning. However, if play therapy techniques can be utilized in this area, it is possible to maintain interest during learning, remembering the underlying philosophy that the child works when he plays if the play is toward a definite end. The play therapy approach can be one of teaching the child to use the device, setting up the kinds of problems that can only be solved with the help of the prosthesis and, at the same time, reinforcing partial successes and helping the child work through emotional feelings in relationship to failures. Here, the process of conditioning is quite effective, and if this is combined with the improvement of cognitive ability so the child will understand where he is failing and why he needs the prosthesis, play therapy can make a very effective contribution toward getting a prosthesis on a retarded child.[219]

In terms of the debilitating diseases and general patient management, the major problem is not to try to get the child to do more, but in a sense to get him to be satisfied to do less, while making sure that he is doing all he is able to do in terms of his intellectual and physical potential. The role of play therapy is to teach the retarded child how to strike this delicate balance between what his physical disability will let him do and what his intellectual disability will keep him from doing. The therapist and the child must explore together the various avenues of play and work to see if they cannot discover a mode of adjustment. Further, the child's disease function may not be stabilized, e.g., muscular dystrophy, so that it is not sufficient to bring the child to a single understanding of the situation, but it is also necessary that he get a more general understanding of the total situation so that each time a change occurs the therapist will be able to work with him in an effort to maintain as much peace and emotional ease as is possible in the face of the deterioration. There is no specific form of play therapy indicated in this area. The usual indications should be followed with the exception that the goals have to be modified to establish a lower level of performance than would be expected of a child at the same level who did not have a debilitating or deteriorating condition. This latter consideration is equally true of problems of convalescence where the disease is not particularly deteriorating but, as we indicated, the child must do much less after the convalescence than he was able to do before the disease. The convalescent period can be used to help him adjust to this fact so that when the convalescence is over, he will be as efficient a person as his physical condition will permit.[220]

Play Therapy and Adjunctive Therapies

Other types of treatment modalities may also need the support of the play therapist. Many of these have already been discussed in the chapters concerning specific forms of play. In some instances it is necessary for the child to have psychotherapy in addition to work in other areas, and we will discuss at this time those instances where both procedures are utilized, i.e., the adjunctive modality as well as play therapy.[221] The first of these instances is the use of play therapy in conjunction with specific training areas, such as special education and prevocational training. Here, we run into two types of difficulties which the play therapist is in a somewhat better position to handle than is the training specialist. The first is the child who, while he may be responding exceptionally well to the specific training is, nonetheless, having sufficient community, home or neighborhood problems that additional support is required over and above that which the teacher can provide. The second is the instance of the child who has become, in a sense, overly used to the training area. Here a variety situation may be necessary to catch certain elements to which the teacher, the training specialist or the child has become inured, and which a new person, not that well acquainted with the child, may pick up immediately, and thus provide for more rapid progress.

As to the first difficulty, it is quite often difficult for the training specialist to deal with the special problems that may arise in the home and at the same time devote the necessary amount of energy to the classroom or shop situation. Part of this we have discussed in the previous chapter relating to parents. However, there is also the matter of giving the child a place or opportunity to vent some of his feelings of hostility and aggression, and to play through some of the situations which arise in the home so that he can be in a better position to find an improved level of adjustment. This would obviously be disruptive to a special education setting. It is difficult if a child had a particularly unpleasant experience at home, for him to come into class and spend the class time trying to work through his own feelings regarding this experience for, while this might be very valuable in terms of the total group situation, it would clearly rob some of the educational function of the class. This happens occasionally and the teacher can usually take it in stride for, as we said, it may be even valuable to take class time to work this through as a learning experience for the whole class. But, if this is a constant and chronic condition, the problem eventually becomes sufficiently disruptive for the teacher to feel that more would be gained if the child could be removed from the class. In order to prevent this from occurring, it sometimes helps to bring the child into play therapy and for the play therapist to work with the teacher in planning the particular curriculum most fitting for this child while at the same time treating the emotional problem created by the child's relationship with his home. Thus, the role of the play therapist as a school psychologist in support of training and rehabilitation areas is also a very important function.[222]

The second aspect is, in a sense, related to the first, because the play therapist again must function as a school psychologist. Quite often a new or different approach or a new or different setting will get further with a particular child's problem than a constant reiteration of an old approach or setting. This is not to say that the old approach or setting was wrong, that the teacher is less capable than the therapist or anything of this sort, but rather that the effect of newness may have such an impact upon the child that there will be clear-cut behavioral changes. This seems to work effectively within institutional structures and would seem to be able to work equally effectively in community areas. Thus, bringing the child into S-S play therapy with someone to whom he is not used, whose behavior he cannot predict, not because he has a problem which the teacher could not normally handle, but because the problem has become so chronic that the teacher's approaches no longer make any impression, may sufficiently upend his expectations to bring about a behavioral change.

Remedial Areas

Much of the same type of approach and same type of situation exists in conjunction with remedial areas. We have already pointed out that specialists in remedial areas such as speech therapy, music therapy, occupational therapy, recreation therapy, etc.,[223] are doing things which would be recognized by a psychotherapist or play therapist as therapy, and that there would not thus be a need under usual circumstances for a child to be receiving both services. However, the two exceptions which we listed above in regard to special education and prevocational training may, under certain circumstances, also exist in relationship to remedial areas. Of these two, the most important is probably again the one relating to the child's community difficulties, particularly if the remedial therapist or special therapist is trying to reach certain specific goals with the child, and the pressures from outside sources are slowing down this process. If this is in a private clinic, this means an increased time and learning expenditure, if it is in an institution or a public clinic, it still means that the child is not able to function or work as rapidly as one would hope. Quite often, bringing in another person who is not necessarily more expert in this area than the therapist in question, but who is able to function as a different person, dealing with a different aspect of the problem, may speed the whole thing up. This is like the old saw that if it takes one carpenter ninety days to build a house, hopefully, it might take two carpenters only forty-five days. If we can approach some of the children's problems with this point of view, there may be a real time economy by introducing play therapy as support of the remedial and special therapies in which the child finds himself. Again, this is not to say that the play therapist can do it better, but possibly by each therapist taking a certain portion of the problem, the whole process may move more rapidly. This is not segmenting the child, but rather segmenting certain specific spotlight areas of the problem so that the child, in a sense, is getting twice as much therapy as before. This should not be considered a regular thing, but under certain circumstances may be useful. One of the circumstances which may make it necessary is the child that has been in therapy for a long time, and a change of scene or a change of person may bring about a certain affectivity which was lost because of the staleness of the program.

Research Problems

Now we come to the question of the methods of research used in connection with play therapy. First, our approach to research is defined primarily as any systematic inquiry. It is our position that different areas of inquiry are at different levels of development, that these different areas require different types of questions and different methodology. Without getting into the old controversary of basic versus pure, laboratory versus field, it is our contention that one does not produce a certain product just because he has a certain tool, the carpenter does not make a bird house because he has a saw, but rather the worker obtains the tools necessary to construct, or in our case, test the products that he hopes to produce. In this connection, we would mention the comments of Edgar Doll,[224] who has set these questions into a plausible and sensible context, recognizing that both so-called applied and so-called basic scientists, laboratory and field researchers all have their contribution to make, as long as they are dealing with parts of the same question. With this general approach stated, we recognize that we will have to delimit the field, the possibilities for contributing research efforts in this area being practically unlimited. We have chosen first to propose some of the questions which appear to be most relevant to further effort, and next to suggest possible procedures whereby the efficacy of the psychotherapy methods that we have described might be brought to a higher level of verification. With the above in mind, we would insist that we are not suggesting a watered down, sloppy, soft minded approach to research questions; but rather that we are interested in rigor, accuracy and precision, and we are only suggesting that methodologies which better fit the context of the inquiry be used. In the area of psychotherapy, the matters of inquiry are often closely tied to particular individuals so that the usual procedure of getting a sample of individuals who can be considered alike is impossible. Therefore, some of the recommendations of Sidman and Skinner[225] in regard to testing the efficacy of treatments using smaller numbers of subjects and often, only one subject, and the whole idiographic research approach, would seem to be in most cases better suited for the types of questions that the area of psychotherapy raises. In other words, if a treatment can be demonstrated to have sufficient power to make clearly demonstrable changes, large numbers of cases are not needed.

With the above in mind, we might say in a more popular vein that it seems illogical that things which are overtly obvious to the naked eye, cannot be demonstrated through careful research. Thus, a child comes into therapy behaving in a certain manner, he goes out behaving in another manner, and it should be possible to demonstrate through proper procedures what it is that brought about this change. The change is obvious to everyone, and whether this can be sufficiently demonstrated and tested so as to set up an objective procedure which can be utilized in many settings, becomes the major issue. It seems to be almost a crime that information which is thus clearly obvious to those who are in contact with the child, cannot be translated into more regular scientific tools.

Relationship of Cognition and Learning

We are in no position at this time to set up a handbook for research in play therapy; however, we would like to point out that there are probably three major areas which should be examined. The first has to do with the relationship of cognition and learning. Cognition theorists and learning theorists have done tremendous amounts of research. Yet, as we have tried to demonstrate throughout the whole discussion of the play therapy problem, we seem to be dealing with an admixture of elements from both schools. Certainly the material from learning theory has been utilized in play therapy and has proven to be effective. However, success seems to be as dependent on development of the cognitive powers of the child as on some other explanation relating to learning theory. That the child has emotions, that these emotions and thoughts modify his behavior, and further that his emotions, interacting with those of the therapist, further change his behavior, is an observable entity which seems clear to everyone except the "scientist." We hope that those who are interested in this area will work through a means of studying the qualities of cognition and learning to combine and produce an adequate cognitive-learning theory. This seems to be what play therapy utilizes, and it would make our work much smoother and the treatment potential of the therapist much more powerful and more effective if such a theory could be formulated.

Refinement of Play Therapy Techniques

Secondly, the obvious area which has to be considered is the whole question of the refinement of play therapy techniques. This becomes immediately apparent when one sets out to write a book of this type. It is very difficult to describe, in writing, all the procedures used in a play therapy situation, and yet, unless this can be done, there is little likelihood that therapists in different parts of the world will be able to use the techniques which have been found to be effective. If it were possible to define some sort of one-to-one relationship between the therapist's behavior and the patient's response, then it would be possible to have a more communicative type of therapy manual and the whole program could move forward at a much more rapid and effective pace.[226]

Problems of Social Learning and Carry-over

The third aspect, is a process of research into theories. We need to know much more about the whole process of social learning and carry-over. We have hinted in this book that our experience demonstrates that improvement of emotional or adaptive maturation seems to have an effect on the physical maturation of the child and, in the example we used it was shown that one can treat the problem of enuresis by playing marbles. This seems totally illogical when analyzed from a strictly objective point of view, and yet since it happens, we cannot discard it because of the seeming lack of logic. Rather, we have to search through the processes which tie this concept to reality and produce, as we say, some sort of social learning theory which can explain through careful research procedures, exactly what the rules or laws of carry-over are in relation to this type of treatment.

Thus, we have a number of questions, and following through with the scientific method, we are in a position to set up hypotheses towards the development of theories which will, hopefully, lead to laws. However, the tools do not seem to be at hand; in a sense we have a pile of steel and only woodworking tools, and it is necessary that we develop tools that can be utilized with the more modern material. This, we think is the major problem of research in this area, and it will remain a problem until this particular factor, as represented by the simile which we have just used, can be corrected. It is not that research cannot be done, only that research cannot be done utilizing the old methods. But research must be done, because all behavior is lawful, and any human phenomena which can be seen and recognized as existing by other humans, must be testable and measurable in the long run. It becomes the responsibility of the scientist to find the ways of testing and measuring it.[227]

ADDITIONAL NOTES

197. Heber (1961), *op. cit.*, Part I.

198. Leland, H., "What is a Mentally Retarded Child?" *J. Psychiatr. Nursing*, 1964, pp. 27-32.

199. Schlesinger, B., *Higher Cerebral Functions and Their Clinical Disorders*, Grune & Stratton, N. Y., 1962, points out that this single mindedness is equally disturbing to the neurologist, who also must use a more "integrated" approach, circa p. 379.

200. Leland, H., "Some Psychological Characteristics of Phenylketonuria," *Psychological Reports*, 1957, 3, pp. 373-376. Also, Johnson, J. L. & Juul, K. D., "Learning Problems in a Schizophrenic Child," *Exceptional Child.*, 1960, 27, pp. 135-138, 146, conversely suggests that the approach used with brain damaged children might be most effective with schizophrenic children.

201. Denhoff, E., "Emotional and Psychological Background of the Neurologically Handicapped Child," *Except. Child.*, 1961, 27, pp. 347-349, makes this point very well when he stated "The emotional and psychological make-up of the neurologically handicapped child is influenced by underlying organic deficit which results in a variety of overt and hidden disabilities."

202. There is an interesting account of this area by Cleverdon, Dorothy and Rosenzweig, L., "A Work-Play Program for the Trainable Mental Deficient," *AJMD*, 1955, 60, pp. 56-70.

203. . . . "A Special Census of Suspected Referred Mental Retardation, Onondaga County, New York," *Technical Report of the Mental Health Research Unit*, New York State Department of Mental Hygiene, Syracuse Univ. Press, 1955, pp. 84-127.

204. Rothstein, J., *Mental Retardation*, Holt, Rinehart & Winston, N. Y., 1961, pp. 1-4.

205. Goldberg, B. and Max, P., "Postnatal Psychological Causes of Mental Retardation," *Canadian Med. Assoc. Jr.*, 1962, 87, pp. 507-510.

206. Stein, Zena and Susser, M., "Mental Retardation A 'Cultural' Syndrome"; and Stein, Zena and Susser, M., "Some Effects of Social Selection on Educationally Subnormal Populations" in Proceedings of London Conference, 1960, Vol. I, *op. cit.*, pp. 171-173 and 174-178, indicate the cultural origins of the child help determine both the diagnosis and the eventual placement.

207. The over-all question of the proper treatment modality for children who present what is probably an admixture of various etiological factors, both cultural and organic, has been raised over the years. The most recent conclusions, as expressed in a number of papers presented at the *London Conference on the Scientific Study of Mental Deficiency*, London, Eng., 1960, seem to support those of your present authors. See also Heiser, K. F., "Psychotherapy for the Mentally Retarded Child," *Train. School Bull.*, Vineland, N. J., 1951, 48, pp. 111-119; Sarason, S. B. and Gladwin, T., "Psychological and Cultural

Problems in Mental Subnormality: A Review of Research," *AJMD*, 1958, 62, pp. 1115-1307; Woodward, Mary, "Early Experiences and Later Social Responses of Severely Subnormal Children," *Brit. J. Med. Psychology*, 1960, 33, pp. 123-132; Bender, Lauretta "Organicity in Schizophrenic Children (Functioning at a Defective Level)"; Benton, A. L., "Some Aspects of the Concepts of Psychogenic Mental Deficiency," Milner, K. L., "The Treatment of Delinquent Mental Defectives by Psychotherapy," and Sloan, W., "Behavior Problems and Psychotherapy in the Mentally Retarded," all in *Proceedings of the London Conference*, 1960, *op. cit.*, pp. 411-417, 243-250, 282-262, 223-229.

208. This note has been cited on page 204.

209. Nichtern, S., "The Biological Treatment of Mental Retardation: The Use of Electro-Convulsive Treatments," *Proceedings of the London Conference*, 1960, *op. cit.*, pp. 199-204.

210. Nichtern, *op. cit.*, feels it is effective. However, Pronko, N. H., Sitterly, Rene and Berg, K., "Twenty Years of Shock Therapy in America, 1937-1956; An Annotated Bibliography," *Genetic Psychology Mono.*, 1960, 62, pp. 233-329, has not included any specific references to ECT and mental retardation.

211. Leland, H., Goldberg, B., and Bair, H., "Electroconvulsive Therapy with the Mentally Retarded," Unpublished manuscript, Parsons State Hosp. & Traing. Center, Parsons, Kans. Presented to the Kansas State Hospitals by "Tele-Com.," 1959.

212. Bender, Lauretta and Keeler, W. R., "The Body Image of Schizophrenic Children Following Electroshock Therapy," *Amer. J. Orthopsychiat.*, 1952, 22, pp. 335-355.

213. Buchan, L. G., "A Pilot Study: An Investigation into the Methodology of Psychopharmacological Therapy," (unpublished Master's thesis, Kansas State College of Pittsburg, Pittsburg, Kansas, 1960).

214. Becker, D. R., "The Effects of a Parapsychopharmacological Agent on Raters' Attitude," (unpublished Master's thesis, Kansas State College of Pittsburg, Pittsburg, Kansas, 1961).

215. Bair, H. V., & Leland, H., "Triflupromazine (Vesprin) in the Treatment of Mentally Retarded Children," paper presented to the 85th Annual Meeting Amer. Assoc. on Ment. Defic., Cincinnati, Ohio, May, 1961.

216. Bender, Lauretta, "Group Activity on a Children's Ward as Methods of Psychotherapy," *Amer. J. Psychiat.*, 1937, 93, pp. 1151-1173.

217. Cruickshank, W. M. and Cowen, E. L., "Group Therapy with Physically Handicapped Children, I," *Jr. Ed. Psych.*, 1948, 39, pp. 193-215, and Cowen, E. L., and Cruickshank, W. M., "Group Therapy with Physically Handicapped Children, II: Evaluation," *Jr. Ed. Psych.*, 1948, 39, pp. 281-297, outline some of the possibilities in this area.

218. Michael-Smith, H. and Kastein, Shulamith, *The Special Child*, New School for Special Child., Seattle, Wash., 1962.

219. In this regard, it has been shown that individuals with this type of injury tend to communicate more about their injuries than do those with a less "visible" type: White, R. K., Wright, Beatrice A. and Dembo, Tamara, "Studies of Adjustment to Visible Injuries: Evaluation of Curiosity in the Injured," *J. Abnorm. & Soc. Psych.*, 1948, 43, pp. 13-28. This should make this type of child even more responsive to therapeutic procedures.

220. Pond, D. A., "Epilepsy and Mental Deficiency," Proceedings of London Conference, 1960, *op. cit.*, pp. 207-209, classes epilepsy as this type of problem and we would agree that the play therapy needs seem similar.

221. Maisner, Edna A., "Contributions of Play Therapy Techniques to Total Rehabilitative Design in an Institution for High Grade Mentally Deficient and Borderline Children," *AJMD*, 1950, 55, pp. 235-250.

222. Hirschberg, J. C., "The Roles of Education in Treatment of Emotionally Disturbed

Children Through Planned Ego Development," *Amer. J. Orthopsychiat.*, 1953, 23, pp. 684-690, discusses this question in terms of emotional disturbance. The areas he outlined seem to apply equally well to the retarded.

223. Examples of this type of approach by various special therapies include among others: Dupont, A., Heeboll-Nielsen, Kr., & Holle, Britta, "Moron (Debile) Children: Physical Treatment, Training and Education," proceedings of London Conference, 1960, *op. cit.*, pp. 547-555 and Benoit, E. P., "The Play Problem of Retarded Children," *AJMD*, 1955, 60, pp. 41-55, in Recreation Therapy; Murphy, Mary M., "A Large Scale Music Therapy Program for Institutionalized Low Grade and Middle Grade Defectives," *AJMD*, 1958, 63, pp. 268-273 and Hartley, Ruth E., Frank, L. K., and Goldenson, R. M., *Understanding Children's Play*, N. Y., Columbia Univ. Press, 1952, pp. 298-339, in Music Therapy-Patrick, Donna "Retardate in Work Adjustment Program," *A. J. Occup. Ther.*, 1960, 14, pp. 297-300; Menzel, Mariella Z., "Psychotherapeutic Techniques Among the Mentally Deficient," *AJMD*, 1952, 56, pp. 796-802 and Soper, R. L., "Occupational Therapy: Its Contribution to the Training of Mentally Deficient Patients at the Newark State School ; *AJMD*, 1946, 51, pp. 296-300, in Occupational Therapy; and Jackson, Lydia, "Non-Speaking Children," *Brit. J. Med. Psych.*, 1950, 23, pp. 87-100; in Speech.

224. Doll, E. A., "The Meaning of Research," in *Readings on the Exceptional Child*, (Trapp and Himelstein, Ed.), Appleton-Century-Crofts, N. Y., 1962, pp. 13-18.

225. Sidman, M., Operant Techniques in A. J. Bachrach (Ed.), *Experimental Foundations of Clinical Psychology*, New York, Basic Books, 1962, pp. 170-210; and Skinner, B. F., "A Case History in Scientific Method," *Amer. Psychologist*, 1956, 11, pp. 221-233.

226. Siegel, G. W., "Adult Verbal Behavior in 'Play Therapy' Sessions with Retarded Children," *Jr. Sp. & Hr. Disorders*, 1963, Mono. Suppl. 10, pp. 34-38, reverses the field and uses a 'play therapy' setting for basic research. This type of effort is also to be applauded.

227. The following is a random selection of some of the more effective research efforts in areas which we feel are either closely allied to the problems we have raised or refer directly to play therapy processes. We are not offering these as prototype studies, but rather as examples of approaches which can be usefully used:

Baer, D. M., "Effect of Withdrawal of Positive Reinforcement on an Extinguishing Response in Young Children," *Child Development*, 1961, 32, pp. 67-74;

Canter, G. N., "Basic Research in Learning With Mentally Retarded Children and Its Educational Implications" in *Frontiers of Elementary Education IV*, (V. J. Glennon, Ed.), Syracuse Univ. Press, 1957, pp. 88-96;

Dahl, L. J. (Ed.) "Symposium on Research Design and Methodology in Mental Retardation," *AJMD*, 1959, 64, pp. 227-432;

Degtyar, F. N., "Development of Association in Younger Pre-School Children," *Pavlov*, 1961, 11:1, (Elsevier Publishing Co., Amsterdam), pp. 58-62;

Eisenberg, L., Landowne, Eleanor J., Wilner, D. M. and Imber, D. S., "The Use of Teacher Ratings as a Mental Health Study: A Method for Measuring Effectiveness of a Therapeutic Nursery Program," *A. J. Pub. Health*, 1962, 52, pp. 18-28;

Josiah Macy Jr. Foundation, *The Central Nervous System and Behavior*, trans. from Russian Med. Lit; U.S. Dept. HEW, PHS, Bethesda, Md., 1959, passim, includes: Lebedinskaya, Ye. I. and Polyakova, A. G., "Certain Age Modifications of the First and Second Signal Systems in Children Two to Seven Years of Age," pp. 488-499; Umanskiy, L. I., "Experimental Study of Typological Characteristics of the Nervous System in Children (from play material)" pp. 973-988;

Lebo, D., "The Present Status of Research on Non-Directive Play Therapy," *J. Consult. Psych.*, 1953, 17, pp. 177-183;

Levin, H. and Wardwell, Elinor, "Research Uses of Doll Play," *Psych. Bull.*, 1962, 59, pp. 27-56;

Linn, L., "A Philosophy of Psychiatric Research," *Mental Hospitals*, 1963, 14, pp. 21-22, 24;

Lofquist, L. H., "Psychological Research and Rehabilitation," A.P.A., Wash., D. C., 1960;

Luria, A. R., "Verbal Regulation of Behavior" in *The Central Nervous System and Behavior*, 1960, *op. cit.*, pp. 359-423;

——— "The Role of Language in the Formation of Temporary Connections" in *Psychology in the Soviet Union*, *op. cit.*, pp. 115-129.

. . . "Language Studies of Mentally Retarded Children," *Jr. Sp. & Hr. Disorders*, Mono. Suppl. 10, 1963, passim.

XIV. General Comments and Considerations

We have tried to cover a great deal of ground, possibly too much, in the area of play therapy and mental retardation. It was necessary to present what would normally be considered a relatively small aspect of the total problem on an extremely large canvas, because so many of the factors relating to problems of treatment in mental retardation are still in the hypothetical or exploratory stages.

There are one or two points that seem to be comparatively clear to most individuals working in the field, and certain elements keep recurring over and over again. Thus, it is usually agreed that mentally retarded individuals have a dependency relationship which continues over a long period of time and cannot be alleviated by early termination of rehabilitation procedures.

It is often noted that the retarded individual has behaviors which make him distinct from his normal peers, not only in terms of intelligence, which is obvious, but also in terms of the manner in which he reacts to certain stimuli, the manner in which he draws his cues from the surrounding environment, and particularly in the manner in which he develops.[228] Further conceptualizations drawn from the way normal children play and the function of play in the development of learning and growth in the normal individual, are highly problematical questions in relationship to the mentally retarded. But, insofar as we are dealing with damaged individuals, though many of the aspects of their growth and development are very similar to the normal individual, many aspects are different, and it is necessary for persons working with the mentally retarded to learn how to separate these two groups of behaviors.

WHAT IS A THERAPIST

The problem of recognizing developmental similarities and differences raises the supplementary question of just who should be considered properly qualified to carry out the procedures of play therapy. This is an extremely difficult question to answer. The obvious answer is not the best answer, because we cannot simply say that the individual must be a qualified psychiatrist or clinical psychologist. Much as that answer may seem to be indicated by the problems presented, there is still the problem that there are not enough individuals trained in those disciplines, and, as we have described, many of the problems relating to mental retardation are not specifically the same types of problems that the traditional training of the psychiatrist or clinical psychologist necessarily encompasses.

Training and Qualification of Therapists

We have then to think about individuals who, in a sense, have become specialists in the area of mental retardation, individuals trained in programs oriented toward the special needs of individuals who are brain damaged and emotionally disturbed. The training and qualifications of these individuals would seem to be primarily related to knowledge of the physical and neurological make-up of the human being, knowledge of what research has revealed to us through experimental work in the areas of learning and cognition and other similar fields, basic knowledge of most treatment modalities, and knowledge of skills and techniques leading to nontraditional or different ways of approaching some of these problems. In other words, the qualified psychotherapist working with the mentally retarded must, in many respects, be a jack of most psychological trades. First and foremost, he has to have an experimental outlook. If he is an individual who demands precedent, who has to be absolutely sure of what he is doing before he goes ahead, he really belongs in another field, because the work with the mentally retarded has not yet reached the point where this kind of precedent, this kind of sureness, can be had. Further, while everything he does has to be based on a certain amount of conceptualization concerning the present philosophical or theoretical points of view concerning the mentally retarded, it nonetheless becomes obvious that he is, in effect, creating his own theory or his own school as he goes along. That is to say, many of the conclusions, erroneous or otherwise, that have been drawn around human behavior, based either on the analysis of the behavior of laboratory animals or on some subjective philosophizing around behavior of humans (in terms of the literature, usually college sophomores), does not necessarily provide proper food for thought in terms of individuals who are different from the start. The behavior of the laboratory animal, who is more often than not a whole animal, is not going to correlate in any meaningful way with the behavior of the damaged human. Thus, forgetting whether or not there is an easy transfer from laboratory psychology to field psychology or from animals to humans in terms of the usual debate on the question, it becomes abundantly clear that since we are not dealing with whole human brains, in the sense of their being undamaged, whatever transfer might be possible between data is going to be distorted in an additional way because of their particular situation. Now this can give rise either to a feeling that nothing is known or can be known, or to a feeling that, as we have cited before, 'all behavior is lawful' and that even in the case of damaged organisms there is a pattern which can be discovered as well as laws that can be evolved. Therefore, the training and qualifications of a play therapist as a specialist in mental retardation primarily becomes a training in how to look at a situation and in a sense how to ask the right questions. The most highly qualified play therapist is essentially going to be the individual who is willing to seek with his patient, the best and most feasible ways of gaining behavioral changes, not the individual who has the most concrete previous knowledge of specific schools of psychotherapy.

Here, we would like to emphasize the fact that there is a wealth of information from education sources, primarily on the nature of human play, and it becomes extremely important that some of this material work its way once again into our literature on play therapy. It is not so much a matter of re-evolving a theory of play as it is of recognizing that since play is conceived as the manner in which children work, the whole early preparation for life experiences of the mentally retarded is going to have to be considered to orbit around the problems of their play.[229] This is true because the retarded have to be started on preparations for vocational existence much earlier than the normal child, and because of the need for constant reiteration and constant reinforcement of behaviors.

Supervision

The play therapist, to be really effective, must also find himself in a position where he can interact with other people during therapy. Thus, the processes of supervision which have been utilized for such a long time in the teaching of psychotherapy with adults, have to be introduced on a much more intensive basis in the training of play therapists. In no other area of psychotherapy is the problem of supervision so important as in the area of play therapy where, as we have pointed out in previous chapters, so much of what comes forth has to be interpreted in terms of the conceptualization of popular reality. Since we can never expect a play therapist or any other type of therapist to have such complete control of all the facets of the field that he would be easily able to interpret all behaviors in terms of popular reality by himself, we will have to anticipate that the only fully effective type of play therapy exists in terms of interactions between two or more individuals. This may raise a question concerning multiple therapists, and if sufficient numbers of individuals are available, this is probably a useful approach. But, neglecting that, at least in the traditional approach of the therapy period plus a period of supervision, more than one head is put to work on the problem presented by the child and more than one manner of viewing the results can be brought to bear on the problem, thus hopefully producing a sufficient and useful solution as to the ways and means of dealing with it.

What we are saying here, in effect, is that the problem of who is to do play therapy is a much more involved one than the mere definition of university degrees or certificates. Play therapy has to be conducted by an individual who has a specialized way of looking at life in general and mental retardation in particular. Hopefully, people who have become interested in the field and have received special training in the universities which give degrees in this specific area[230] are also trained with this frame of reference, and it is our experience that the majority of them can claim to fit this category.

Research Function of Therapists

But, the important factor again is that play therapy as it exists with the mentally retarded is really another form of research, and that the best therapist is an individual who has a clinical orientation but has at the same time a research frame of reference,[231] and is willing to approach all of his work with the same rigor and same discipline that is normally demanded of the experimental psychologist. This means that in a sense he has a willingness to sacrifice certain subjectivities regarding his patient in favor of the long term results. This, of course, does not mean that he ever subjects his patients to some of the things to which laboratory animals are subjected because he is still dealing with human beings, but it does mean that he cannot, in the name of misplaced sympathy, refuse to do certain things with his patient if his doing them may produce a sounder, happier, more constructive personality organization.

Conversely, of course, he cannot set up procedures that tend to tie the patient to the therapy situation. Thus, it is clear from much work in experimental psychology that certain types of conditioning would probably produce results which were much cleaner and much faster than psychotherapy results. It is obvious that, by using traditional conditioning practices, patients could be set up in a highly structured kind of environment where every behavior grows out of the previous behavior in a Rube Goldberg type of relationship so that the patient has only to be conditioned to perform certain specific acts while the rest of the situation organizes itself around him automatically. The problem here is that life is not so constructed and this type of patient would never again be able to return to normal community living because he would not find in the community the type of controlled environment which this sort of experimental procedure demands. Therefore, it is necessary that a certain amount of a subjective or at least popular reality approach be used and that the mistake of confusing objectivity with science not be made. As we have pointed out earlier in the book, it is the responsibility of the scientist to deal with the truth as he sees it, and there is no implication that this truth is necessarily the cold objective truth that would be seen for all time. Rather, it is a truth based on the popular reality of the moment, and it is in that area of science that the psychotherapist as an experimentor has to function.

OTHER PROBLEM AREAS

Expected Gains from Therapy

We have raised from time to time the problem of whether treatment objectives have been attained. Without rehashing the material already presented in the various chapters on this question, we would like at this point to comment briefly on expected gains in therapy.[232] An individual is brought into psychotherapy so that he can learn to function better in his social community. This is true of adults or children, the mentally normal or mentally retarded, or anyone else. The whole conceptualization of psychotherapy has grown out of the fact that individuals, when placed in certain circumstances where they are subjected to suggestibility from other individuals whom they have learned to respect, seem to change their behavior in reference to either the direct or implied suggestions of this second individual who, for practical purposes, is called the therapist. As far back as we can go into recorded history we find examples of patriarchs, prophets, and soothsayers imposing this kind of authority and supervision over more dependent individuals and getting them, through one means or another, to modify their behavior for purposes either fair or foul. Therefore, when we come to the general question of gains in psychotherapy, we have to ask not why we do what we do, but rather why we do certain specific things. In other words, what is it that the retarded individual needs to have in order to survive in a modern civilized community? This is a much more difficult question than would appear on the surface, because it seems to be the course of the modern civilized community to produce increasing numbers of retardates, not in terms of previous definitions of mental retardation, but in terms of the fact that individual members of the community constantly have to know more and more in order to survive at even the average level. Thus, we find many things taught in the first grade in grammar school today that did not even exist when most of us reading this book went to school, e.g. such things as problems of space travel, information concerning certain types of mathematical principles, etc. With this in mind, we are going to have to think not only in terms of what the individual has to know to survive, but what kinds of behaviors have to be demonstrated in order to permit survival. In other words, intelligence as such becomes really less important than the adaptive behavior of the individual because even the normal person's intelligence is not going to be able to fully cope with the educational demands of the future unless a number of procedures in public educations, etc., are also modified to meet these needs.

Therapy Forms are Similar to Life Expectations

Thinking from the above frame of reference, it was the intention of the authors to set up forms of play therapy which, in effect, are forms of behavior required of the individual for survival in the community. Thus, in setting up four different ways of dealing with play therapy, we have tried to deal with four major aspects of community living which seem to cause the greatest difficulty to the retarded individual. The community is divided as we have divided play therapy, into highly structured, less structured, and totally unstructured elements of the environment. Thus, at the most primitive level, the individual finds himself daily faced with unstructured stimuli in the form of wind, ruin, and sunshine, etc., in an unstructured situation in the form of the open community without any particular demands being placed upon him at that point in time. The most primitive kind of adjustment that has to be made in terms of daily living is an adjustment equivalent to that recreated in the U-U type of situation, and one of the first difficulties one has with the mentally retarded individual at the more primitive level is his ability, for example, to adjust to the fact that it is raining and he is outside without an umbrella or some other type of protection. Beyond this level we find ourselves faced with the same types of unstructured environmental forces but modified by the fact that we are not in a totally open situation. Thus, using the example above, the individual finds himself in the rain, but now instead of being in a loose situation where he can run away or go into the house or use his own particular responses, he finds himself downtown where there are certain buildings that cannot be entered, where there are certain places where it is unsafe to go, and others where it is safe. In other words, he is actually in a U-S type of situation in which proper discrimination, proper determinations of behavior, are required if he is to be able to successfully cope with these kinds of environmental forces.

At another level we find situations in which the individual is receiving from his community extremely strong, highly structured stimuli, with no particular ready-made or ever present social enforcement surrounding them. Thus, it is expected that individuals, for instance, will wear proper clothing when they are on the street, that they will take care of body functions in a certain manner in certain places, that they will react toward their fellow man in certain peaceful manners, instead of striking out at will. In other words, there are highly structured relationships required of the individual in the community with no specific structured procedures required. Thus, we have the free field again in the face of structured stimuli, which is similar to the S-U form of play therapy where the materials, or in this case the stimuli, are clearly defined, but what is to be done with them is still left open to the discriminations and imagination of the individual. Thus, if the individual is hungry, this is highly specific. It becomes even more highly specific if it represents a certain time of day or a certain break in other activities so that this is not only a hunger derived from the function of the individual's stomach, but also from the cultural habituation to being hungry at a certain time of the day, etc., and yet he finds himself without money or away from home, or in other circumstances which make it impossible for him to eat at that moment. How he deals with that problem is really the answer to whether or not he is going to be able to remain as a free individual in the community, or whether other controls will have to be imposed upon him, and so again the response to this type of S-U circumstance is highly important to his total adjustment to community living.

And finally, given these same external controls, the individual will find himself in an extremely highly structured situation similar to that represented by the S-S form. That is to say, he has these highly structured stimuli represented by specific concrete elements, but at the same time finds himself not free to make a decision, but forced rather to go along with the decisions which are made for him. Thus, he cannot dash across the street to get food even if he has money, but must rather wait for stop lights to change. He cannot, in the middle of other types of situations, think only in terms of his own needs, but must learn to delay gratifications for an extended period of time because of the controls the environment has placed upon him for one reason or another, and again his ability to survive is quite often dependent on his ability to learn to delay these gratifications.

Society itself seems to structure itself around the retardate in terms of these same U-U, U-S, S-U, and S-S situations, and if the individual, as a child, can learn to cope with these problems and, as a child, through his play, can learn to respond in a controlled manner, then the possibility of our being able to presume that he may also be able to carry this learning into daily living as an adolescent and as an adult, becomes much greater than would exist if he had never had this previous experience during the developmental period. Thus, the major gains to be expected from play therapy are essentially the ability to know the kinds of things that life will expect on one hand, and the ability to have had success experiences dealing with these life demands on the other. This creates a personality pattern which is fairly comfortable within the demands of the community and can thus be permitted to remain in the community as a contributing element.[233]

An Approach to Prevention

Another aspect of the more general question is the problem of prevention. Now it is obvious by definition that play therapy or psychotherapy occurs after the event; that is, individuals have to be in some sort of emotional trouble before they are brought to a therapist and we are certainly not recommending that all retarded children be brought automatically to play therapy as a way of preventing trauma. We do not have that many play therapists, and we certainly would not want that many patients. However, one aspect of prevention has sometimes been overlooked. The individual as he moves on in society, grows older, and creates new problems or finds new problems created around him, because of the natural "traumas" of the aging process; "traumas" in the sense that new responsibilities are added, behaviors are expected of him because he is an adult which were not expected of him as a child, etc. Most of these difficulties are things which normally could not be predicted by any amount of counseling or preguidance, because they grow out of the individual's relationship to his environment. Thus, the previously mentioned fact of a continuing dependency relationship becomes an extremely important facet in considering both the question of gains in therapy and the prevention of serious problems. One of the things that every retarded individual has to learn is that regardless of how well trained he is, regardless of how well adjusted he may be, there are still going to be situations arising with which he cannot cope immediately. This, in a sense, is part and parcel of being retarded. An understanding has to be developed that the individual is handicapped, is not able to function at the same level as other individuals, and will from time to time need additional help. Thus, we can conceive of play therapy as being a means of preventing more serious disturbances from developing at an older age.

There is another type of prevention in which play therapy has a role. This second type of prevention is related to the adjustment of everybody in the community regardless of their intelligence, and has to do with the adjustments which the individual must make to the social and economic changes in a culturally growing community. The economic problems which beset any nation today have a constant tendency to throw out of employment, or out of the regular flow of economic life of the community, large numbers of individuals who have become marginal for various reasons. If we are going to conceive of the mentally retarded filling some sort of economic role in the community, we are going to have to recognize that they are going to be in the van of these marginal workers and every time there is any sort of a dislocation, they are going to be the first ones effected. In general, we have no argument with this fact. We would not want to advocate that the mentally retarded be used to replace able-bodied individuals in the labor market unless it means that these able-bodied individuals would have the opportunity for better education and/or for better and higher level jobs. But to presume that because the retarded individual is available, that he probably would work for a cheaper wage and would be less demanding as far as working conditions, etc., and thus is a logical person to put into the labor market in times of stress, is not only an unhealthy and false presumption, but leads to a degeneration of the retarded individual and society as a whole. Rather, what we are saying is that there is a role for the retarded individual in providing on the general market various types of service occupations which still require the kind of labor which many retarded adults can provide. To be able to function, however, retarded individuals have to have certain types of training and the training has to be started when they are very young. Therefore, when we talk about prevention in this area, we are talking about the prevention of these people becoming so totally economically dependent that they cannot function even in the areas where the community has need for them as productive individuals. The things learned in play therapy will and must carry the individual in very good stead, and will provide a type of prevention which will permit the individual who has successfully completed play therapy to know how also to compete successfully in the labor market even though it is recognized that it will always be at a marginal level. Thus, play therapy seems to serve two preventive functions for the child in that, on one hand, it prevents more serious disorders and emotional upsets developing later from increased responsibility relating to aging, and secondly it prevents his becoming an additional public trust as a result of lack of experience, lack of training, lack of motivation, and lack of understanding. These factors cannot be put forth as the major basis for play therapy, but certainly must be mentioned as additional reasons for considering the retarded individual as a good candidate for play therapy, even though as mentioned earlier in the book, the specific gains may be less than those with individuals of normal intelligence.

Utilization of Community Resources

In this same regard, we have to recognize that another major problem is related to training the individual how to utilize community facilities. We are constantly faced with the problem of an individual finding himself in a decision making situation in which he has had no previous experience and he does not know where to turn or who to ask. As we mentioned above, it is impossible for the therapist or the guidance counselor or anyone else to predict all the situations that may arise in a community area, so that it is not possible even in the best organized program to provide for the patient to have "been there once" in every type of situation. It is possible, however, to give the patient sufficient understanding as to the general functioning of community facilities that he will gain a feeling of security and confidence in being able to approach public officials of one sort or another, to seek out their aid and counsel when unpredictable circumstances arise in his environment. Thus, it becomes necessary for the individual to learn how to approach community facilities, what they are there for, what their function is, under what circumstances they will receive people, etc. Play therapy cannot become an educational procedure of teaching the child how to fill out forms and blanks, etc., this is the function of another area, but it can as we say, instill sufficient confidence in the individual concerning his relationships with authoritative adults and public officials that he will at least be willing to approach the various bureaus and offices for the purpose of seeking help when unpredictable environmental events occur.

Finally, we must again make the point, in terms of the relationship of the child to the community, that it is always the responsibility of the well to help the sick, of the more able to help the less able. This has been the underlying creed of this book. It, in a sense, has been the underlying creed of most individuals working with the handicapped or other less able individuals, and it certainly cannot be shunted to one side as a bit of useless philosophy. The problem of the handicapped individual is clearly the community's problem and the community must accept this fact, even though there is no exact or positive return to the community in terms of concrete economic gain. We have pointed out that there is a possibility of some economic gain anyway, but this should not be the main motivating reason. The main reason has to be that there are people who need help, they are able to benefit from the help that the psychotherapist can give, and the community has to learn to accept its less able members as well as they accept the more able members without insisting that the retardate make the kind of contribution that sometimes even the more able member is not always able to make. Further, we might say that it is not necessarily exploitation of the retardate to utilize him in what we would consider the more menial situations within the community, because we are at the same time giving him the status of being wanted, being useful, and to some extent earning his own way. Thus, while it would clearly be exploitation to force an able-bodied man of normal or superior intelligence to serve us in such a menial manner, it is actually a compliment to the retardate to ask him to carry out some of these tasks, and in this way he becomes a living part of the human situation rather than merely an appendage to it.

SUMMARY AND CONCLUSIONS

We have tried to point out that play therapy is feasible with the mentally retarded, that the development of man as a human being makes the play form of therapy a very logical form of therapeutic procedure in the sense that it seems to fill the need of completing what was otherwise a missed or defective area in the development of the individual. We have pointed out in earlier chapters that primitive man seems to have developed from a lower form to the present through the procedure of handed experience. We have tried to evolve a process utilizing this kind of experience in developing psychotherapy forms which, as we have just stated, seem to be consistent with the kinds of demands the community makes on the older individual. Since we are dealing with the mentally retarded, it becomes extremely important that he be exposed as a child to the kinds of things to which he will be exposed as an adult. Finally, we have tried to relate these various psychotherapeutic procedures to other procedures going forth simultaneously and to conceptualizations of adaptive behavior and measured intelligence, as a way of rounding out a gross theory of mental retardation as it relates to child growth and development. All of these efforts are of necessity incomplete and certainly almost everything said in this book is going to require revision and review as the result of improved research methods and experimental processes. From this point of view we find ourselves somewhat in the position of the individual who is trying to put out a fire through the use of the bucket brigade, recognizing that modern fire fighting equipment would do this much more rapidly and much more efficiently but, noentheless, feeling the need to put the fire out, and not having the modern equipment, the bucket brigade is utilized. This book serves in the area of psychotherapy with the mentally retarded a bucket brigade type function. It is hoped that there is enough stimulating material in it to get other observers and other workers in the field interested in improving upon the technique, giving them sounder experimental bases and, in short, developing a much more workable procedure for accomplishing the objectives which we have outlined.

President Kennedy's Message and Report

We must recognize that the whole area of mental retardation is subject to this same kind of review and that the problems which we have found surrounding the inability to achieve a sound theory of psychotherapy equally surround the problems of diagnosis, rehabilitation, treatment, etc., in relationship to the whole area of mental retardation. What seems to be important is that people are now beginning to become aware of the deficit, partly due to the efforts of the late President Kennedy in his history making address to Congress[234] which established for the first time a public policy authored by our chief executive. The pioneering efforts made by President Kennedy, and specifically the legislation which he sponsored, probably have helped the field move ahead more rapidly since 1963 than it has at any other time in history. The area has been further aided by the tremendous work done by the group of highly dedicated individuals who made up the President's Panel on Mental Retardation. Some of the specific recommendations which came out of the report of the panel can become specific recommendations for us in expanding therapeutic and research services to mentally retarded children:

1. High priority should be given to developing research centers on mental retardation at strategically located universities and at institutions for the retarded. (p. 24)
2. The Federal Government should develop a comprehensive, continu-

ing program for the collection and analysis of population statistics on the incidence, prevalence, and personal and socio-economic characteristics of the mentally retarded. (p. 29)

3. Federal fellowship programs should be extended to provide opportunities for students to prepare for research careers in mental retardation in conjunction with training in one of the basic behavioral or social sciences. (p. 44)

4. Deprivation of adequate opportunities to learn and other environmental factors may adversely influence the intellectual development of children; therefore communities should undertake programs to modify these conditions. (p. 61)

5. In view of the critical shortage of personnel and the need for volunteers in health, welfare, and education—particularly in areas of extreme deprivation—it is recommended that a domestic Peace Corp be organized to provide stimulus to volunteer community service groups. (p. 70)

6. Every person suspected of mental retardation should have the benefit of expert comprehensive diagnosis and evaluation. (p. 82)

7. State governments should lift all present restrictions barring retarded children with physical handicaps from service available to other children. To increase the capability of the states to provide services for retarded children under the state crippled children's program, additional earmarked funds should be made available to that program. (p. 85)

8. The physical and emotional needs of the retarded are neglected. Adequate treatment of these needs is essential to their total well-being. (p. 86)

9. There should be available in every community a 'fixed point of referral and information' which provides a life consultation service for the retarded. (p. 92)

10. Institutional care should be restricted to those whose specific needs can be best met by this type of service. (p. 135)

11. An expanded program of information and education on mental retardation is essential for the general public and pertinent professional organizations. (p. 157)[235]

Thus, we find that the field of mental retardation is not specifically tied to any one area of discipline, but rather that it involves all major aspects of living experience and all major professional disciplines are required to help alleviate its problems. Again, we want to underline our concern in the aspect of this problem which we have described as *adaptive behavior*. This is the primary problem relative to whether or not the individual is institutionalized or whether or not he receives the available services which the community develops or even whether or not he is able to continue to live, in terms of proper utilization of medical care, etc. Therefore, the whole problem of play therapy or the learning and cognition processes upon which such a program is based, becomes one of the core problems in dealing with many of the mentally retarded individuals, particularly those who are most apt to come to the attention of public authorities. We do not want to overstate our case; there is no implication that this program would necessarily be useful with or even is intended to apply to the whole group of mentally retarded in the community. Certainly those individuals who have been able to make their own adjustment or are able to utilize community facilities without emotional trauma, do not fit under this conceptualization. But, recognizing that the numbers of retarded children who become severe community problems and who find themselves constantly on the books of one agency after another can be reduced by the kinds of procedures we have outlined, we have offered this program.[236]

Thus, play therapy or psychotherapy is not a panacea and in no way provides for the cure or elimination of mental retardation, nor does it provide for even the cure of emotionally disturbed individuals who are mentally retarded. However, it does provide for one more way of alleviating some of the more extreme difficulties in which we find our patients, and thus adds one more tool to the kit which will be useful in solving those aspects of the problem which, so far, have kept the community from functioning and going forward in a fully activated manner.

ADDITIONAL NOTES

228. Berkson, G., "Responsiveness of the Mentally Deficient," *AJMD*, 1961, 66, pp. 277-286, stated for example, "taken as a group, mentally deficient subjects respond less intensely and for shorter duration than do normals to short duration stimuli," p. 284.

229. We have not attempted to develop a generalized theory of play, though we have cited such theoretical concepts as were necessary to the foundation of our play therapy system. However, there are a number of historically important works upon which most modern concepts still depend, these include: Freobel, F., *Pedagogics of the Kindergarten*, (Josephine Jarvis, Trans.), D. Appleton & Co., N. Y., 1895; Groos, K., *The Play of Animals*, D. Appleton & Co., N. Y., 1898; Groos, K., *The Play of Man*, D. Appleton & Co., N. Y., 1908; Dewey, J. (1916), *op. cit.*; Adler, A., *Understanding Human Nature*, Garden City Pub. Co., N. Y., 1927; Schlosberg, H., "The Concept of Play," *Psychol. Review*, 1947, 54, pp. 229-231. It is interesting to note that Major, D. R., *The Elements of Psychology*, R. G. Adams & Co., Columbus, Ohio, 1914 and Erikson, E. H., "Growth and Crises of the Healthy Personality," in *Personality in Nature, Society and Culture*, (Kluckhohn, C., et al, Eds.) 2nd. Ed., Alfred A. Knopf, N. Y., 1956, make almost identical points concerning play and raise similar alternatives, thus showing how limited the growth of understanding has been in the intervening years. This is a badly neglected area for research and theoretical investigation.

230. At the time of this writing, George Peabody College for Teachers, Nashville, Tenn., and Oklahoma State Univ., Stillwater, Okla., have specialized programs leading to degrees in Mental Retardation as a specialty of Psychology.

231. Shapiro, A., "Problems of Psychotherapy," Proceedings of the London Conf., Vol. I, *op. cit.*, pp. 263-270.

232. Hobbs (1962), *op. cit.*, pp. 741-747.

233. Smirnov, A. A., "Child Psychology" in Simon (1957), *op. cit.*, ". . . to confront the child with authoritative demands will not serve; nor is a knowledge of moral codes sufficient. Practical moral experience is necessary which can give rise, not to merely formal knowledge, but to real moral conviction and moral behavior . . ." pg. 186.

234. Kennedy, J. F., *Mental Illness and Mental Retardation*, Message to Congress from the President of the United States, February 5, 1963, Washington, D. C., discusses problems of Prevention, Community Services and Research in Mental Retardation.

235. *National Action to Combat Mental Retardation*, The President's Panel on Mental Retardation, U.S. Govt. Printing Office, Washington, D. C., 1963, passim.

236. For further discussion of psychotherapy and mental retardation, see Sarason, S. B., *Psychological Problems in Mental Deficiency*, 3rd. Ed., Harper Bros., N. Y., 1959.

Author Index

Subject Index